The Massachusetts Political Almanac 1999

VOLUME TWO

THE EXECUTIVE BRANCH

1999 EDITION

THE GOVERNOR

THE CONSTITUTIONAL OFFICERS

THE EXECUTIVE OFFICES

INDEPENDENT STATE AGENCIES

THE SUPREME JUDICIAL COURT

CENTER FOR LEADERSHIP STUDIES
P.O. BOX 400
CENTERVILLE, MA 02632
TELEPHONE: (800) 833-7600
(508) 775-4323
FAX: (800) 886-7310
INTERNET: http://www.the-mpa.com

The Massachusetts Political Almanac,
Volume Two - 1999 edition.
ISBN 0-926766-25-2 (Volume II)
ISBN 0-926766-26-0(2-Volume Set)

The Massachusetts Political Almanac 1999

PUBLISHER
Stephen G. Lakis

EDITOR
Carolyn Barnes

Table of Contents

Introduction

Now in its tenth year of publication, *The Massachusetts Political Almanac, Volume II, The Executive* is an annual compendium of information on the executive branch of government in the Commonwealth of Massachusetts. It serves as a complement to its parent publication, *Volume I, The Legislature.*

This comprehensive reference book provides a complete overview of the executive branch of state government, including the functions of the Governor and constitutional officers, organization of the six executive secretariats and four departments that report to the Governor, complete office descriptions, biographical profiles of key executive branch officials, and office and agency organizational charts. An overview of the judicial branch is also provided, including a brief history and current description of the Massachusetts judiciary system, along with the profiles and photos of the Supreme Judicial Court Justices. Independent Agencies are listed with a description of their functions.

Each year, *The Executive* is updated to reflect changes in every facet of the executive offices since the previous year — including changes in personnel, reshuffling in organization, additions and/or deletions of agencies, and modifications in agency descriptions.

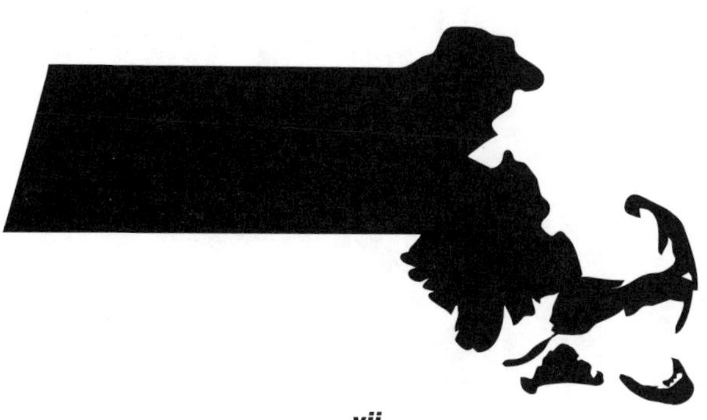

SECTION I

The Constitutional Officers

Governor
A. Paul Cellucci
State House, Room 360
Boston, MA 02133 ____________ (617) 727-9173

Secretary of the Commonwealth
William F. Galvin
State House, Room 337
Boston, MA 02133 ____________ (617) 727-9180

Attorney General
Thomas Reilly
One Ashburton Place, 20th Floor
Boston, MA 02108 ____________ (617)727-2200

State Treasurer & Receiver General
Shannon O'Brien
State House, Room 227
Boston, MA 02133 ____________ (617)367-6900

State Auditor
A. Joseph DeNucci
State House, Room 230
Boston, MA 02133 ____________ (617)727-2075

Office of the Governor and the Lt. Governor

The Governor is the chief executive officer of the Commonwealth of Massachusetts and the commander-in-chief of the state's military forces. His primary responsibility is the administration of all agencies and departments that make up the executive branch.

In consultation with the six cabinet secretaries, who are appointed by the Governor and serve at his pleasure, he determines policy for his administration and works to gain legislative approval of his programs.

The executive secretariats of the Commonwealth are currently:

- *Executive Office for Administration and Finance*
- *Executive Office of Elder Affairs*
- *Executive Office of Environmental Affairs*
- *Executive Office of Health and Human Services*
- *Executive Office of Public Safety*
- *Executive Office of Transportation and Construction*

The Governor is responsible for preparation of the state's annual budget. He has the authority to accept or to veto all legislative enactments, subject to an override by a vote of two-thirds of the members present in each chamber of the legislature, and to convene the Governor's Council. With the consent of the Governor's Council, he can call special sessions of the General Court, nominate judicial officers, and grant pardons.

In case of the absence, death, or disability of the Governor, the Lieutenant Governor performs all of the duties incumbent on the chief executive officer and has all of his constitutional powers. She assists the Governor in administering the executive agencies, advises the Governor on administrative policies, and works with the legislature to enact those policies into law. The Lieutenant Governor is a voting member of the Governor's Council and presides over the council in the Governor's absence.

Under the current administration, the executive offices of the Governor and Lieutenant Governor have been consolidated.

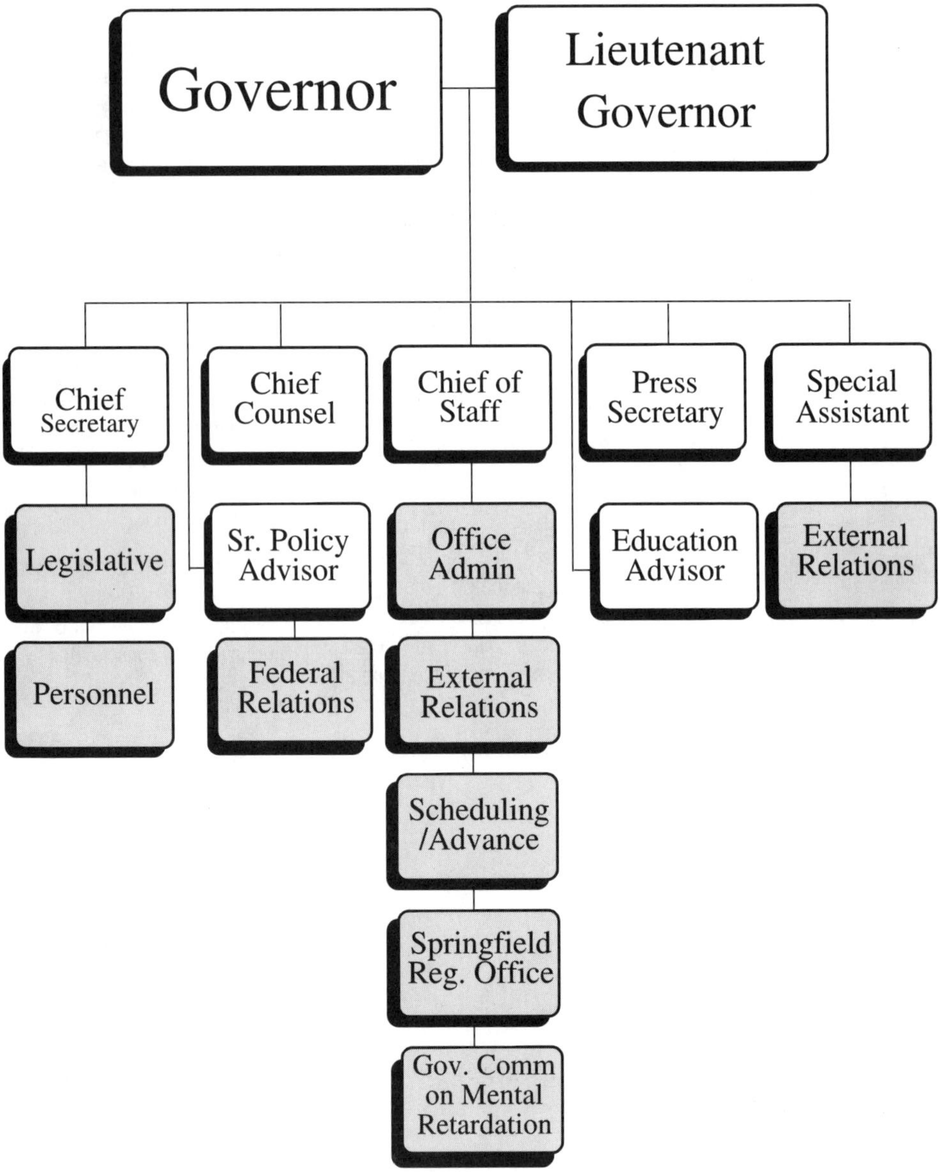
Governor
Lieutenant Governor
Chief Secretary
Chief Counsel
Chief of Staff
Press Secretary
Special Assistant
Legislative
Sr. Policy Advisor
Office Admin
Education Advisor
External Relations
Personnel
Federal Relations
External Relations
Scheduling /Advance
Springfield Reg. Office
Gov. Comm on Mental Retardation

Office of the Governor and Lt. Governor

Governor	***Argeo Paul Cellucci***	*(617) 727-9173*
Lt. Governor	***Jane Swift***	*727-9173*
Chief of Staff	***Virginia B. Buckingham***	*727-9173*
Deputy Chief of Staff	***Russell D. Aims***	*727-3600*
Assistant Chief of Staff	***Elizabeth S. Morse***	*727-3600*
Assistant Chief of Staff	***Catherine M. McDonald***	*727-9173*
Assistant Chief of Staff/Fed. Relations	***William S. Smith***	*727-3600*
Special Assistant	***Jennifer D. Carey***	*727-3600*
Chief Secretary	***Stephen J. O'Neill***	*727-5787*
Deputy Chief Secretary	***Stephen R. Doody***	*727-5787*
Deputy Chief Secretary	***Charles B. King***	*727-5787*
Chief Legal Counsel	***Paul W. Johnson***	*727-2065*
Deputy Chief Legal Counsel	***Laurie R. Wallach***	*727-2065*
Advisor on Education	***Michael J. Sentance***	*727-2339*
Dir. Planning & Scheduling	***Yvonne E. Boyle***	*727-3600*
Director of Legislative Affairs	***Robert J. Garrity***	*727-7238*
Administrator of Governor's Commission on Mental Retardation	***Elizabeth R. Closs***	*727-0517*
Press Secretary	***Ilene D. Hoffer***	*727-2759*
Director of Federal/State Relations (Washington Office)	***Charles Steele***	*(202) 624-7713*
Director of External Affairs	***Barbara G. Burke***	*727-6250*
Director of Office Administration	***Theresa E. Dolan***	*727-5415*
Regional Office Director (Western Massachusetts)	***Peter J. Abair***	*(413) 784-1200*

Argeo Paul Cellucci

Governor

Office of the Governor
Address: State House, Suite 360, Boston, MA 02133
Telephone: (617) 727-9173 **Fax:** (617) 727-9725
Staff: Kellie A. Cullen O'Neill, Special Assistant; Jacquelyn Phelan, Special Assistant

PERSONAL INFORMATION:
Born: April 24, 1948
Place of Birth: Marlboro
Marital Status: married (Janet) **Children:** 2
Education: Boston College (B.S., Accounting, '70); Boston College School of Law (J.D., '73)
Previous Employment: Lieutenant governor (1991-97); Massachusetts Senate ('84-'90); Massachusetts House of Representatives ('76-'84); Town of Hudson (Board of Selectmen, '71-'77); Attorney
Years in Current Position: 1 **Years in State Service:** 22

1999 PRIORITIES:
Ensuring Massachusetts children get a first-rate education; cutting the personal income tax from 5.95% to 5%; providing access to affordable quality health care for all citizens; protecting the public safety and curbing domestic violence.

ORGANIZATIONS:
Massachusetts and American Bar Associations; Sons of Italy

Jane Swift

Lieutenant Governor

Office of the Governor
Address: State House, Suite 360, Boston, MA 02133
Telephone: (617) 727-9173 **Fax:** (617) 727-9725

PERSONAL INFORMATION:
Born: Feb. 24, 1965 **Place of Birth:** North Adams
Marital Status: married (Charles Hunt) **Children:** 2
Education: Trinity College (B.A. '87)
Previous Employment: Director, Office of Consumer Affairs & Business Regulation; Director of Regional Airport Development, Massachusetts Port Authority; State Senator, Berkshire, Hampden, Hampshire and Franklin District; Legislative Aide, State Senator Peter Webber' G. Fox & Co, Retail Sales Manager
Years in Current Position: new **Years in State Service:** 11

ORGANIZATIONS:
Trustee Board Member of the Massachusetts 4-H Foundation, Corporator for the Massachusetts College of Liberal Arts

Stephen J. O'Neill

Chief Secretary

Office of the Governor
Address: State House, Suite 280, Boston, MA 02133
Telephone: (617) 727-5787 **Fax:** (617) 727-8136
Staff: Diane Reynolds, Executive Assistant
Reports to: Gov. A. Paul Cellucci

PERSONAL INFORMATION:
Born: August 27, 1966 **Place of Birth:** Boston
Marital Status: married (Kellie)
Education: Merrimack College ('89); Suffolk University Law School ('98)
Years in Current Position: 2 **Years in State Service:** 8

JOB DESCRIPTION:
Serves as Governor's Chief Secretary

Virginia B. Buckingham

Chief of Staff

Office of the Governor
Address: State House, Suite 360, Boston, MA 02133
Telephone: (617) 727-9173 **Fax:** (617) 727-9723
Staff: Russell D. Aims, Deputy Chief of Staff; Elizabeth Morse, Catherine M. McDonald, William S. Smith, Assistant Chiefs of Staff; Laura Hennessey, Special Assistant
Reports to: Gov. A. Paul Cellucci; Lt. Governor Jane Swift

PERSONAL INFORMATION:
Born: Sept. 14, 1965
Place of Birth: Waterbury, CT
Education: Boston College (B.A. '87)
Marital Status: married (David A. Lowy)
Previous Employment: Weld for Senate Campaign (Campaign Manager); Office of the Governor (Press Secretary); Office of the Governor (Assistant Press Secretary); Weld-Cellucci campaign (Press Aide); The Tocco Group (Director of Client Services); Associated Builders and Contractors, MA/RI chapter (Director of Public Affairs)
Years in Current Position: 2 **Years in State Service:** 7

JOB DESCRIPTION:
Serves as Governor's Chief of Staff.

Elizabeth S. Morse
Assistant Chief of Staff

Office of the Governor
Address: State House, Suite 360, Boston, MA 02133
Telephone: (617) 7273600 **Fax:** (617) 727-8685
E-mail: Elizabeth.S.Morse@state.ma.us
Reports to: Virginia Buckingham, Chief of Staff

PERSONAL INFORMATION:
Born: January 18, 1969 **Place of Birth:** Concord
Education: Colby College (B.A., Government, '91)
Previous Employment: Hale & Dorr (Legal Assistant); Office of the Governor (Assistant to Deputy Chief of Staff); Executive Office of Communities & Development (Director of Policy and Chief of Staff)
Years in Current Position: 1 **Years in State Service:** 5

JOB DESCRIPTION:
Governor's Office liaison with the offices of Health & Human Services, Economic Development, and Elder Affairs.

Catherine M. McDonald
Assistant Chief of Staff

Office of the Governor
Address: State House, Suite 360, Boston, MA 02133
Telephone: (617) 727-9173 **Fax:** (617) 727-9723
Reports to: Virginia Buckingham, Chief of Staff

PERSONAL INFORMATION:
Born: Jan. 17, 1964 **Place of Birth:** Boston
Marital Status: married (Peter Ferrara) **Children:** 1
Education: Northeastern University (B.S. '88); Suffolk University Law School (J.D. '95)
Previous Employment: McDermott, Will & Emery
Years in Current Position: 1 **Years in State Service:** 5

Russell D. Aims

Deputy Chief of Staff

Office of the Governor
Address: State House, Suite 360, Boston, MA 02133
Staff: Christina Campbell, Administrative Assistant
Telephone: (617) 727-3600
E-mail: Russell.Aims@state.ma.us
Reports to: Chief of Staff Virginia Buckingham

PERSONAL INFORMATION:

Born: July 9, 1961 **Place of Birth:** Bridgeport, CT
Education: University of Wyoming (B.S., Political Science, '83)
Previous Employment: Governor's Office (Assistant Chief of Staff, '93-'97); Executive Office for Administration and Finance (Special Assistant to Secretary, '93); Division of Capital Planning and Operations (Special Assistant to Commissioner, '91-'93); Executive Office of Communities and Development (Special Assistant to Secretary, '91); Massachusetts House of Representatives (Senior Research Analyst, '87-'91); New England Conservatory of Music (Assistant Director of Admissions/International Student Advisor, '83-'88)
Years in Current Position: 1 **Years in State Service:** 10

William S. Smith

Assistant Chief of Staff/Federal Relations

Office of the Governor
Address: State House, Room 360, Boston, MA 02133
Telephone: (617) 727-3600
Fax: (617) 727-8685 **E-mail:** billsmith@state.ma.us
Reports to: Chief of Staff Virginia Buckingham

PERSONAL INFORMATION:
Born: September 23, 1959
Place of Birth: Rockville Centre, NY
Marital Status: married (Laura) **Children:** 1
Education: Georgetown University (B.A., History, '81); Catholic University (M.A., Political Philosophy, '85)
Previous Employment: Massachusetts Executive Office of Economic Affairs; various positions in the federal, legislative and executive branches (Washington, D.C.)
Years in Current Position: 1 **Years in State Service:** 4.5

JOB DESCRIPTION:
Provide analysis and advice to the Chief of Staff and the Governor on federal policy impacting Massachusetts.

1999 PRIORITIES:
As Congress makes significant changes, to protect the interests of Massachusetts taxpayers consistent with the national interests.

Jennifer D. Carey

Special Assistant to the Governor

Office of the Governor
Address: State House, Room 360, Boston, MA 02133
Telephone: (617) 727-3600 **Fax:** (617) 727-8685
E-mail: Jennifer.Davis.Carey@state.ma.us
Staff: Jennifer N. Ramos, Administrative Assistant
Reports to: GovernorA. Paul Cellucci

PERSONAL INFORMATION:
Born: October 2. 1956 **Place of Birth:** Brooklyn, New York
Marital Status: married (Robert) **Children:** 3
Education: Harvard and Radcliffe, (A.B. '78); Harvard Graduate School of Education (Ed.M; Ed.D.)
Previous Employment: Bancroft School (Upper School Administrative Team); Harvard and Radcliffe Colleges (Admissions Officer; Dir. of Minority Recruitment Program)
Years in Current Position: new **Years in State Service:** new

JOB DESCRIPTION:
Coordinate and direct projects of Governor's Advisory Commission (Latin American, African American, Native American, Asian American, Gay & Lesbian Youth); oversee constituent concerns; community outreach; develop education policy; serve as liaison to Legislative Black Caucus.

1999 PRIORITIES:
To continue to work to fully implement education reform, to bring the issues of the Commissions to the Governor's table.

ORGANIZATIONS:
Girls, Inc. (Board of Directors); YWCA (Policy Committee); MLK Breakfast Committee, (Essay Committee); Massachusetts Academy of Arts, Science Advisory Board

Charles B. King

Deputy Chief Secretary

Office of the Governor
Address: State House, Room 280, Boston, MA 02133
Telephone: (617) 727-5787
Fax: (617) 727-8136 **E-mail:** Charles B. King@state.ma.us
Reports to: Chief Secretary Stephen O'Neill

PERSONAL INFORMATION:
Born: November 1, 1960 **Place of Birth:** Worcester
Marital Status: single
Education: Nichols College (B.A. '87)
Previous Employment: MA Division of Insurance
Years in Current Position: 1 **Years in State Service:** 2

JOB DESCRIPTION:
Managing the daily operations of the Chief Secretary's Office

Stephen R. Doody

Deputy Chief Secretary

Office of the Governor
Address: State House, Room 280, Boston, MA 02133
Telephone: (617) 727-5787
Fax: (617) 727-8136
E-mail: Stephen.R.Doody@state.ma.us
Reports to: Chief Secretary Stephen O'Neill

PERSONAL INFORMATION:
Born: November 7, 1966 **Place of Birth:** Weymouth
Marital Status: single
Education: University of Massachusetts/Amherst (B.A. '89)
Previous Employment: The Patriot Ledger (High School Sports Correspondent); Governor's's Office of External Relations (Correspondence Aide); Office of the Chief Secretary (Personnel Officer, Personnel Director, Deputy Chief Secretary)
Years in Current Position: 1 **Years in State Service:** 7

JOB DESCRIPTION:
Help manage the daily operations of the Chief Secretary's office.

Paul W. Johnson

Chief Legal Counsel to the Governor

Office of the Governor
Address: State House, Room 271, Boston, MA 02133
Telephone: (617) 727-2065 ext. 360
Fax: (617) 727-8290 **E-mail:** PWJohnson@state.ma.us
Staff: Sharon Jones, Administrative Assistant
Reports to: Governor A. Paul Cellucci

PERSONAL INFORMATION:
Born: November 7, 1950 **Place of Birth:** Rochester, MN
Marital Status: married (Paula J. Popeo) **Children:** 2
Education: Harvard College (B.A., '72); Harvard Law School (J.D., '75)
Previous Employment: Smith, Duggan & Johnson (Partner); Civil Division, U.S. Attorney's Office (Chief); Massachusetts Department of the Attorney General (Assistant Attorney General)
Years in Current Position: 2 **Years in State Service:** 7

JOB DESCRIPTION:
Advise the Governor on legal matters, including legislation and the selection of judges.

Laurie R. Wallach

Deputy Chief Legal Counsel

Office of the Governor
Address: State House, Room 271, Boston, MA 02133
Telephone: (617) 727-2065 **Fax:** (617) 727-8290
Reports to: Chief Legal Counsel Paul Johnson

PERSONAL INFORMATION:
Education: Yale College (B.A. '81); Cambridge University (M. Phil); Yale Law School (J.D. '86)
Previous Employment: Ropes & Gray (Associate); Office of the Independent Counsel, Iran-Contra (Associate Independent Counsel); The Honorable Jon O. Newman, U.S. Court of Appeals for the Second Circuit (Law Clerk)
Years in Current Position: 2 **Years in State Service:** 2

Yvonne E. Boyle

Director of Planning & Scheduling

Office of the Governor
Address: State House, Suite 360, Boston, MA 02133
Telephone: (617) 727-3600 **Fax:** (617) 727-9723
Staff: Lara Whelan, Deputy Scheduler for Mrs. Cellucci; Wendy Abraham, Assistant Deputy Scheduler
Reports to: Governor A. Paul Cellucci

PERSONAL INFORMATION:
Born: September 20, 1945
Place of Birth: West Virginia **Children:** 2
Education: University of Miami (B.A., Education, '67)
Previous Employment: Dan Daly for U.S. Senate (Scheduler and Event Coordinator); Edgartown Schools (Teacher)
Years in Current Position: 8 **Years in State Service:** 10

JOB DESCRIPTION:
To coordinate requests for appointments with the Governor, both inside and outside the State House. To review correspondence and phone requests for meetings with or appearances by the Governor. To oversee the scheduling of the Governor's calendar.

ORGANIZATIONS:
Edgartown Yacht Club; Charlestown Republican Committee

Robert J. Garrity

Deputy Director of Legislative Affairs

Office of the Governor
Address: State House, Room 160, Boston, MA 02133
Telephone: (617) 727-7238 **Fax:** (617) 727-8840
Staff: Alison Wilkie, Chris Ragusa
Reports to: Chief of Staff Stephen O'Neill

PERSONAL INFORMATION:
Born: June 21, 1971 **Place of Birth:** Attleboro
Marital Status: married (Kim) **Children**: 2
Education: Northeastern University (B.S.)
Previous Employment: Deputy Director of Legislative Affairs (Office of the Governor); Executive Office of Environmental Affairs (Legislative Director); State Senator Lucile Hicks (Legislative Aide)
Years in Current Position: new **Years in State Service:** 5

JOB DESCRIPTION:
Implement Governor's legislative agenda; act as liaison between legislators and administration; coordinate administration review of all bills laid before the Governor.

ORGANIZATIONS:
Norfolk Personnel Board (1960-present); Republican Town Committee

Ilene D. Hoffer

Press Secretary

Office of the Governor
Address: State House, Room 265, Boston, MA 02133
Telephone: (617) 727-2759 **Fax:** (617) 727-9416
E-mail: ihoffer@state.ma.us
Staff: Bridget Goertz, Operations Manager
Reports to: Governor A. Paul Cellucci

PERSONAL INFORMATION:
Born: Dec. 31, 1970 **Place of Birth:** Chicago
Education: Tufts University (B.A. '92)
Previous Employment: Deputy Press Secretary, Governor's Office; Issues Director, Weld-Cellucci Re-election '94; Speechwriter, Governor's Office.
Years in Current Position: new **Years in State Government:** 5

JOB DESCRIPTION:
Act as chief spokesperson for the Cellucci administration.

Elizabeth R. Closs
Administrator of Governor's Commission on Mental Retardation

Office of the Governor
Address: One Ashburton Place, Rm 805 Boston, MA 02108
Telephone: (617) 727-0517 **Fax:** (617) 727-0887 **E-mail:** bcloss@state.ma.us
Staff: Barbara Mazzella, Alison Cohen, Policy Analyst; Emily Micolonghi, Executive Assistant
Reports to: Chief of Staff Virginia Buckingham

PERSONAL INFORMATION:
Born: July 5, 1959 **Place of Birth:** Richmond, VA
Education: Vassar College (A.B., '80); Harvard University (M.T.S., '83); Simmons College School of Social Work (M.S.W., '87) **Children:** 2
Previous Employment: Bay Core Human Services (MR Residential Director)
Years in Current Position: 3 **Years in State Service:** 3

JOB DESCRIPTION:
Support 11-member volunteer commission to achieve its priorities; policy analysis, planning events, monitoring in-house complaint process.

1999 PRIORITIES:
Support 11-member volunteer commission to define and achieve its priorities; develop major report on school-to-work transition for youth with disabilities; continue to work with Department of Mental Retardation to reduce the waiting list and inappropriate nursing home placements.

ORGANIZATIONS:
American Association on Mental Retardation

Barbara G. Burke
Director of External Relations

Office of the Governor
Address: State House, Room 111, Boston, MA 02133
Telephone: (617) 727-6250 **E-mail:** Barbara G.Burke@state.ma.us
Fax: (617) 727-9725
Reports to: Chief of Staff Virginia Buckingham

PERSONAL INFORMATION:
Born: July 23, 1957 **Place of Birth:** Boston
Education: University of Massachusetts (B.A. '90, M.Ed. '93)
Previous Employment: Executive Assistant to Governor's Chief Legal Counsel
Years in Current Position: 1 **Years in State Service:** 19

JOB DESCRIPTION:

To manage the Office of External Relations with responsibility for the Governor's correspondence, constituent services and proclamations.

Theresa E. Dolan

Director of Office Administration

Office of the Governor
Address: State House, Room 487, Boston, MA 02133
Telephone: (617) 727-5415 **Fax:** (617) 727-8685
E-mail: tdolan@state.ma.us
Staff: Susan A. Carter, Dep. Dir.; Audrey Schindler, Admin. Assistant
Reports to: Chief of Staff Virginia Buckingham

PERSONAL INFORMATION:
Born: June 25, 1948 **Place of Birth:** Boston
Marital Status: single
Education: Regis College (B.A., '70); Simmons College Graduate School of Management (M.B.A., '78)
Previous Employment: Massachusetts Department of Public Health (Special Assistant to Deputy Commissioner); Massachusetts General Hospital (Unit Manage)
Years in Current Position: 14 **Years in State Service:** 16

JOB DESCRIPTION:
To oversee the internal accounts payable, payroll, purchasing, payroll, human resources, benefits, accounting, administrative, and budget functions for the Office of the Governor.

ORGANIZATIONS:
American Cancer Society, Central Boston Unit (Board of Directors; Executive Committee; Service Committee); Affiliated Community VNAs of the South Shore, Inc. (Board of Directors' Member, Management Board)

Peter J. Abair

Director

Western Regional Office of the Governor
Address: 436 Dwight Street., Rm 300, Springfield, MA
Telephone: (413) 784-1200 **Fax:** (413) 784-1202
E-mail: peter.abair@state.ma.us
Staff: Michell Borgatti, Administrative Assistant; Mary Jenewin-Caplin, Deputy Director
Reports to: Chief of Staff Virginia Buckingham

PERSONAL INFORMATION:
Born: Jan. 17, 1965 **Place of Birth:** Pittsfield
Marital Status: married (Linda) **Education:** Boston University (B.A. '86))
Previous Employment: Mass. Executive Office of Education (Director of Governmental Affairs & Parent Information), State Senator Lucile P. Hicks (Legislative Assistant); U.S. Rep. Silvio O. Conte (Legislative Aide)
Years in Current Position: 1 **Years in State Service:** 6

JOB DESCRIPTION:
Report to the Governor and his cabinet on issues affecting western Massachusetts; serve as intermediary between citizens in Western Massachusetts and state agencies; provide greater access to state government for Western

Mass. citizens. The western regional office serves the four counties of ; Berkshire, Franklin, Hampden, and Hampshire.

PRIORITIES FOR 1999:
Work with regional leaders on promoting continued regional economic development and job creation; and ensure continued provision of state services to the citizens of western Massachusetts.

ORGANIZATION:
Pioneer Valley Plan for Progress; Berkshire Council for Growth

Governor's Executive Council

The Governor's Executive Council is composed of the Lieutenant Governor and eight individuals who are elected from districts composed of five contiguous state senatorial districts. Councilors serve two-year terms and are compensated in the amount of $15,600 per year. The Council is responsible for providing advice and consent in the following areas:

- Warrants for payment of bills of the Commonwealth
- Pardons and commutations
- Judicial and quasi-judicial appointments by the Governor
- Veterans' appeals
- Compilation and certification of election results
- Prorogation of the legislature
- Calling a special session of the legislature
- Disability retirement for judges
- Appointments of notaries public and justices of the peace

The Governor's Council can be reached at the following address:

The Governor's Council

The State House, Room 184
Boston, MA 02133
(617) 727-2756

Extension 0 (for office)

Governor's Executive Council

First District	***David Francis Constantine***	*(617) 727-2756 ext. 1*
Second District	***Kelly A. Timilty***	*(617) 727-2756 ext. 2*
Third District	***Marilyn Petitto Devaney***	*(617) 727-2756 ext. 3*
Fourth District	***Christopher A. Iannella Jr.***	*(617) 727-2756 ext. 4*
Fifth District	***Patricia A. Dowling***	*(617) 727-2756 ext. 5*
Sixth District	***Michael J. Callahan***	*(617) 727-2756 ext. 6*
Seventh District	***Dennis P. McManus***	*(617) 727-2756 ext. 7*
Eighth District	***Edward M. O'Brien***	*(617) 727-2756 ext. 8*

David Francis Constantine

1st District

Address: State House, Room 184, Boston, MA 02133
Telephone: (617) 727-2756 **Fax:** (617) 742-4722
Staff: George Cronin, Administrative Secretary

PERSONAL INFORMATION:
Born: Nov. 11, 1937 **Place of Birth:** New Bedford
Education: Stonehill College (B.S. '59); Tufts School of Dental Medicine (D.M.D. '63); Boston School of Graduate Dentistry "65)
Public Office: Board of Health (Member), New Bedford, ('77-87); Board of Health (Chairman) New Bedford, (1987-present)

JOB DESCRIPTION:
Approve executive appointments to judicial and quasi-judicial state positions; approve payment of weekly warrant; approve pardons and commutations

ORGANIZATIONS:
American Association of Oral & Maxillofacial Surgeons; ADA; Mass. Dental Society, S.E. District & N.E. Dental Society; Mass. Association of Health Boards; Knights of Columbus; Sussaquin Lions Club.

Kelly A. Timilty

2nd District

Address: State House, Room 184, Boston, MA 02133
Telephone: (617) 727-2756 **Fax:** (617) 742-4722
Staff: George Cronin, Administrative Secretary

PERSONAL INFORMATION:
Born: Oct. 14, 1962
Education: University of Maryland, (M.D., B.A. '86)
Public Office: Executive Council, 1995-2000

JOB DESCRIPTION:
Approve executive appointments to judicial and quasi-judicial state positions; approve payment of weekly warrant; approve pardons and commutations

Christopher A. Iannella, Jr.

4th District

Address: State House, Room 184, Boston, MA 02133
Telephone: (617) 727-2756 **Fax:** (617) 742-4722
Staff: George Cronin, Administrative Secretary

PERSONAL INFORMATION:
Born: Nov. 6, 1952 **Place of Birth:** Boston
Education: Boston College; Suffolk Law School
Public Office: Executive Council, 1985-90; 1993-00.

JOB DESCRIPTION:
Approve executive appointments to judicial and quasi-judicial state positions; approve payment of weekly warrant; approve pardons and commutations

Patricia A. Dowling

5th District

Address: State House, Room 184, Boston, MA 02133
Telephone: (617) 727-2756 **Fax:** (617) 742-4722
Staff: George Cronin, Administrative Secretary

PERSONAL INFORMATION:
Born: Dec. 10, 1957 **Place of Birth:** Lawrence
Education: Skidmore College; Suffolk University Law School
Public Office: Executive Council 1995-00; Mayor City of Lawrence 1998-01.

JOB DESCRIPTION:
Approve executive appointments to judicial and quasi-judicial state positions; approve payment of weekly warrant; approve pardons and commutations

ORGANIZATIONS:
Massachusetts Bar Association; Essex County Bar Association; Lawrence Bar Association; Lawyers Concerned for Lawyers; Greater Lawrence YWCA, Board of Advisors.

Dennis P. McManus

7th District

Address: State House, Room 184, Boston, MA 02133
Telephone: (617) 727-2756 **Fax:** (617) 742-4722
Staff: George Cronin, Administrative Secretary

PERSONAL INFORMATION:
Born: April 18, 1967 **Place of Birth:** Worcester
Education: University of Massachusetts (B.A. '89); Suffolk University Law School (J.D. '93)
Public Office: Executive Council 1999-2000

JOB DESCRIPTION:
Voting on executive nominations to judicial and quasi-judicial state positions; voting on pardons and commutations as recommended by the Executive; voting on payment of weekly warrant

ORGANIZATIONS:
Knights of Columbus, Worcester County Bar Association

Edward M. O'Brien

8th District

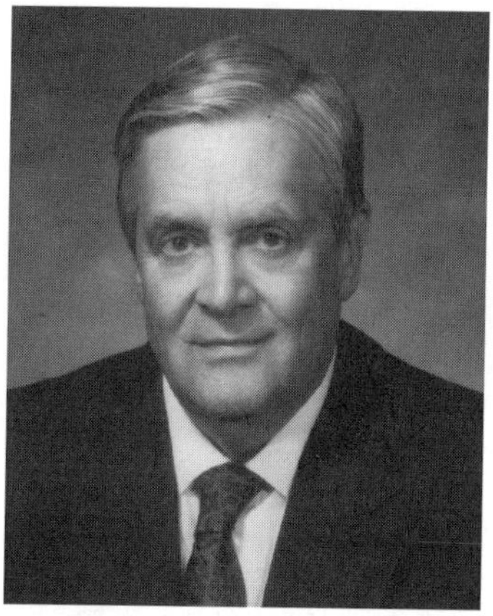

Address: State House, Room 184, Boston, MA 02133
Telephone: (617) 727-2756 **Fax:** (617) 742-4722
Staff: George Cronin, Administrative Secretary

PERSONAL INFORMATION:
Born: March 30, 1933
Place of Birth: Easthampton
Marital Status: married (Ann Lewonis O'Brien)
Children: 5
Education: Yale (B.A. '54); Boston College Law School (J.D. '57)
Public Office: Secretary to the Governor (Furcolo), 1958-61; Hampshire County Commissioner, 1968-72; Executive Council, 1971-74; 1979-00.

JOB DESCRIPTION:
Approve executive appointments to judicial and quasi-judicial state positions; approve payment of weekly warrant; approve pardons and commutations

1999 PRIORITIES:
Improvement of Massachusetts judiciary.

ORGANIZATIONS:
Knights of Columbus, Pulaski Club, Friends of Sinn Fein, Hampshire, Hampden and Massachusetts Bar Associations, Democratic State Committee

Secretary of the Commonwealth

The Secretary of the Commonwealth is the chief record-keeping, public information, and elections officer of the Commonwealth. The responsibilities of this office include the maintenance of public records, administration of elections, storage of historical data, preservation of historical sites, registering of corporations, and filing and distribution of regulations and public documents. The Office of the Secretary of the Commonwealth is divided into the following administrative and functional units:

- *Archives Division*
- *Central Voter Registration*
- *Central Services Division*
- *Citizen Information Service*
- *Commonwealth Museum*
- *Corporations Division*
- *Elections Division*
- *Government Affairs Division*
- *Massachusetts Historical Commission*
- *Personnel Division*
- *Publications Division*
- *Public Records Division*
- *Rules and Regulations Division*
- *Securities Division*
- *State House Bookstore*
- *State Records Center*
- *Tours and Government Education Division*

Archives Division

The Archives Division is charged with storage, preservation, and management of the historic documents of the Commonwealth. The division operates an archives research room at Columbia Point, which is open to the public.

Citizen Information Service

The Citizen Information Service is the state's primary information and referral system. It offers information on state programs and services and directs callers to the governmental office that can best handle their inquiries.

Commonwealth Museum

The Commonwealth Museum features exhibits on the people, places, and politics of Massachusetts. The museum provides educational materials, traveling exhibits, and special programs.

Corporations Division

The Corporations Division maintains a registry of all business and non-profit corporations organized in Massachusetts and all out-of-state corporations doing business in the state. Information processed by the division includes the names and addresses of all corporate officers and the amount of stock issued. The Corporations Division also oversees the registration of trusts, limited partnerships, trademarks, and service marks.

Elections Division

The Elections Division administers all state and county elections. It prints and distributes nomination papers for candidates, certifies the signatures on nomination papers and initiative and referendum petitions, prints ballots, trains local election officials, and tabulates election results. The office provides information on laws and regulations governing the election process.

Massachusetts Historical Commission

The Massachusetts Historical Commission oversees historic preservation programs and administers the funding of such endeavors. Its goal of identifying and protecting the cultural heritage of the Commonwealth is addressed in conjunction with local historical commissions, which work with the state agency in formulating preservation plans. The Massachusetts Historical Commission is the liaison through which local commissions gain listings in the National Register of Historic Places, and it oversees the office of the State Archaeologist.

Public Records Division

The Public Records Division is a repository for many types of public records. The office can provide descriptions of the management information systems held by the various state agencies. Lobbyists and their employers must register and file their semi-annual financial disclosure reports with this office. It administers the campaign finance reports of candidates for federal office. The Public Records Division also keeps on file listings of ward and town political committees, pardons, and criminal renditions from other states. The Commissions Section of the office swears in and renews the certification of notaries public and justices of the peace. It also maintains a file of all local option statutes adopted by the cities and towns of the Commonwealth and the names of all appointed and elected officials serving on local and regional boards and authorities.

Rules and Regulations Division

The Rules and Regulations Division is responsible for publishing all acts and resolves passed during the legislative session, as well as updates to the Code of Massachusetts Regulations, the vehicle by which statutes are executed in the Commonwealth. This division also publishes executive orders issued by the constitutional officers and advisory opinions released by the attorney general and certain other state agencies. The Rules and Regulations Division publishes a listing of contract opportunities for purchase of goods and services by the state and provides information on local, regional, and state capital planning and operations projects. All of the publications listed above are available in the State Bookstore.

Securities Division

The Securities Division administers the state's Uniform Securities Act and regulates the activities of securities issuers and agents doing business in Massachusetts. The division licenses stockbrokers and brokerage firms and investigates citizen complaints about alleged fraudulent business practices. This office also certifies that stocks and other investments traded in the Commonwealth comply with certain filing and financial disclosure requirements.

State Records Center

The State Records Center maintains files of all non-current records of state agencies and departments. Records of agencies may not be destroyed without prior approval of the Records Conservation Board. A required records retention period is either established in statute or determined by the board.

Tours and Government Education Division

The Tours and Government Education Division provides two types of free, guided tours of the State House to groups and individuals — one focusing upon artistic, architectural, and historic points of interest, and the other presenting a functional overview of state government and the legislative process.

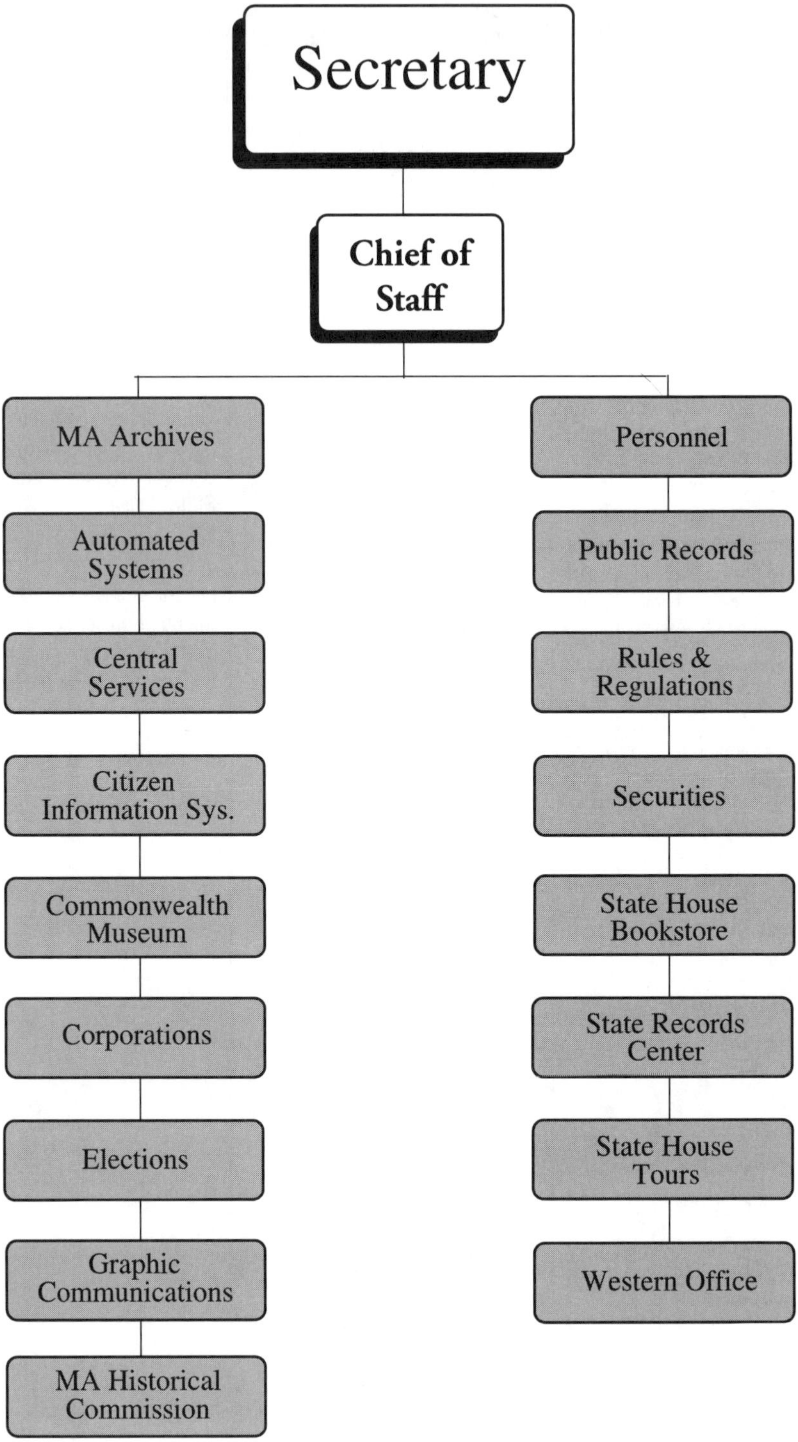
Secretary
Chief of Staff
MA Archives
Automated Systems
Central Services
Citizen Information Sys.
Commonwealth Museum
Corporations
Elections
Graphic Communications
MA Historical Commission
Personnel
Public Records
Rules & Regulations
Securities
State House Bookstore
State Records Center
State House Tours
Western Office

Office of the Secretary of the Commonwealth

Secretary of the Commonwealth	**William F. Galvin**	(617) 727-9180
Chief of Staff	**John K. McCarthy**	727-9180
Executive Assistant	**William B. Stewart**	727-2804
Legal Counsel	**Laurie Flynn**	727-4919
Special Assistant/Budget Director	**Philip L. Shea**	727-0556
Assistant Secretary	**Michael A. Maresco**	727-9180
Reigstry of Deeds	**Kevin R. Harvey**	727-2804

Directors:

Massachusetts Archives	**John D. Warner, Jr.**	727-2816
Automated Systems Division	**Kevin Thibault**	727-6400
Central Services Division	**Corolette Goodwin**	727-4590
Citizen Information Service	**Josephine Albanese**	727-7030
Commonwealth Museum	**Mary McCarthy-Collins**	727-9268
Corporations Division	**Laurie Flynn**	727-4919
Elections Division	**John Cloonan**	727-2828
Graphic Communications	**Josephine Fatta**	727-8437
Mass. Historical Commission	**Judith McDonough**	727-8470
Human Resources	**Bobbi Baker**	727-4918
Public Records	**Kelly MacWilliam**	727-2832
Rules and Regulations	**Steven Kfoury**	727-2831
Securities Division	**Matthew Nestor**	727-3548
State House Bookstore	**Janice Coughlin**	727-2834
State Records Center	**Anthony DeSantis**	727-2470
State House Tours	**Mary Rinehart-Stankiewicz**	727-3676

William F. Galvin

Secretary of the Commonwealth

Office of the Secretary of the Commonwealth
Address: State House, Room 337, Boston, MA 02133
Telephone: (617) 727-9180 **Fax:** (617)727-0556

PERSONAL INFORMATION:
Born: September 17, 1950
Marital Status: married (Eileen) **Children:** 1
Education: Boston College (Cum Laude, B.B., '72); Suffolk University School of Law (J.D., '75)
Previous Employment: Private practice of law
Years in Current Position: 4
Years in State Service: 18 ('75-'91 in Massachusetts House of Representatives)

JOB DESCRIPTION:
Serve the public as the information officer of the Commonwealth, the chief election officer, the regulator of all sales of securities, the Massachusetts Historical Commission, and all corporate registries; responsible for the promulgation of rules and regulations; custodian of official archives; and keeper of public records.

1999 PRIORITIES:
To implement the so-called Motor Voter Law; to promote economic growth by ease of corporate registration, better information for citizens making investments in securities.

John K. McCarthy

Chief of Staff

Office of the Secretary of the Commonwealth
Address: State House, Room 337, Boston, MA 02133
Telephone: (617) 727-8002 **Fax:** (617) 742-4722
Staff: Nancy Driscoll, Administrative Assistant

PERSONAL INFORMATION:
Born: May 12, 1958 **Place of Birth:** Boston
Marital Status: married (Linda) **Children:** 2
Education: Boston College (A.B., Economics/ Political Science, '80); Suffolk University School of Law (J.D., '88)
Previous Employment: Law firm of Carter and Carter (Attorney); Raytheon Company (Contract Administrator)
Years in Current Position: 2 **Years in State Service:** 4.5

JOB DESCRIPTION:
Responsible for management of 20 divisions with staff of 220 employees and annual budget of $13 million. Perform all statutory functions on behalf of the Secretary in his absence.

1999 PRIORITIES:
Increase office revenues while maintaining office administrative costs. Continue to expand policies in investor protection, voter participation, historic preservation and access to public records.

ORGANIZATIONS:
Massachusetts Bar Association; Norwood Democratic Town Committee; Massachusetts Moderators Association

Laurie Flynn

Legal Counsel to the Secretary of the Commonwealth/ Director of the Corporations Division

Office of the Secretary of the Commonwealth
Address: One Ashburton Place, Room 1710, Boston, MA 02108
Telephone: (617) 727-4919 **Fax:** (617) 742-4528

PERSONAL INFORMATION:
Education: Suffolk University ('78); Suffolk University Law School ('81)
Years in Current Position: 5 **Years in State Service:** 13

ORGANIZATIONS:
International Association of Corporate Administrators; Boston Bar Association; Massachusetts Bar Association

Philip L. Shea

Budget Director

Office of the Secretary of the Commonwealth
Address: One Ashburton Place, Room 1710, Boston, MA 02108
Telephone: (617) 727-0556 **Fax:** (617) 723-1372
Staff: Ruth Bitto, Lisa Perna, Administrative Assistants

PERSONAL INFORMATION:
Born: October 19, 1941 **Place of Birth:** Lowell
Marital Status: married (Keli Rae) **Children:** 4
Education: Bentley College ('62)
Previous Employment: Business Consultant (Self-Employed); Conifer Bank (Vice-President/Assistant to President); John J. Hurley and Co., C.P.A. (Senior Tax Accountant); Massachusetts State Senate ('79-'84); Massachusetts House of Representatives ('73-'79); Lowell City Council ('70-'73)
Years in Current Position: 4 **Years in State Service:** 16

JOB DESCRIPTION:
Administrative responsibility for all fiscal matters relating to the Secretary of the Commonwealth's office.

1999 PRIORITIES:
Continue to work with the fiscal affairs personnel of the various executive offices and legislative committees on behalf of the Secretary of the Commonwealth.

ORGANIZATIONS:
Bentley College Alumni Association; Lowell Boys Club Alumni Association (past Vice-President); Camp Paul for Exceptional Children (past Treasurer); Greater Lowell Mental Health Advisory Board (past Member)

Kevin R. Harvey

Assistant Secretary of the Commonwealth for Legislation

Office of the Secretary of the Commonwealth
Address: State House, Room 337, Boston, MA 02133
Telephone: (617) 727-2804 **Fax:** (617) 742-4722

PERSONAL INFORMATION:
Born: June 25, 1957 **Place of Birth:** Peabody
Marital Status: married (Robin)
Education: Salem State College (Ed/Business Administration, '80)
Years in Current Position: 4 **Years in State Service:** 15

JOB DESCRIPTION:
Responsible for all legislative activities.

ORGANIZATIONS:
Salem City Councilor ('85-present)

Michael A. Maresco

Assistant Secretary of the Commonwealth

Office of the Secretary of the Commonwealth
Address: State House, Room 337, Boston, MA 02133
Telephone: (617) 727-9180 **Fax:** (617) 742-4722
E-mail: MMaresco@SEC.state.ma.us

PERSONAL INFORMATION:
Born: June 20, 1962 **Place of Birth:** Malden
Marital Status: married (Kathleen)
Education: Suffolk University (B.S. and B.A., Marketing, '85); University of Massachusetts, McCormack Institute (M.S.P.A., June '94)
Years in Current Position: 6 **Years in State Service:** 18

JOB DESCRIPTION:
Lobbying for office legislative agenda and budget matters and representing the Secretary at various committees and meetings. Serve as Secretary's official designee to the Massachusetts Historic Commission.

1999 PRIORITIES:
FY'2000 Budget, Reauthorization of the Massachusetts Preservation Project Fund, Census/Redistricting Issues

ORGANIZATIONS:
Marshfield Democratic Town Committee; Marshfield Sons of Italy; Pope John XXIII High School Advisory Board; Newton Sons' of Italy; Elected member of the Marshfield Board of Assessors.

Attorney General

The Attorney General is the highest legal and law enforcement officer of the Commonwealth. The Attorney General advises and represents the Commonwealth in matters in which it has legal interest, and is the chief prosecutor for the state and represents the state in legal proceedings in which it is the defendant. The Attorney General may also represent the public in affirmative litigation.

The Office of the Attorney General is divided into the following bureaus:

- *Executive Bureau*
- *Business and Labor Protection Bureau*
- *Criminal Bureau*
- *Family and Community Crimes Bureau*
- *Government Bureau*
- *Public Protection Bureau*

Executive Bureau

The Executive Bureau is charged with the overall responsibility for administration, supervision, policy-setting and training of staff in the Office of the Attorney General. In addition, the bureau handles a number of specialized functions, including constituent relations and legislative affairs.

Within the Executive Bureau the First Assistant Attorney General is the principal legal advisor to the Attorney General responsible for reviewing and approving case-related matters including amicus requests and authorizing legal positions of the office. The Chief of Staff is responsible for implementation of policies and priorities; supervision of legislative and press operations, budget and personnel office. The Chief of Staff also advises and consults with the Attorney General and First Assistant Attorney General. The Legal Counsel to the Attorney General is responsible for addressing employee related issues including internal ethical and conflicts of interest questions, establishing office-wide policies on a range of issues, organizing and conducting office-wide training on personnel matters, and handling special legal projects as required by the First Assistant General and the Attorney General. The First Assistant Attorney General staff oversees intergovernmental affairs of the Office including legislative initiatives and relations with the National Association of Attorneys General, the Dept. of Justice and other Attorneys General offices. The Legislative Liaison assists in preparing, filing, and monitoring legislation on behalf of the Attorney General and other legislation important to the office.

Business and Labor Protection Bureau

The Business and Labor Protection Bureau is comprised of the following divisions:

- *Unemployment Fraud Division*
- *Fair Labor and Business Practices*
- *Insurance Fraud Division*
- *Medicaid Fraud Control Unit*

Pursuant to its authority under the Massachusetts General Laws Chapter 151A Section 47, the Unemployment Fraud Division enforces the actions involving employer tax fraud and misrepresentations to obtain unemployment benefits. These cases are prosecuted in the District and Superior courts.

While the division primarily receives referrals from the Division of Employment and Training (DET), it also generates its own independent actions. Through the use of resources in other divisions in the Business and Labor Protection Bureau, the Unemployment Fraud Division targets complex and sophisticated schemes involving various combinations of employment security fraud, prevailing wage, and workers compensation violations. This interdisciplinary effort has been instrumental in the division's investigation and successful prosecution of egregious violators.

The Fair Labor and Business Practices Division investigates and prosecutes employers who fail to contribute to the unemployment fund and employees who make fraudulent claims. It also prosecutes individuals who defraud the unemployment fund by way of complex schemes. The division also investigates and prosecutes general contractors and subcontractors for failure to pay prevailing wages to their employees on public work projects; and prosecutes employers who fail to pay wages, minimum wage, overtime pay, and vacation pay. It investigates and prosecutes violations of child labor laws and work-related injuries to minors, grants workplace procedure waivers, and inspects workplace safety on construction sites, industrial sites, and in the manufacturing industry. It also investigates work-related fatalities throughout the state.

The Medicaid Fraud Control Unit investigates and prosecutes allegations of fraud and larceny of providers in the Medicaid system–doctors, pharmacists, nursing home owners and administrators, and other providers of health care goods and services. It also investigates and prosecutes care givers in nursing homes who abuse, neglect, and mistreat residents in long-term care facilities.

The Insurance Fraud Division investigates and prosecutes all types of insurance fraud and related larcenies in superior and district courts. Most of the division's cases are investigated by the Massachusetts Insurance Fraud Bureau, a private agency operated by the insurance industry. The division works closely with the Massachusetts State Police, the Governor's Auto Theft Strike Force, and the Department of Industrial Accidents. Referrals are also received from attorneys, judges, local police departments, and federal agencies.

Criminal Bureau

The Criminal Bureau investigates and prosecutes all criminal cases in which the state is a plaintiff. It provides district attorneys and local law enforcement officials with technical investigative assistance and works in conjunction with federal law enforcement agencies on matters of shared jurisdiction. The Criminal Bureau is functionally divided into the following offices:

- *Appellate Division*
- *Economic Crimes Division*
- *Environmental Crimes Strike Force*
- *Safe Neighborhood Initiative*
- *Narcotics & Organized Crime/Special Investigations*
- *High Technology Crimes Unit*
- *Asset Forfeiture Unit*
- *Public Integrity*

Family and Community Crimes Bureau

The Family and Community Crimes Bureau is responsible for policy and program development in four areas: issues affecting children, the elderly, and persons with disabilities, including abuse, neglect, and financial exploitation; juvenile justice; and domestic violence. It oversees the work of the Victim Witness Assistance Board and supervises the Victim Compensation and Assistance Division. It works closely with the Government Bureau and the Consumer Protection Division of the Public Protection Bureau, and other agencies, including the Executive Office of Elder Affairs and the Massachusetts Office of Victim Assistance, on issues of common concern.

Government Bureau

The Government Bureau litigates on behalf of executive branch agencies and departments, usually when agency rules or regulations are challenged. The Bureau is divided administratively into the Administrative Law Division, the Trial Division, and the Environmental Protection Division. The Administrative Law Division defends state officials and agencies against lawsuits challenging the legality of government operations. It is responsible for rendering formal advisory opinions of the Attorney General, and it reviews new home rule charters and municipal bylaws for constitutionality. In addition, this office initiates affirmative litigation on behalf of the state and its agencies.

The Trial Division represents the Commonwealth and its agencies in all civil litigation and is made up of the following offices:

- *Contracts*
- *Real Estate*
- *Torts*
- *Eminent domain*

Public Protection Bureau

The Public Protection Bureau prosecutes civil cases in which the state is a plaintiff and conducts affirmative litigation for individuals and state agencies involved in applicable lawsuits. This bureau investigates consumer complaints and represents the public interest in consumer matters, environmental protection, civil liberties, and other areas. The office is made up of the following divisions:

- *Consumer Protection and Antitrust*
- *Civil Investigation*
- *Civil Rights and Civil Liberties*
- *Public Charities*
- *Regulated Industries*

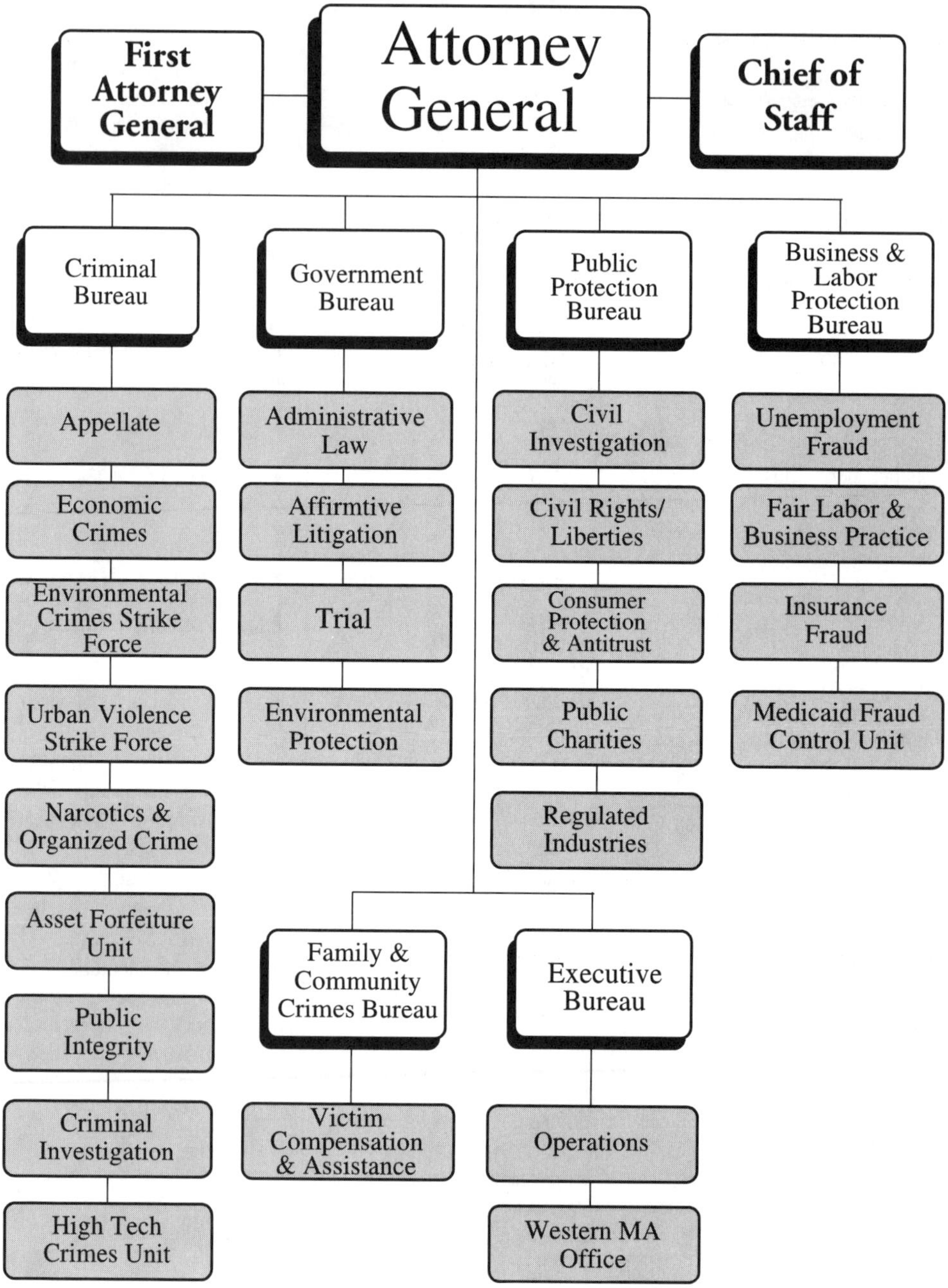
Attorney General
First Attorney General
Chief of Staff
Criminal Bureau
Government Bureau
Public Protection Bureau
Business & Labor Protection Bureau
Appellate
Economic Crimes
Environmental Crimes Strike Force
Urban Violence Strike Force
Narcotics & Organized Crime
Asset Forfeiture Unit
Public Integrity
Criminal Investigation
High Tech Crimes Unit
Administrative Law
Affirmtive Litigation
Trial
Environmental Protection
Civil Investigation
Civil Rights/ Liberties
Consumer Protection & Antitrust
Public Charities
Regulated Industries
Unemployment Fraud
Fair Labor & Business Practice
Insurance Fraud
Medicaid Fraud Control Unit
Family & Community Crimes Bureau
Victim Compensation & Assistance
Executive Bureau
Operations
Western MA Office

Office of the Attorney General

Attorney General	**Thomas Reilly**	(617) 727-2200

EXECUTIVE BUREAU

First Assistant Attorney General	**Dean Richlin**	727-2200
Chief of Staff	**Vacant**	
Acting Deputy Chief of Staff	**Jill Reilly**	727-2200
Acting Deputy Chief of Staff	**Jeff Shapiro**	727-2200
Chief, Western Massachusetts Office, Springfield	**Judy Zeprun-Kalman**	(413) 784-1240
Director of Operations	**Frank Velluto**	727-2200
Librarian	**Karin Thurman**	727-2200
Legal Counsel to the Attorney General	**LaDonna Hatton**	727-2200
Directors:		
Budget	**Vacant**	727-2200
Human Resource Management	**Diana LaRochelle**	727-2200
Communications	**Brian Heffron**	727-2200
Information Technology	**Paula Durant**	727-2543
Intergovernmental Affairs	**Jason Queenin**	727-2200

GOVERNMENT BUREAU

Bureau Chief	**Alice E. Moore**	727-2200
Deputy Bureau Chief	**Peter Sacks**	727-2200
Affirmative Litigation Coordinator	**Ernest Sarason, Jr.**	727-2200
Appeals Coordinator	**John Bowman**	727-2200
Bureau Training Coordinator	**Pierce O. Cray**	727-2200
Division Chiefs:		
Administrative Law	**Judith Yogman**	727-2200

Trial	**John Bigelow**	*727-2200*
Environmental Protection	**James R. Milkey**	*727-2200*

BUSINESS AND LABOR PROTECTION BUREAU

Acting Bureau Chief	**Stuart T. Rossman**	*727-2200*
Deputy Bureau Chief	**Anthony E. Penski**	*727-2200*
Fair Labor & Business Practices Division	**Barbara Piselli**	*727-2200*
Insurance Fraud Division	**John Ciardi**	*727-2200*
Medicaid Fraud Control Unit	**Nicholas J. Messuri**	*727-2200*
Unemployment Fraud Division	**Gina Walcott**	*727-2200*
Chief Prosecutor	**David R. Marks**	*727-2200*

CRIMINAL BUREAU

Bureau Chief	**Gerard T. Leone**	*727-2200*
First Deputy Bureau Chief	**Kurt Schwartz**	*727-2200*
Deputy Bureau Chief	**Susan Spurlock**	*727-2200*
Deputy Bureau Chief of Litigation	**Mark Smith**	*727-2200*
Division Chiefs:		
Appellate	**Pam Hunt**	*727-2200*
Criminal Investigations	**Det./Lt. Mark Delaney**	*727-2200*
Economic Crimes	**Carol A. Starkey**	*727-2200*
Environmental Crimes	**Martin Levin**	*727-2200*
Financial Investigations	**Paul Stewart**	*727-2200*
Narcotics and Special Investigations	**Mark Smith**	*727-2200*
Public Integrity	**Jeremy Silverfine**	*727-2200*
High Technology Crime Unit	**Gregory Motta**	*727-2200*

PUBLIC PROTECTION BUREAU

Acting Bureau Chief	**Freda K. Fishman**	727-2200
Division Chiefs:		
Consumer Protection/Antitrust	**William Porter**	727-2200
Civil Rights/Civil Liberties	**Richard W. Cole**	727-2200
Public Charities (Acting)	**Eric Carriker**	727-2200
Regulated Industries	**George Dean**	727-2200
Civil Investigations	**Karen Ortolino**	727-2200

FAMILY AND COMMUNITY CRIMES BUREAU

Bureau Chief (Acting)	**Joseph Whalen**	727-2200
Division Chief, Victim Compensation and Assistance	**Judith Beals**	727-2200

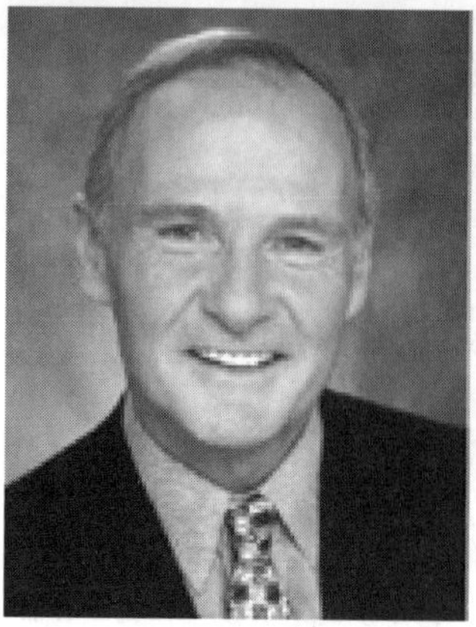

Thomas Reilly
Attorney General

Office of the Attorney General
Address: One Ashburton Place, 20th Floor, Boston, MA 02108
Telephone: (617) 727-2200 **Fax:** (617) 727-6016
Staff: Diane McDonald, Assistant
Reports to: Governor A. Paul Cellucci

PERSONAL INFORMATION:
Place of Birth: Springfield
Marital Status: married (Ruth) **Children:** 3
Education: American International College (B.A. '64); Boston College Law School (J.D. '70)
Previous Employment: Civil Rights Division of the Attorney General's Office; District Attorney Middlesex County
Years in Current Position: 7 **Years in State Service:** 25

JOB DESCRIPTION:
The Attorney General serves as the Commonwealth's chief lawyer and law enforcement official, supervising a diverse legal staff of approximately 200 lawyers. The Office of the Attorney General is divided into six bureaus: Executive, Government, Criminal, Business and Labor Protection, Public Protection, and Family and Community Crimes.

James R. Milkey
Chief, Environmental Protection Division

Government Bureau
Address: 200 Portland Street, Boston, MA 02114
Telephone: (617) 727-2200 **Fax:** (617) 727-9665
Staff: Marianne Ricca, Secretary
Reports to: Government Bureau Chief Peter Sacks

PERSONAL INFORMATION:
Born: December 17, 1956
Place of Birth: Hartford, CT
Marital Status: married (Cathie Jo Martin) **Children:** 2
Education: Harvard College (A.B., '78); Harvard Law School (J.D., '83); Massachusetts Institute of Technology (M.C.P., '83)
Previous Employment: Pace Law School (Visiting Associate Professor, '94-'95); Massachusetts Office of the Attorney General ('84)
Years in Current Position: 3 **Years in State Service:** 14

JOB DESCRIPTION:
Supervise and manage 14 Assistant Attorneys General in the Environmental Protection Division.

1999 PRIORITIES:
Air pollution, brownfields, and environmental justice issues.

ORGANIZATIONS:
Boston Bar Association

Stuart T. Rossman

Acting Bureau Chief

Business and Labor Protection Bureau
Address: 200 Portland Street, Boston, MA 02114
Telephone: (617) 727-2200
Reports to: Attorney General Thomas Reilly
Fax: (617) 722-3067

PERSONAL INFORMATION:
Marital Status: Married (Shelley)
Children: 2
Education: University of Michigan (B.A., Political Science, '75); Harvard Law School (J.D., '78)
Previous Employment: Gaston & Snow (Partner, '87-'91; Associate, '78-'87)
Years in Current Position: 4
Years in State Service: 7

JOB DESCRIPTION:
Responsible for supervising and managing a staff of 40 attorneys and 60 staff members and inspectors assigned to the Fair Labor & Business Practices Division, the Division of Employment and Training, the Insurance Fraud Division, and the Medicaid Fraud Control Unit.

ORGANIZATIONS:
United Jewish Appeal Young Leadership Cabinet (past National Chair); Bureau of Jewish Education (Board of Directors and Vice President); South Area Soloman Schechter Day School (Board of Directors); Massachusetts Bar Association; Boston Bar Association; Volunteer Lawyers Project of the Boston Bar Association (Chair, Board of Directors); Jewish Community Relations Council of Boston (Board of Directors and Vice President); Combined Jewish Philanthropies of Boston (Board of Directors and Executive Committee); Northeastern University Law School (Lecturer)

Nicholas J. Messuri

Chief

Medicaid Fraud Control Unit
Address: 200 Portland Street, Boston, MA 02114
Telephone: (617) 727-2200 x3405
Fax: (617) 722-2008
E-mail: nicholas.messuri@ago.state.ma.us

PERSONAL INFORMATION:
Born: August 24, 1960
Place of Birth: Somerville
Marital Status: married (Tina)
Children: 2
Education : Northeastern ('82)
Previous Employment: Middlesex County District Attorney's Office.
Years in Current Position: 3
Years in State Service: 13

JOB DESCRIPTION:
Chief of the Attorney General's Health Care Fraud Division. Oversight of prosecutors and investigators of healthcare providers in Massachusetts.

Anthony E. Penski

Deputy Bureau Chief

Business and Labor Protection Bureau
Address: 200 Portland Street, Boston, MA 02114
Telephone: (617) 727-2200 **Fax:** (617) 722-3067
Reports to: Attorney General Thomas Reilly and Stuart T. Rossman

PERSONAL INFORMATION:
Marital Status: Married (Michelle) **Children:** 2
Education: University of Massachusetts (B.S. '68); Suffolk University Law School (J.D. '74)
Previous Employment: Municipal Counsel, City of Gardner and towns of Athol, Hubbardston, and Templeton
Years in Current Position: 4 **Years in State Service:** 11

JOB DESCRIPTION:
Responsible for oversight and management of a staff of approximately 35 assistant Attorneys General and 60 investigatory and support staff assigned to the Fair Labor & Business Practices Division, the Unemployment Fraud Division, the Insurance Fraud Division and the Medicaid Fraud Control Unit. Also serves as the Attorney General's Veterans' Affairs Coordinator.

ORGANIZATIONS:
Chairman, Massachusetts Contributory Retirement Appeal Board; Massachusetts Bar Association, Public Law Council Member and current Chair of the Government Lawyers Practice Group; City Solicitors and Town Counsel Association; Veterans of Foreign Wars; Polish American Veterans of Massachusetts; Faculty Member, New England Municipal Clerks Institute and Academy.

Carol A. Starkey

Chief, Economic Crimes Division

Criminal Bureau
Address: One Ashburton Place, Boston, MA 02108
Telephone: (617) 727-2200 **Fax:** (617) 727-5755
Staff: Olivia M. Blanchette, Secretary; Paul Stewart, Director of Financial Investigators for all division chiefs; includes seven Assistant Attorneys General and one Special Assistant Attorney General
Reports to: Bureau ChiefGerard T. Leone

PERSONAL INFORMATION:
Born: December 6, 1961 **Place of Birth:** Denver, CO
Marital Status: single
Education: University of Colorado at Boulder ('84); Suffolk University Law School (J.D., '88)
Previous Employment: Bristol County District Attorney's Office (Assistant District Attorney, Superior Court Prosecutions)
Years in Current Position: 2 **Years in State Service:** 9

JOB DESCRIPTION:
Manage staff comprised of Assistant Attorneys General, civilian investigators, and state police officers to investigate and prosecute white-collar crime.

1999 PRIORITIES:
Prosecute all categories of white-collar offenses including larcenies, tax evasion, securities fraud, and schemes to defraud by professionals such as attorneys, physicians, accountants, investment advisors, and others.

ORGANIZATIONS:
Teacher of the Urban Strike Force (sponsored by AGO); public speaker on topics of domestic violence, elder abuse, and economic crimes throughout the Commonwealth.

Richard W. Cole

Chief, Civil Rights/Civil Liberties Division

Public Protection Bureau
Address: One Ashburton Place, 19th Floor, Boston, MA 02108
Telephone: (617) 727-2200 **Fax:** (617) 727-5762
Reports to: Acting Bureau Chief Freda Fishman

PERSONAL INFORMATION:
Education: George Washington University (B.A., Political Science, '71); Boston University School of Law (J.D., '74)
Previous Employment: Stahlin, Bergstresser & Cole, P.C. (Partner, '88-'91); Greater Boston Legal Services (Managing Attorney, '78-'84)
Years in Current Position: 7 **Years in State Service:** 7

JOB DESCRIPTION:
Supervise Assistant Attorneys General and staff in the division; enforce Massachusetts Civil Rights Act, representing Commonwealth to combat credit, housing and employment discrimination, unequal educational opportunities; enforce voting rights and First Amendment protection; address allegations of police misconduct through extensive training, policy changes, and, if appropriate, legal action.

ORGANIZATIONS:
Massachusetts Bar Association Chair, Community Education Committee, Member, Policy Research Committee; Committee on Sections; Massachusetts Bar Foundation (Fellow); John Payne Music School, Inc. (President and Director); Governor's Commission on Hate Crimes; National Chair, Civil Rights Working Group of the National Association of Attorneys General; National Co-chair, Attorney General Reno's Working Group on State and Local Law Enforcement Training on Hate Crimes.

State Treasurer & Receiver General

The State Treasurer and Receiver General is responsible for the management of state funds and is the sole party authorized to make payments from those funds. The Treasurer collects revenues from municipalities and the federal government. State agencies that collect revenues are required to deposit all receipts and the revenues received with this office. The Treasurer and Receiver General is charged with the investment management of all state financial assets and the debt service attached thereto. This office is responsible for the issuing, marketing, and accounting of state bonds, notes, and securities. The Treasurer's office administers the state's payroll, pays all bills of the state, and enforces abandoned property laws. The office oversees the State Retirement Board, the Emergency Finance Board, and the State Lottery Commission. Additionally, the office oversees the Massachusetts Cultural Council and the administration of bonuses awarded to veterans of the Vietnam and Korean Wars.

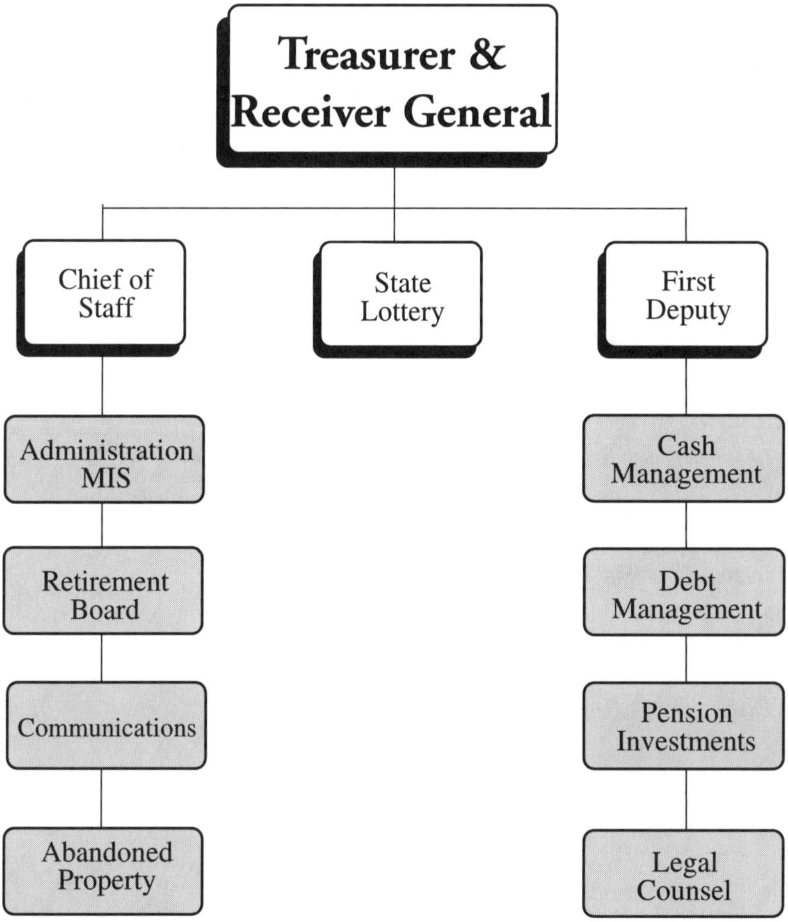
Treasurer & Receiver General
Chief of Staff
State Lottery
First Deputy
Administration MIS
Retirement Board
Communications
Abandoned Property
Cash Management
Debt Management
Pension Investments
Legal Counsel

Treasurer and Receiver General	**Shannon O'Brien**	(617) 367-6900
First Deputy Treasurer	**Michael Travaglini**	367-6900
Chief of Staff/Deputy Treasurer	**Lynda Tocci**	367-6900
Deputy Treasurer/Cash Management	**Elizabeth A. Pearce**	367-3900
Deputy Treasurer/Debt Management	**Jeffrey S. Stearns**	367-3900
Deputy Treasurer/General Counsel	**vacant**	367-3900
Assistant Treasurer/Unclaimed Property	**Neil J. Harrington**	367-3900
Assistant Treasurer/Admin & Finance	**Kyle J. Keady**	367-3900
Assistant Treasurer/Debt Management	**Patrick F. Landers**	367-3900
Assistant Treasurer/Human Resources	**Michael J. O'Halloran**	367-3900
Assistant Treasurer/Communications	**Dwight D. Robson**	367-6900
Assistant Treasurer/Cash Management	**Amelia Viscomi**	367-3900
Executive Director State Board of Retirement	**vacant**	367-3900
Executive Director, State Lottery	**vacant**	781-849-5500

Shannon O'Brien

Treasurer and Receiver General

Office of the State Treasurer and Receiver General
Address: State House, Room 227, Boston, MA 02133
Telephone: (617) 367-6900 **Fax:** (617) 248-0372
Sraff: Dina Conlen, Special Assistant

PERSONAL INFORMATION:
Born: April 30, 1959 **Place of Birth:** Boston
Marital Status: married (R. Emmet Hayes)
Education: Yale University (B.A. '81); Boston University School of Law ('85)
Previous Employment: Health Care Executive, State Senator, State Representative, Attorney
Years in Current Position: new **Years in State Service:** 8

JOB DESCRIPTION:
The State Treasurer and Receiver General is responsible for the management of state funds and is the sole party authorized to make payments from those funds. The Treasurer collects revenues from municipalities and the federal government and is charged with the investment management of state financial assets and the debt service attached. The office is responsible for issuing, marketing, and accounting of state bonds, notes, and securities. It administers the state payroll, pays bills of the state, and enforces abandoned property laws. The office oversees the State Retirement Board, the Emergency Finance Board, the State Lottery Commission, and the Massachusetts Cultural Council, as well as the administration of bonuses awarded to veterans of the Vietnam and Korean Wars. The Treasurer serves as Chair of the Massachusetts Lottery Commission, Chair of the State Retirement Board, Member of the Massachusetts Municipal Depository Trust and Member of the Massachusetts Emergency Finance Board.

Michael Travaglini

First Deputy Treasurer

Office of the State Treasurer and Receiver General
Address: State House, Room 227, Boston, MA 02133
Telephone: (617) 367-6900 **Fax:** (617) 248-0372
Reports to: Treasurer and Receiver General Shannon O'Brien

PERSONAL INFORMATION:
Born: Nov. 7, 1962 **Place of Birth:** Boston
Marital Status: single
Education: Harvard (B.A. '85); Georgetown University Law Center (J.D. '90)
Previous Employment: Chief of Staff, Boston Redevelopment Authority (1996-98); Executive Officer, Boston Retirement System (1994-96)
Years in Current Position: new **Years in State Service:** new

JOB DESCRIPTION:
Supervise and manage the financial policy section of the State Treasurer. The section includes cash management, debt management and pension investment. Also serves as the chief financial advisor to the State Treasurer.

Lynda Tocci
Chief of Staff, Deputy Treasurer

Office of the State Treasurer and Receiver General
Address: State House, Room 227, Boston, MA 02133
Telephone: (617) 367-6900 **Fax:** (617) 720-4341
Reports to: Treasurer and Receiver General Shannon O'Brien

PERSONAL INFORMATION:
Born: Nov. 21, 1967 **Place of Birth:** Boston
Education: Wheaton College (B.A. '89) Simmons Graduate School of Management (M.B.A., '98)
Previous Employment: US Trust Bank, Director of Public Relations
Years in Current Position: new **Years in State Service:** new

JOB DESCRIPTION:
Implement policies and priorities; advise and consult with Treasurer, First Deputy and Executive Director of Lottery.

Elizabeth A. Pearce
Deputy Treasurer/Cash Management

Office of the State Treasurer and Receiver General
Address: One Ashburton Place, 12th Floor, Boston, MA 02108
Telephone: (617) 367-3900 **Fax:** (617) 523-1068
Staff: Jane Waldron, Administrative Assistant
Reports to: First Deputy Treasurer Michael Travaglini

PERSONAL INFORMATION:
Education: University of New Hampshire (B.A.)
Previous Employment: Town of Greenburgh, Deputy Comptroller
Years in Current Position: new **Years in State Service:** new

JOB DESCRIPTION:
Responsible for the oversight of the Commonwealth's cash management, short-term investments, commercial paper and banking activities.

Jeffrey S. Stearns

Deputy Treasurer, Debt Management

Office of the State Treasurer and Receiver General
Address: One Ashburton Place, 12th Floor, Boston, MA 02108-1608
Telephone: (617) 367-3900 **Fax:** (617) 227-1973
Reports to: First Deputy Treasurer Michael Travaglini

PERSONAL INFORMATION:
Born: Feb. 20, 1958 **Place of Birth:** Oshkosh, WI
Marital Status: married (Mary) **Children:** 2
Education: Washington University (B.A. '80); Kennedy School of Government, Harvard (Master of Public Policy)
Previous Employment: State of Massachusetts, Office of Fiscal Affairs, Executive Office of Transportation
Years in Current Position: 5 **Years in State Service:** 15

JOB DESCRIPTION:
Structuring and issuing debt for the Commonwealth including bonds, notes, commercial paper; payment of debt service obligations.

Neil J. Harrington

Assistant Treasurer/Unclaimed Property

Office of the State Treasurer and Receiver General
Address: One Ashburton Place, Boston, MA 02108
Telephone: (617) 367-3900 **Fax:** (617) 248-3944
Reports to: Chief of Staff Lynda Tocci

PERSONAL INFORMATION:
Born: June 23, 1956 **Place of Birth:** Salem
Marital Status: married (Sarah) **Children:** 4
Education: St. Louis University (B.A. '78, M.A. '81); Boston University - doctoral studies.
Previous Employment: Mayor, City of Salem, 1990-97; Massachusetts Board of Regents of Higher Eduction, Administrative Assistant to the Chancellor (1981-89)
Years in Current Position: new **Years in State Service:** 8

JOB DESCRIPTION:
Manage and supervise the Abandoned Property Division which is responsible for the collection of unclaimed funds and securities from individuals and businesses in Massachusetts, and the notification of the availability of such assets to their rightful owners or heirs.

Kyle J. Keady

Assistant Treasurer/Administration and Finance

Office of the State Treasurer and Receiver General
Address: One Ashburton Place, 12th Floor, Boston, MA 02108
Telephone: (617) 367-3900, **Fax:** (617) 367-3645
E-mail: KKeady@tre.state.ma.us
Staff: Peter Navarro, Director of MIS
Reports to: Lynda Tocci, Chief of Staff

PERSONAL INFORMATION:
Born: Nov. 9, 1963 **Place of Birth:** Groton
Children: 1
Education: University of Lowell (B.S. '85)
Years in Current Position: 3 **Years in State Service:** 13

JOB DESCRIPTION:
Responsible for the oversight of administration, procurement, financial operations, and management information systems.

Michael J. O'Halloran

Assistant Treasurer/Human Resources

Office of the State Treasurer and Receiver General
Address: One Ashburton Place, 12th Floor, Boston, MA 02108
Telephone: (617) 367-7770 **Fax:** (617) 723-1438
Reports to: Chief of Staff Lynda Tocci

PERSONAL INFORMATION:
Born: July 15, 1966 **Place of Birth:** Boston
Marital Status: married (Lynne) **Children:** 2
Education: Suffolk University (B.S.); Antioch University (M.A.)
Previous Employment: Director of Human Resources in State Auditor's Office
Years in Current Position: 1 **Years in State Service:** 1

JOB DESCRIPTION:
Oversight of Human Resources operations.

ORGANIZATIONS:
Certified mediator; Adjuct Professor of Negotiation, Bentley College.

Dwight D. Robson

Assistant Treasurer/Communications

Office of the State Treasurer and Receiver General
Address: One Ashburton Place, 12th Floor, Boston, MA 02108
Telephone: (617) 367-3900 **Fax:** (617) 248-0372
Reports to: Chief of Staff Lynda Tocci

PERSONAL INFORMATION:
Born: April 5, 1971 **Place of Birth:** Lawrence
Marital Status: Married (Lena)
Education: University of Massachusetts - Lowell (B.A.)
Previous Experience: Harshbarger Committee (Press Secretary); Legislature's Education Committee (Chief of Staff); Kerry Committee (Deputy press Secretary)
Years in Current Position: new **Years in State Service:** 2

JOB DESCRIPTION:
Coordinate all external communications for the Department of State Treasurer, including press relations and speech writing.

Amelia Viscomi

Assistant Treasurer/Cash Management

Office of the State Treasurer and Receiver General
Address: One Ashburton Place, 12th Floor, Boston, MA 02108
Telephone: (617) 367-3900, **Fax:** (617) 523-1068
Staff: Jane T. Waldron, Administrative Assistant
Reports to: Elizabeth Pearce, Deputy Treasurer

PERSONAL INFORMATION:
Education: Boston College (B.A. '84)
Years in Current Position: 1 **Years in State Service:** 14

JOB DESCRIPTION:
Cash flow management; cash flow forecasting; oversee short-term investments; manage federal receipts; control disbursements; manage commercial paper program; warrant management.

ORGANIZATIONS:
Treasury Management Association of New England

Auditor of the Commonwealth

The Massachusetts Office of the State Auditor (OSA) is operated under the direction of State Auditor A. Joseph DeNucci.

As mandated by the Massachusetts General Laws, this office conducts audits of all departments, offices, commissions, institutions, and activities of the Commonwealth. The Auditor also makes determinations regarding the privatization of state services, and conducts audits of vendors and contractors that do business with the state.

The office of the State Auditor is divided into the following four divisions:

- *Division of Audit Operations*
- *Division of Local Mandates*
- *Division of Information Technology*
- *Division of Administration*

Division of Audit Operations

This division examines the diverse operations of state government in order to ensure that state funds are expended in an appropriate and legal manner.

When auditing a department, agency, or authority, the Office of the State Auditor uses trained and experienced personnel to report on financial, operational, administrative, and programmatic issues. The OSA also looks for compliance with laws and regulations. It checks efficiency and economy in agency operations, and effectiveness in achieving mandated goals.

OSA audit reports help administrators through recommendations and technical assistance. They therefore go beyond the safeguarding and enhancement of the Commonwealth's assets by creating solutions to improve an agency's financial and managerial operations.

Division of Local Mandates

The Division of Local Mandates (DLM) was established by Proposition 2-1/2, which strictly limits the amount of revenue Massachusetts cities and towns may raise to support local services. At the same time, this legislation provides that any post-1980 state law or regulation requiring additional expenditures by any city or town must be funded by the state or be subject to local acceptance.

In this context, DLM measures the financial impact of state laws and regulations governing municipal services and works with state legislators and administrators to avoid placing additional cost burdens on local budgets. Issues range from solid waste management to tax abatements to education

Division of Information Technology

The Information technology Audit Division conducts electronic date processing audit at the various departments, agencies and authorities of the Commonwealth. Technical assistance and training are provided to auditees and OSA staff where appropriate.

In addition, the Information Technology Audit division works closely with the Audit Operations division in the production of integrated audits, which provide a combined analysis of an entity's information technology, financial, and performance issues.

Finally, the Information Technology Audit Division continues to update survey information pertaining to state agency computer-related operations, including Year 2000 readiness and compliance.

Division of Administration

The Division of Administration's role is defining and balancing the multiple priorities of the OSA. This division includes the departments of budget, communications, legal, intergovernmental, and personnel to support the audit function.

Among the division's responsibilities are communicating the result of audit reports to state and agency officials and the public, drafting an annual legislative package that addresses audit findings, and providing a variety of training programs to help audit staff meet required professional standards.

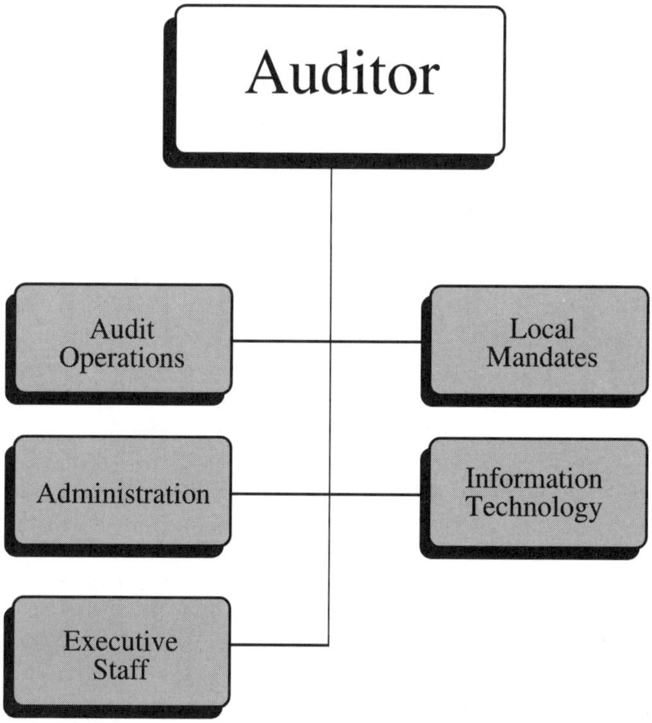
Auditor
Audit Operations
Local Mandates
Administration
Information Technology
Executive Staff

Auditor of the Commonwealth	**A. Joseph DeNucci**	*(617) 727-2075*

DEPUTY AUDITORS

Audit Operations	**Robert Powilatis**	*727-6200*
Intergovernmental Relations	**Myrna Malec**	*727-2075*
Administration/Local Mandates	**Kenneth Marchurs**	*727-6200*
Information Technology Audits	**John Beveridge**	*727-6200*
Policy and Executive Affairs	**Francis Shannon**	*727-2075*

EXECUTIVE AFFAIRS

Chief of Staff	**Richard Sewall**	*727-2075*

AUDIT OPERATIONS

Directors:

Audit Support	**Nick D'Alleva**	*727-6200*
Contract Audits	**Paul A. Sweeney**	*727-6200*
Federal Audits	**Henry A. Malionek**	*727-0025*
State Audits	**Howard N. Olsher**	*727-6200*
Authority Audits	**Edward McDonough**	*727-0025*

ADMINISTRATION

Directors:

General Counsel	**John Parsons**	*727-6200*
Budget	**Elizabeth A. Capstick**	*727-6200*
Community Affairs	**Maryanne Kelley**	*727-2075*
Communications	**Glenn A. Briere**	*727-6200*
Personnel/Human Resources	**vacant**	*727-6200*
Information Systems	**Paul McLaughlin**	*727-6200*

DIVISION OF LOCAL MANDATES

Director	**Tom Collins**	*727-0980*

A. Joseph DeNucci

Auditor of the Commonwealth

Office of the State Auditor
Address: State House, Room 230, Boston, MA 02133
Telephone: (617) 727-2075
Fax: (617) 727-3014
Staff: Robert Powilatis, First Deputy Auditor for Audit Operations; Kenneth Marchurs, Deputy Auditor for Administration and Local Mandates; John Beveridge, Deputy Auditor for MIS/EDP; Frank Shannon, Deputy Auditor for Policy and Executive Affairs, Myrna Malec, Deputy Auditor for Intergovernmental Relations

PERSONAL INFORMATION:

Born: August 30, 1939
Place of Birth: Newton
Marital Status: married (Barbara) **Children:** 5 (6 grandchildren)
Previous Employment: Massachusetts House of Representatives, 10th Middlesex District; ('77-87; House Chairman, '81-'87) Committee on Human Services and Elderly Affairs
Years in Current Position: 12

JOB DESCRIPTION:

The Office of the State Auditor, one of six constitutional offices, is operated under the direction of State Auditor A. Joseph DeNucci. As mandated by the Massachusetts General Laws, the primary responsibility of the Auditor is to conduct an audit once every two years of all departments, offices, commissions, institutions, and activities of the Commonwealth. The Auditor also has authority to audit the thousands of vendors that contract with the Commonwealth and is required to review, analyze, and subsequently certify or reject all initiatives to privatize state services. In addition, the Auditor is responsible for the Division of Local Mandates, which is charged primarily with determining the financial impact of legislation and regulations on cities and towns.

ORGANIZATIONS:

State Inspector General's Council; Emergency Finance Board; State Comptroller's Advisory Board; New England Intergovernmental Audit Forum; Newton Boys and Girls Club (Board of Directors); Association of Government Accountants; Public Employee Retirement Administration Commission

SECTION II

The Executive Offices

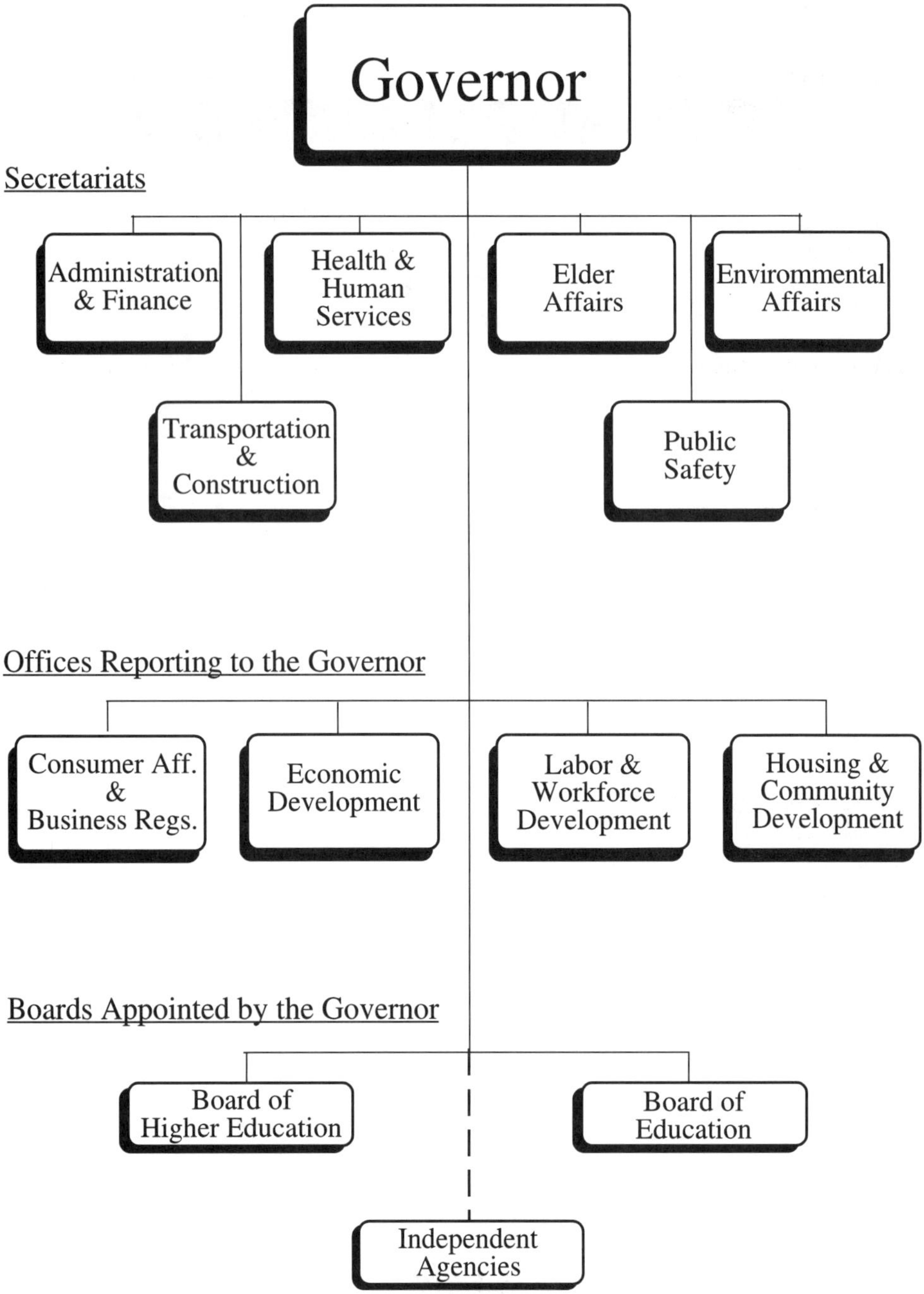
Governor
Secretariats
Administration & Finance
Health & Human Services
Elder Affairs
Environmental Affairs
Transportation & Construction
Public Safety
Offices Reporting to the Governor
Consumer Aff. & Business Regs.
Economic Development
Labor & Workforce Development
Housing & Community Development
Boards Appointed by the Governor
Board of Higher Education
Board of Education
Independent Agencies

Cabinet Secretariats and Departments

SECRETARIATS

Administration and Finance
State House, Room 373
Boston, MA 02133
Andrew S. Natsios, Secretary 727-2040

Elder Affairs
One Ashburton Place
Boston, MA 02108
Lillian F. Glickman Secretary 727-7750

Environmental Affairs
100 Cambridge Street, Room 2000
Boston, MA 02202
Robert A. Durand, Secretary 727-9800

Health and Human Services
One Ashburton Place, Room 1109
Boston, MA 02108
William O'Leary, Secretary 727-0077

Public Safety
One Ashburton Place, Room 2133
Boston, MA 02108
Jane Perlov, Secretary 727-7775

Transportation and Construction
10 Park Place, Room 3510
Boston, MA 02116
Kevin J. Sullivan, Secretary 973-8080

DEPARTMENTS

Consumer Affairs and Business Regulation
One Ashburton Place, Room 1411
Boston, MA 02108
Daniel A. Grabauskas, Director 727-7755

Economic Development
One Ashburton Place, Room 2101
Boston, MA 02108
Carolyn Boviard, Director 727-8380

Housing and Community Development
100 Cambridge Street, Room 1804
Boston, MA 02202
Jane W. Gumble, Director 727-7765

Labor and Workforce Development
One Ashburton Place, Room 1402
Boston, MA 02108
Angelo Buonopane, Director 727-6573

Administration & Finance

The Executive Office for Administration and Finance is responsible for the administrative function and fiscal policy of the executive branch of state government, including administrative planning, policy formulation, and financial and managerial oversight and control. This office is charged with the preparation of the Governor's annual budget recommendations and the implementation and monitoring of legislative action.

The office is divided into four major functional units: Administration, Fiscal Affairs, Finance, and Strategic Planning.

The *Administrative Division* oversees 15 state commissions and agencies:

- *Appellate Tax Board*
- *Board of Library Commissioners*
- *Civil Service Commission*
- *Department of Personnel Administration*
- *Department of Procurement and General Services*
- *Division of Administrative Law Appeals*
- *Group Insurance Commission*
- *Massachusetts Commission Against Discrimination*
- *Office of Dispute Resolution*
- *Division of Employee Relations*
- *Office on Disability*
- *Public Employees Retirement Association*
- *Teachers Retirement Board*
- *State Office of Affirmative Action*
- *Office of Veterans' Services*

The *Fiscal Affairs Division*, through the Budget Bureau, is responsible for assisting the Governor in the development, presentation and implementation of the state's annual operating budget. The bureau manages the financial planning activities of the state government and reviews and evaluates all requests for appropriations. The Budget Bureau oversees state agency applications for federal monies to ensure compliance with state law, reviews grant applications, coordinates the review and processing of all federal funds, and monitors federal grant program spending.

The *Finance Division* is responsible for oversight and management of the general fiscal affairs of the Commonwealth. Five offices and departments fall under its jurisdiction:

- *Office of Debt Management*
- *Department of Revenue*
- *Division of Capital Planning and Operations*
- *Office of the Comptroller*
- *Office of Information Technology*

Appellate Tax Board

The Appellate Tax Board is a quasi-judicial administrative board that hears and decides appeals of state and local tax assessments in the Commonwealth. These include requests for abatements of personal property and motor vehicle excise taxes denied by local boards of assessors. Abatements of income, estate, sales, and use taxes rejected by the Department of Revenue are also reviewed by the Appellate Tax Board. The chairman of the Appellate Tax Board reviews, evaluates, and edits all decisions, orders, and opinions of the Board.

Board of Library Commissioners

The development of public library services in the state of Massachusetts is the role of the Board of Library Commissioners. The Board offers technical assistance to library organizations and personnel across the state. The Board also administers both federal and state grants to libraries and offers guidance to governmental agencies. A computer-based resource sharing library consortia; a Talking Book program for the blind, visually impaired, and handicapped; and a Machine Lending Service for the talking book tapes all fall under the auspices of the Board of Library Commissioners.

Civil Service Commission

The Civil Service Commission is a quasi-judicial body (composed of four commissioners and a chairman) that is responsible for the implementation of the merit system in the area of public employee personnel administration.

The Commission hears appeals under Chapters 30 and 31 of the General Laws to determine whether just cause exists for the discharge, removal, suspension, transfer, or reduction in rank of civil service employees. Appeals relating to actions, or failures to act, by the Department of Personnel Administration regarding classification of positions, eligibility, and fairness of the selection process are also heard by the Commission.

Department of Personnel Administration (DPA)

The Department of Personnel Administration administers the civil service system for positions in state agencies and also in the state's municipalities in order to establish and maintain a merit system of personnel administration within the state. The DPA sets policies and standards for public personnel practices on the basis of basic merit principles. It provides personnel services and administers written examinations for the purpose of hiring and promoting state and municipal employees. All information regarding applications, exams, and scheduling is handled by this department.

Operational Services Division

Under the direction of the Purchasing Agent, the Department of Procurement and General Services is responsible for the purchase of goods and social services by the executive branch.

The Division of Commodities Procurement oversees the purchase of goods and the disposition of state property through the following offices:

- *Bureau of Information Technology Acquisitions*
- *Bureau of Commodities*
- *Bureau of Inventory Control, Surplus Property, and Collective Purchasing*
- *Bureau of Administration*

The Division of Purchased Services is responsible for implementing and coordinating the selection, pricing, procurement, contracting, administration, monitoring, and post audit of social service programs. These duties are performed by the following offices:

- *Program Pricing Bureau*
- *Master Service Contracting Bureau*
- *Bureau of Technical Support*
- *Audit Bureau*

Division of Administrative Law Appeals

The Division of Administrative Law Appeals is an independent state agency established to conduct adjudicatory hearings of appeals to and from various state agencies. Such hearings are either constitutionally or statutorily required. Hearings conducted at agency request include those of the Office for Children, the Department of Public Health, and the Division of Registration. Hearings conducted by specific statutory authority include appeals from the Rate Setting Commission, the Civil Service Commission, and the Board of Registration in Medicine.

Group Insurance Commission

The Group Insurance Commission is responsible for designing, contracting, and monitoring the provisions of life and health insurance for state employees, retirees, and their families, and for providing long-term disability insurance to active employees. The Commission also administers health and life insurance programs to retired municipal employees and teachers in certain governmental units.

Massachusetts Commission Against Discrimination (MCAD)

The Massachusetts Commission Against Discrimination was created by statute to enforce laws that prohibit discrimination in public accommodations based on race, color, national origin, sex, sexual orientation, religious creed, blindness, deafness, or disability. The Commission also enforces laws prohibiting discrimination in credit based on age, marital status and public assistance, as well as discrimination in the areas of education, employment, and housing. Complaints of discrimination in any of these areas are filed with the Commission, which investigates the complaints and adjudicates the cases at public hearings.

Office of Dispute Resolution

Funded by charges to user agencies and to the public, the Office of Dispute Resolution selects, screens, trains, and assigns mediators to resolve major environmental, housing, and regulatory stalemates and to settle civil lawsuits, thereby providing a valuable cost-saving service to the courts, public agencies, and the public. Educational programs are also provided by the office in an effort to reduce the occurrence, magnitude, and cost of disputes.

Division of Employee Relations

The Division of Employee Relations is responsible for negotiating and administering the labor relation contracts for the over 60,000 employees in 12 bargaining units in the executive branch. Only employees whose titles are covered under collective bargaining agreements in the executive branch are handled by this office. Employees of the legislature and constitutional officers bargain with the Human Development Resource Bureau, while employees of the state's institutions of higher learning deal with the Higher Education Coordinating Council.

Office on Disability

Created in 1981, the Office on Disability seeks to eliminate discrimination against people with disabilities and to guarantee accessible housing, transportation, and equal job opportunities in both the public and private sectors. This office serves as an advocate and a technical advisor to individuals who have been discriminated against on account of a disability. In addition, the Office on Disability initiates and advocates for legislation to ensure civil and human rights of people with disabilities.

Public Employee Retirement Association (PERA)

This agency was created to develop uniform regulations and standards for the process of retirement in the Commonwealth. It has the authority to review all accidental and ordinary disability pensions granted by a retirement board. The agency oversees 106 state, county, and municipal pension systems and has the authority to access all books and records and to examine the financial affairs of any system.

Teachers Retirement Board

The Teachers Retirement Board administers the retirement system of public school teachers in Massachusetts.

State Office of Affirmative Action

The State Office of Affirmative Action is responsible for the implementation, monitoring, and enforcement of affirmative action in all agencies within the executive branch of state government. This agency sets policy, implements procedures, and designs systems to ensure equal opportunity and to eliminate present and past discriminatory practices. It also acts as a civil rights agency in conjunction with the Massachusetts Commission Against Discrimination for state employees who have been the victims of sexual harassment or employment discrimination.

Department of Veterans' Services

The Department of Veterans' Services is a need-based assistance program that provides medical, financial, and service benefits to veterans and their families. The office funds the local veterans assistance programs in the Commonwealth's cities and towns so that they can administer the primary assistance programs. It establishes policy, proposes legislation, and represents the interests of veterans in matters coming before the state legislature. In addition it acts as an agent for all departments of the Commonwealth before the Department of Veterans' Affairs in securing a federal compensation that may be available. The office also assists individual veterans in obtaining information regarding pensions, educational benefits, tax exemptions, annuities, and home loans.

Office of Information Technology

The Office of Information Technology is responsible for providing information technology services to the executive branch. The office supports the major statewide computerized administrative systems and a personal computer network that links most secretariats and departments. Within the office are four bureaus:

- *Bureau of Computer Services*
- *Bureau of Systems Services*
- *Bureau of Telecommunications*
- *Bureau of Technology Planning*

Office of the Comptroller

The Comptroller's Office is responsible for the accounting policies and practices of the Commonwealth, oversight of management and expenditure functions, and the publication of official financial reports. The office operates the state's accounting, financial management, and payroll systems as well as maintains a file of all vendors that do business with the state. In addition, the Comptroller's Office administers the annual Single State Audit on behalf of the federal government and the state. The office also prepares the periodic warrants for the Governor's Council.

Department of Revenue

The Department of Revenue administers the state's tax system by collecting income, sales, estate, corporate, use, and other taxes. It offers tax payer assistance services, audits tax returns, and enforces the state tax code. The department also has supervisory responsibility over local taxes and related matters, provides technical assistance to municipalities, and oversees the distribution of local aid to cities, towns, and regional school districts. The department is further responsible for administering the state's child support enforcement program.

Division of Capital Asset Management

The Division of Capital Asset Management is responsible for the acquisition, disposition, construction, leasing, and development of real estate on behalf of the Commonwealth. In addition, the agency is responsible for planning and coordinating all capital projects on behalf of state agencies.

Bureau of State Office Buildings

- *Office of Project Management*
- *Office of Real Estate Development*
- *Office of Leased Management*
- *Office of Finance and Administration*
- *Office of Programming*
- *Office of Court Facilities*
- *Office of Mental Health Facilities*

Administration

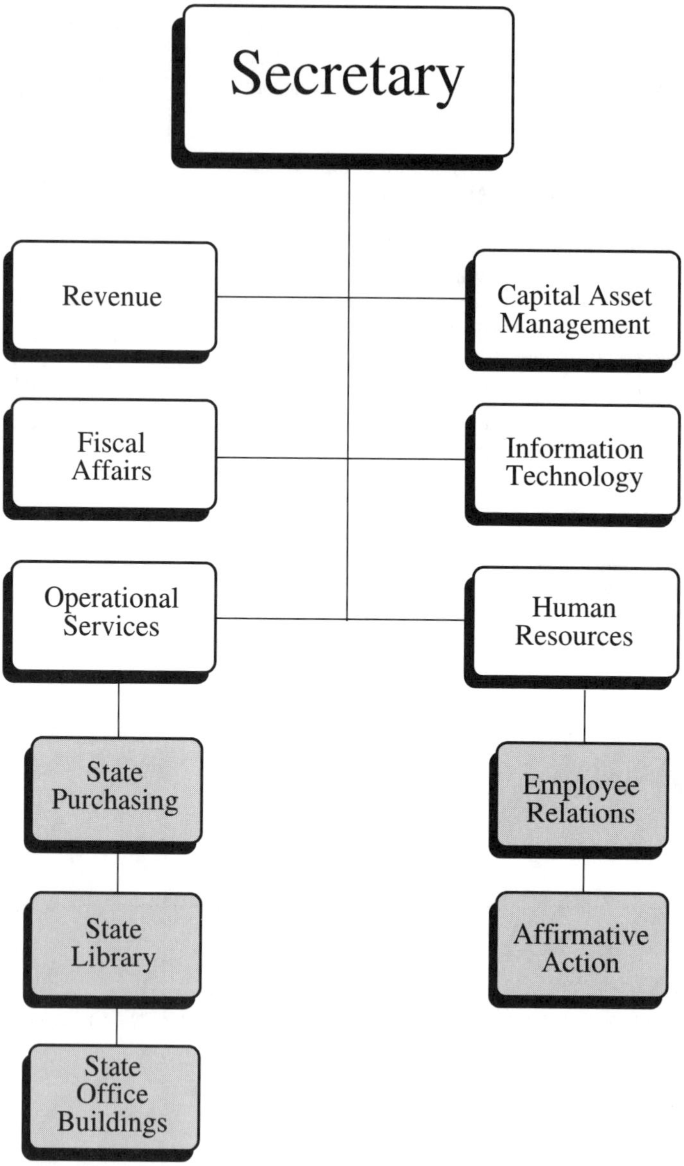

Boards and Commissions

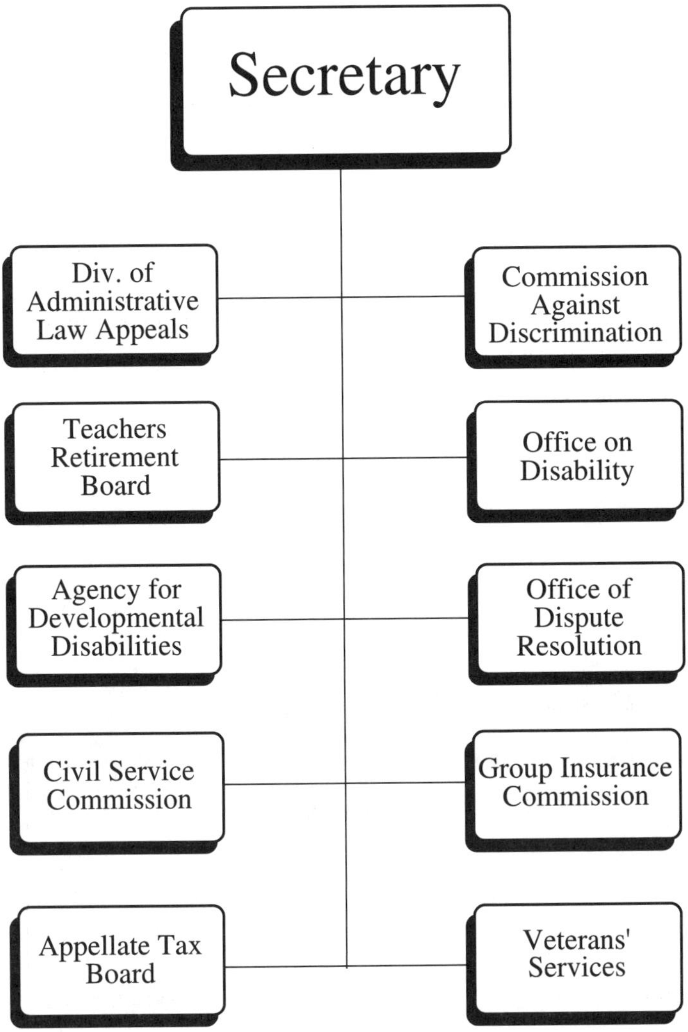
Secretary
Div. of Administrative Law Appeals
Commission Against Discrimination
Teachers Retirement Board
Office on Disability
Agency for Developmental Disabilities
Office of Dispute Resolution
Civil Service Commission
Group Insurance Commission
Appellate Tax Board
Veterans' Services

Secretary	**Andrew S. Natsios**	(617) 727-2040
Chief of Staff	**Kristen Keel**	727-2040
Assistant Secretary, Management & Operations	**Rosemarie Day**	727-2040
Assistant Secretary, Capital Resources	**Lowell R. Richards III**	727-2040
Director of Communications	**Joseph Landolfi**	727-2040
General Counsel	**Christopher J. Supple**	727-2040

Directors:

Director of Capital Budgeting	**vacant**	727-2040
Director of Debt Finance	**Catherine R. Frazer**	727-2040
Director of Fiscal Research	**vacant**	727-2040
Director of Information Technology	**David Lewis (Acting)**	727-2040
Director of Operations	**Jody Ryan**	727-2040
Director of State and Local Relations	**Melissa Cummings**	727-2040

DIVISION OF ADMINISTRATIVE LAW APPEALS

Chief Administrative Magistrate	**Christopher F. Connolly**	727-7060
First Administrative Magistrate	**Robert E. Tierney**	727-7060

STATE OFFICE OF AFFIRMATIVE ACTION

Director	**Mark David Bolling**	727-7441

APPELLATE TAX BOARD

Chairman	**Kenneth Gurge**	727-3100
Commissioner	**Timothy F. O'Brien**	727-3100

FISCAL AFFAIRS DIVISION

Director	**Thomas M. Graf**	727-2081

DIVISION OF CAPITAL ASSET MANAGEMENT

Commissioner	**Lark Jurev Palermo**	727-4050
Assistant Commissioner/ General Counsel	**Jamie Lewis Keith**	727-4050
Assistant Commissioner for Operations	**Stephen J. Hines**	727-4050

Deputy Commissioner for Construction Services	**Ralph F. Nee**	727-4030
Directors:		
Finance and Administration	**Michael D. Sullivan**	727-4006
Leasing & Staff Office Planning	**Martha Goldsmith**	727-4015
Programming	**Michael B. Williams**	727-4015
Real Estate	**Joan B. Honig**	727-4015
Surplus Property	**Harold Vanasse**	(508) 792-7453

ADMINISTERING AGENCY ON DEVELOPMENTAL DISABILITIES

Director	**Daniel Shannon**	727-6374

OFFICE ON DISABILITY

Acting Director	**Lorraine Greiff**	727-7440

OFFICE OF DISPUTE RESOLUTION

Executive Director	**Fredie D. Kay**	727-2224

OFFICE OF EMPLOYEE RELATIONS

Director	**Kevin Preston**	727-5403

BUREAU OF STATE OFFICE BUILDINGS

Superintendent	**Dennis R. Smith**	727-1100
Dep. Superintendent/Operations	**Leo Colborne**	727-0929
Director of State House Events	**Tammy Kraus DelTorto**	727-1100

CIVIL SERVICE COMMISSION

Chairman	**Christine E. Morris**	727-2293

OFFICE OF THE COMPTROLLER

Comptroller	**Martin J. Benison**	973-2315
Deputy Comptroller	**Elizabeth A. Kilcoyne**	973-2619
General Counsel	**David Marchand**	973-2615

GROUP INSURANCE COMMISSION

Executive Director	**Dolores L. Mitchell**	727-2310
Chief Legal Counsel/Systems Executive Director	**Robert S. Johnson**	727-2310

BOARD OF LIBRARY COMMISSIONERS

Director	**Keith M. Fiels**	267-9400

MASSACHUSETTS COMMISSION AGAINST DISCRIMINATION

Chairman	**Charles E. Walker, Jr.**	727-3990
Commissioner	**Dorca I. Gomez**	(413) 739-2145
Commissioner	**Douglas T. Schwarz**	727-3990

INFORMATION TECHNOLOGY DIVISION

Director	**vacant**	973-0090
Deputy Director	**David Lewis**	973-0735
Bureau Directors:		
Technology Finance Group	**Louis Angeloni**	973-0715
Data Center Services	**Ralph Ragucci**	660-4401
Communication Service	**Lou Macinanti**	973-0962
Enterprise Applications	**Anna dos Santos**	973-0898
Strategic Planning	**Val Asbedian**	973-0762

HUMAN RESOURCES DIVISION

Personnel Administrator	**James J. Hartnett, Jr.**	727-1556
Deputy Personnel Administrator	**Paul Dietl**	727-1556
Assistant Administrator/General Counsel	**James P. McDonagh**	727-3555

OPERATIONAL SERVICES DIVISION

State Purchasing Agent/ Commissioner	**Philmore Anderson III**	727-7500
Assistant Commissioner	**vacant**	727-7500
Deputy Purchasing Agent/ Deputy Commissioner	**Gary J. Lambert**	727-7500
Division of Procurement Directors:		
Administration and Finance	**Ellen L. Phillips**	727-7500

General Counsel	**vacant**	727-7500
Facilities	**Kathleen Reilly**	727-7500
Professional & Institutional Services	**Cheryl L. Traina**	727-7500
Technical Group	**Richard Mordaunt**	727-7500

Division of Purchased Services Directors:

Audit	**Kent Barkhouse**	727-7500
Technical Support	**Tanja Ryden**	727-7500
Program Support	**Ellen Bickleman**	727-7500

PUBLIC EMPLOYEE RETIREMENT ADMINISTRATION

Executive Director	**Robert F. Stalnaker**	666-4446
Deputy Executive Director	**Joseph Martin**	666-4446
Dept. Executive Director	**Joseph Connarton**	666-4446
General Counsel	**Barbara Phillips**	666-4446

DEPARTMENT OF REVENUE

Commissioner	**Frederick A. Laskey**	626-2201
Senior Deputy Commissioner	**Bernard Crowley, Jr.**	626-2201
First Deputy Commissioner and General Counsel	**Donald J. Evans**	626-3200
Office of Tax Policy Analysis	**Howard Merkowitz**	626-2100
Director of Communications	**Ann Murphy**	626-2251
Chief of Staff	**Susan Montgomery**	626-2201

Deputy Commissioners:

Child Support Enforcement	**Amy Pitter**	577-7200
Audit Division	**Frederick Beebe**	887-6757
Information Systems Officer	**Vincent Piccinni**	887-5450
Inspectional Services Division	**John Moynihan**	626-2175
Local Services	**Joseph J. Chessy, Jr.**	626-2300
Processing	**Alan Golobski**	887-5010

Research and Development Division	**Robert E. Nevins**	626-2580
Taxpayer Services	**Sheila LeBlanc**	887-6124
Compliance Division	**Stephen E. Moffatt**	887-6501
Administrative Services Division	**Joseph Scotti**	626-2201

STATE HOUSE LIBRARY

Trustee, Board of Library Commissioners	**Marie J. Parente**	722-2400
Librarian/Director	**Stephen A. Fulchino**	727-2592

TEACHERS' RETIREMENT BOARD

Executive Director	**Thomas R. Lussier**	727-3661
Chief Financial Officer	**John Harrigan**	727-3661
Deputy Executive Director	**Erika Glaster**	727-3661
Director Information Technology	**Joseph Champa**	727-3661
Director of Benefit Services	**Robert K. DeLena**	727-3661
General Counsel	**Joan Schloss**	727-3661

VETERANS' SERVICES

Commissioner	**Thomas J. Hudner, Jr.**	727-3578
Deputy Commissioner	**Walter F. Pero**	727-3578
Director of Administration and Finance	**Thomas G. Kelley**	727-3578
Director of Veteran's State Cemeteries	**Robert C. McKean**	727-3578
General Counsel	**John M. Corey**	727-3578
Director, External Affairs	vacant	727-3578
Director, Operations	**Richard H. Spicer**	727-3578

Andrew S. Natsios

Secretary

Executive Office for Administration and Finance
Address: State House, Room 373, Boston, MA 02133
Telephone: (617) 727-2040 **Fax:** (617) 727-2496
Staff: Kate Almquist, Exeuctive Assistant
Reports to: Governor A. Paul Cellucci

PERSONAL INFORMATION:
Born: Sept. 22, 1949 **Place of Birth:** Philadelphia, PA
Marital Status: married (Elizabeth) **Children:** 3
Education: Georgetown University (B.A. '71); Harvard, Kennedy School of Government (M.P.A. '80)
Previous Employment: Massachusetts House of Representatives (1975-87); Executive Director, Northeast Public Power Association (1987-89); Director, Office of Foreign Disaster Assistance, U.S. Agency for International Development (1989-91); Assistant Administrator, U.S. Aid, 1991-92- Bureau Humanitarian Assistance; Vice President of World Vision (1993-98); Senior Fellow, U.S. Institute of Peace (1998-99). U.S. Army Reserves, 1972-94, Lt. Colonel (retired)) Veteran of the Gulf War
Years in Current Position: new **Years in State Service:** 12

JOB DESCRIPTION:
Governor's Chief Fiscal Advisor, oversight of annual state budget, and oversight of the state workforce.

1999 PRIORITIES:
Reducing state income tax, containing spending, education reform review and depression of the central artery.

ORGANIZATIONS:
AHEPA; International Justice Mission, Board of Directors; Nichols College, Institute for American Values, Advisory Board

Rosemarie Day

Assistant Secretary, Management & Operations

Executive Office for Administration and Finance
Address: State House, Room 373, Boston, MA 02133
Telephone: (617) 727-2040 **Fax:** (617) 727-2040
E-mail: RosemarieDay@state.ma.us
Reports to: Secretary Andrew Natsios

PERSONAL INFORMATION:
Born: July 9, 1966
Place of Birth: Long Beach, CA
Marital Status: Married (Stephen Churchill)
Education: Stanford University (B.A. '88); Kennedy School of Government, Harvard (M.P.P. '92)
Years in Current Position: 1.5
Years in State Service: 12

JOB DESCRIPTION:

Oversight of DCPO, OSD, CBO; Leadership of special initiatives such as reform of construction processes and agency performance improvement programs.

Joseph Landolfi

Director of Communications

Executive Office for Administration and Finance
Address: State House, Room 373, Boston, MA 02133
Telephone: (617) 727-2040 **Fax:** (617) 727-2496
Reports to: Secretary Andrew Natsios

PERSONAL INFORMATION:

Born: July 25, 1951 **Place of Birth:** Beverly
Marital Status: married **Children:** 2
Education: Northeastern University (B.A. '74); Northeastern University (M.S. '79)
Previous Employment: Executive Office of Heath & Human Services, Director of Communications; Dept. of Social Services, Director of Communications.
Years in Current Position: 2 **Years in State Service:** 24

JOB DESCRIPTION:

Oversee and coordinate all media and external communications for the Executive Office and its agencies.

1999 PRIORITIES:

Preparation and presentation of Governor's budget recommendation for FY 2000.

Christopher J. Supple

General Counsel

Executive Office of Administration and Finance
Address: State House, Room 373, Boston, MA 02133
Telephone: (617) 727-2040 **Fax:** (617) 727-2779
E-mail: christopher.j.supple@state.ma.us
Staff: Melissa Cummings, Legislative Director
Reports to: Secretary Andrew Natsios

PERSONAL INFORMATION:

Born: December 15, 1962 **Place of Birth:** Needham
Education: Holy Cross College (B.A., History, '85); Duke University School of Law (J.D., '88)
Previous Employment: Assistant Chief of Staff and Deputy Legal Counsel to Governor Weld and Governor Cellucci; Adjunct Professor of Law, Suffolk University School of Law; Department of Justice, Criminal Division (Trial Attorney); Hale and Dorr (Associate); U.S. District Judge Edward F. Harrington (Law Clerk)
Years in Current Position: 1 **Years in State Service:** 4

JOB DESCRIPTION:

Prepare Governor's budgets, analyze and review budget bills passed by the Legislature, oversee and advise legal staffs of Administration and Finance agencies, act as counsel to the Secretary of A & F, consult with Attorney General's Office on litigation matters, review and approve settlements.

Catherine R. Frazer

Director of Debt Finance

Executive Office for Administration and Finance
Address: State House, Room 373, Boston, MA 02133
Telephone: (617) 727-2040 **Fax:** (617) 727-2779
E-mail: CFrazer@state.ma.us
Staff: Justin DeShaw, Director of Capital Budgeting; John A. Simon, Special Assistant to the Secretary
Reports to: Assistant Secretary Lowell Richards III

PERSONAL INFORMATION:
Born: October 17, 1963 **Place of Birth:** Newton
Marital Status: single
Education: University of Vermont (B.A., '85); Boston College (M.B.A., Finance, '89)
Previous Employment: Bank of Boston (Media Lending Officer)
Years in Current Position: 2 **Years in State Service:** 4

JOB DESCRIPTION:
Primary contact for agencies and investment community. Oversee $13 billion debt outstanding and $900 million capital spending plan. Manage issues by quasi-public agencies and the Massachusetts Water Pollution Abatement Trust.

ORGANIZATIONS:
Massachusetts Educational Finance Authority (Board Member); Neighborhood Association of Back Bay

Christopher F. Connolly

Chief Administrative Magistrate

Division of Administrative Law Appeals
Address: 100 Cambridge Street, Room 904, Boston, MA 02202
Telephone: (617) 727-7060
Staff: Patricia A. English, Assistant
Reports to: Secretary Andrew Natsios

PERSONAL INFORMATION:
Born: December 12, 1946 **Place of Birth:** Boston
Marital Status: married (Kathleen Dillon) **Children:** 4
Education: Marquette University (A.B., '68); Boston College Law School (J.D., '71)
Previous Employment: Suffolk County (District Attorney); Private law practice
Years in Current Position: 19 **Years in State Service:** 22

JOB DESCRIPTION:
Director of state agency established to conduct hearing on appeals to and from various state agencies; responsible for assigning administrative magistrates to conduct said hearings, drafting and promulgating rules and regulations and ensuring a fair and impartial hearing process.

1999 PRIORITIES:
To assign at least as many cases that are filed with the Division in order to keep up with an increasing case load.

ORGANIZATIONS:
Massachusetts Bar Association

Timothy F. O'Brien

Commissioner

Appellate Tax Board
Address: 100 Cambridge Street, Room 1010, Boston, MA 02204
Telephone: (617) 727-3100 **Fax:** (617) 727-6234
Staff: Helen Mary Warren, Assistant
Reports to: Secretary Andrew Natsios

PERSONAL INFORMATION:
Education: Tufts College (B.A., Economics, '67); Boston College Law School (J.D., '73); Harvard Business School (M.B.A., '78); Army War College ('96)
Previous Employment: Attorney and C.P.A. in private practice
Years in Current Position: 2 **Years in State Service:** 8

JOB DESCRIPTION:
Access hearing officer on various appeals from local assessments involving real estate evaluation and on appeals concerning state tax matters; draft findings of fact on report explaining the Board's decisions on cases for which the commissioner acts as the hearing officer.

1999 PRIORITIES:
To expeditiously render decisions.

ORGANIZATIONS:
U.S. Army Reserves (Lieutenant Colonel); Ancient and Honorable Artillery Company; Catholic Lawyers' Guild

Thomas M. Graf

Director

Fiscal Affairs Division
Address: State House, Room 272, Boston, MA 02108
Telephone: (617) 727-2081 **Fax:** (617) 727-1024
E-mail: Tom.Graf@state.ma.us
Staff: David Raines, Administrative Assistant
Reports to: Secretary Andrew Natsios

PERSONAL INFORMATION:
Born: January 20, 1957 **Place of Birth:** Malden
Marital Status: married (Barbara) **Children:** 4
Education: Merrimack College (B.S.,'79); Suffolk University (MBA)
Previous Employment: Governor's Director of Legislative Affairs ('91-'93); Chief of Staff to the Minority Leader
Years in Current Position: 5 **Years in State Service:** 19

JOB DESCRIPTION:
Budget Director for the Commonwealth.

ORGANIZATIONS:
Melrose School Committee ('87-'93); Melrose Youth Soccer; Melrose Little League; Board of Directors, Melrose YMCA.

Lark Jurev Palermo

Commissioner

Division of Capital Asset Management
Address: One Ashburton Place, Boston, MA 02108
Telephone: (617) 727-4050 ext. 303 **Fax:** (617) 727-5363
Staff: Marlene McGivney, Secretary
Reports to: Secretary Andrew Natsios

PERSONAL INFORMATION:
Education: Boston University (B.S., Public Communications); Suffolk University (J.D.)
Previous Employment: Hale and Dorr, Real Estate Department (Partner)
Years in Current Position: 5 **Years in State Service:** 6

JOB DESCRIPTION:
Executive head of the state agency responsible for the Commonwealth's real estate development, construction, and capital planning.

Jamie Lewis Keith

Assistant Commissioner and General Counsel

Division of Capital Asset Management
Address: One Ashburton Place, 15th floor, Boston, MA 02108
Telephone: (617) 727-4050 ext. 376 **Fax:** (617) 727-5363
Staff: Lawyers and administrative staff in the Office of the General Counsel. Contact Person: Virginia Delvecchio, Legal Assistant
Reports to: Commissioner Lark Jurev Palermo

PERSONAL INFORMATION:
Born: July 27, 1957
Place of Birth: Philadelphia, PA
Marital Status: married (Matthew) **Children:** 1
Education: Cornell University (A.B., '79); Boston University School of Law (J.D., '84);
Previous Employment: Real Estate and Environmental Law Departments, Hale and Dorr (Junior Partner); Honorable Bailey Aldrich, U.S. Court of Appeals for the First Circuit (Law Clerk, '84-'85); Museum of Fine Arts, Boston ('79-'81)
Years in Current Position: 4 **Years in State Service:** 5

JOB DESCRIPTION:
Act as chief legal counsel to DCPO and head of the legal department; assist Commissioner in management of, and on major policy matters for, the agency.

ORGANIZATIONS:
Massachusetts and Boston Bar Associations; New England Women in Real Estate

Stephen J. Hines

Assistant Commissioner for Operations

Division of Capital Asset Management
Address: One Ashburton Place, Room 1519, Boston, MA 02108
Telephone: (617) 727-4050 ext. 303 **Fax:** (617) 727-5363
Staff: Donna Bontempo, Executive Assistant
Reports to: Commissioner Lark Jurev Palermo

PERSONAL INFORMATION:
Born: June 5, 1959 **Place of Birth:** Woburn
Marital Status: married (Marybeth) **Children:** 2
Education: College of the Holy Cross (A.B., '81); Boston College Law School (J.D., '84)
Previous Employment: Acting General Counsel for DCPO; Associate General Counsel for DCPO; City of Worcester (Assistant City Solicitor)
Years in Current Position: 5 **Years in State Service:** 10

JOB DESCRIPTION:
Assist Commissioner in the management of the Agency.

ORGANIZATIONS:
Boston Bar Association; Massachusetts Bar Association

Ralph F. Nee

Deputy Commissioner for Construction Services

Division of Capital Asset Management
Address: One Ashburton Place, Room 1519, Boston, MA 02108
Telephone: (617) 727-4030 ext. 512
Staff: Michael J. Lambert, Director of Construction Services, Engineering; Mary Beth Clancy, Assistant Director, Operations
Reports to: Commissioner Lark Jurev Palermo

PERSONAL INFORMATION:
Education: Harvard University, Contract and Construction Law Course; Harvard University, JFK School of Government (Certificate, Public Policy Management); Franklin Technical Institute (Electrical Technology); Lowell Technical Institute (Civil Engineering)
Years in Current Position: 11 **Years in State Service:** 31

JOB DESCRIPTION:
Meet the Commonwealth building asset management needs as determined by the Administration.

ORGANIZATIONS:
S.A.M.E.

Michael D. Sullivan

Director of Finance and Administration

Division of Capital Asset Management
Address: One Ashburton Place, 15th Floor, Boston, MA 02108
Telephone: (617) 727-4006 **Fax:** (617) 727-5363
Reports to: Commissioner Lark Jurev Palermo

PERSONAL INFORMATION:

Education: Suffolk University (B.S., Political Science, '76); Suffolk University (M.P.A., '77)
Previous Employment: Office of the State Auditor; Executive Office of Health and Human Services; Massachusetts General Court
Years in Current Position: 13 **Years in State Service:** 26

JOB DESCRIPTION:

Responsible for the financial and administrative activities of the Division including labor relations, affirmative action, systems, capital budgeting, accounting, contracting and payroll.

Michael B. Williams

Director of Programming

Division of CapitalAsset Management
Address: One Ashburton Place, 15th Fl, Boston, MA 02108
Telephone: (617) 727-4015 **Fax:** (617) 727-6060
E-mail: michael.williams@state.ma.us
Staff: Melissa Robin, Senior Manager; Sherril White, Administrative Manager
Reports to: Commissioner Lark Jurev Palermo

PERSONAL INFORMATION:

Place of Birth: Colombia, South America
Marital Status: married (Carol Waldvogel) **Children:** 2
Education: Boston Architectural Center (Bachelor of Architecture); Miami University, Oxford, OH (Journalism)
Previous Employment: Private sector architecture and planning firm (Senior Associate)
Years in Current Position: 4.5 **Years in State Service:** 10.5

JOB DESCRIPTION:

Responsible for planning and design decisions in developing building programs and master plans; determining the feasibility and cost of state construction projects; setting standards and guidelines for planning and design of state facilities; providing technical review and information as required. Manage staff of planning and design professionals and administrative personnel; direct and oversee the work of consulting architects, engineers, and programmers.

1999 PRIORITIES:

Develop and implement building projects for higher education, public safety, human services, and environmental agencies.

ORGANIZATIONS:

American Institute of Architects, Boston Society of Architects; Boston Athenaeum; Faculty, Boston Architectural Center.

Dennis R. Smith
Superintendent

Bureau of State Office Buildings
Address: State House, Room 1, Boston, MA 02133
Telephone: (617) 727-1100 **Fax** 617-727-7700
E-mail: patrick.reed@state.ma.us
Staff: Gerald Roosa, Deputy Superintendent of Administration; Leo Colborne, Deputy Superintendent for Operations and Engineering; John O'Connell, Facility Manager; Neil Kilpeck, Director of State House Operations; Charles Wolf, Trades Manager; Randy Cabral, Director of Security; Tammy Kraus DelTorto, Executive Assistant.

Reports to: Secretary Andrew Natsios, Commissioner Palermo

PERSONAL INFORMATION:
Born: September 16, 1946 **Place of Birth:** Milford
Marital Status: married (June) **Children:** 3
Education: University of Massachusetts at Lowell (B.M., Education, '68); Suffolk University (M.A., Education, '72)
Previous Employment: U.S. Department of Education (Regional Director); Town of Middleboro (Selectman); Massachusetts State Senate (Aide); U.S. Metric Board, Washington D.C. (Board Member); Mathematics Department (Head /Teacher)
Years in Current Position: 6 **Years in State Service:** 23

JOB DESCRIPTION:
Responsible for property management, buildings and mechanical operations of the State House, McCormack and Saltonstall Buildings, Lindemann Mental Health Center, 100 Nashua Street building, Pittsfield State office Building and the Springfield State Office building. Custodian of historic military flag collection at the State House. Oversee events and conferences held in the State House, McCormack and Saltonstall buildings.

1999 PRIORITIES:
The Bureau mission is to provide safe, secure workplace for customers, assuring that all who enter Bureau facilities have a pleasant business environment and can transit common areas without incident; and to efficiently maintain mechanical structures and buildings, recognizing that they function as places of business, museums of art and history, and sites of public congregation.

ORGANIZATIONS:
Massachusetts Aviation Education Council; Aeronautics Club of New England; New England Historical and Genealogical Society; International Facility Managers Association; Middlesex Club.

Leo Colborne
Dep. Superintendent Operations /Engineering

Bureau of State Office Buildings
Address: One Ashburton Place , Rm107, Boston, MA 02108
Staff: Elizabeth Hemond, Office Manager; Ruth Rodriquez, Clerk, John Cormican, Manger of Building Operations
Telephone: (617) 727-0929 **Fax** (617) 727-2576
E-mail: leo.colborne@state.ma.us

Reports to: Superintendent Dennis R. Smith

PERSONAL INFORMATION:

Born: October 31, 1933
Marital Status: married **Children:** 2
Education: Burdett (one year)
Previous Employment: H.J. Stiles, President Leo Colborne & Son
Years in Current Position: 7 **Years in State Service:** 7

JOB DESCRIPTION:

Maintain efficient day to day operations of Government Center buildings; Oversee major construction projects.

Tammy Kraus DelTorto

Director of State House Events

Bureau of State Office Buildings
Address: State House, Rm 107, Boston, MA 02133
Staff: Tina Fabrizio, Administrative Clerk
Telephone: (617) 727-1100 x 532 **Fax** 617-727-7700
E-mail: tammy.deltorto@state.ma.us
Reports to: Superintendent Dennis Smith

PERSONAL INFORMATION:

Born: Feb. 21, 1967 **Place of Birth:** Middleboro
Marital Status: married (Dean)
Education: Westfield State College (B.S. '89); Northeastern University
Previous Employment: Tele-Dynamics, West Bridgewater Systems Programmer/Trainer
Years in Current Position: 2 **Years in State Service:** 2

JOB DESCRIPTION:

Oversight and management of special events and conferences held in the State House.

Christine E. Morris

Chairman

Massachusetts Civil Service Commission
Address: One Ashburton Place, Room 2112, Boston, MA 02108
Telephone: (617) 727-2293 **Fax:** (617) 727-7590
Staff: Eric Wetzel, General Counsel; Thomas Nee, Chief of Staff; Robert Anzevino, Executive Assistant
Reports to: Governor A. Paul Cellucci

PERSONAL INFORMATION:

Born: July 15, 1947 **Place of Birth:** Lawrence
Marital Status: married (Gabriel Dumont)
Education: University of South Carolina (B.A., '68); Suffolk University School of Law (J.D., '71); Harvard Business School (P.M.D., 81) **Previous Employment:** Massachusetts Executive Office of Labor (Secretary of Labor); Dumont and Morris, Attorneys at Law (Managing Partner); The Morris Company, Real Estate Consulting (President); Xerox Corporation, Systems Division (Regional Sales Manager)
Years in Current Position: 3 **Years in State Service: 8**

JOB DESCRIPTION:
Chairman of quasi-judicial panel hearing disputes with respect to the merit system law and regulations governing state and municipal employment.

Daniel Shannon

Executive Director

Massachusetts Developmental Disabilities Council
Address: 174 Portland St. 5th Fl, Boston, MA 02114
Telephone: (617) 727-6374
Fax: (617) 727-1174
Staff: Adelia DelTrecco, Executive Assistant; Deidre Whelan, Legal Counsel.
Reports to: Secretary Andrew Natsios

PERSONAL INFORMATION:
Born: July 31, 1957 **Place of Birth:** Concord
Marital Status: married (Nancy Joyce) **Children:** 3
Education: Northeaster University (B.S. '80); Suffolk University (M.P.A. 89)
Years in Current Position: 3 **Years in State Service:** 7

Lorraine Greiff

Acting Director

Massachusetts Office on Disability
Address: One Ashburton Place, Room 1305, Boston, MA 02108
Telephone: (617) 727-7440; (800) 322-2020
Fax: (617) 727-0965
Staff: Michael Dumont, Budget Director; Barbara Lybarger, General Counsel, Myra Berloff, Community Services, Penny Goerlach, Special Projects
Web page: http://www.state.ma.us/mod
Reports to: Governor A. Paul Cellucci

PERSONAL INFORMATION:
Place of Birth: Boston
Marital Status: married (Paul) **Children:** 3
Years in Current Position: 4 **Years in State Service:** 14

JOB DESCRIPTION:
Development and management of independent agency within Administration and Finance that is responsible for monitoring and overseeing programs, policies, services, and civil rights pertaining to Massachusetts residents with disabilities. This office serves as Americans with Disabilities Act coordinator for state government.

Martin J. Benison

Comptroller

Office of the State Comptroller
Address: One Ashburton Place, 9th Floor, Boston, MA 02108
Telephone: (617) 973-2315 **Fax:** (617) 727-2163
E-mail: martin.benison@state.ma.us
Staff: Monica A. Middleton, Administrative Assistant
Reports to: Governor A. Paul Cellucci

PERSONAL INFORMATION:
Born: April 9, 1958 **Place of Birth:** Stanford, CT
Marital Status: married (Lauren) **Children:** 3
Education: Boston College (B.A. '80); Harvard JFK School of Government (M.P.A., '97)
Previous Employment: Deputy Comptroller, Commonwealth of Massachusetts
Years in Current Position: new **Years in State Service:** 14

ORGANIZATIONS:
National Association of State Auditors, Comptrollers and Treasures; Government Finance officers Association; Association of Government Accountants

Fredie D. Kay

Executive Director

Massachusetts Office of Dispute Resolution
Address: 100 Cambridge Street, Room 1005, Boston, MA 02202
Telephone: (617) 727-2224 ext. 315 **Fax:** (617) 727-6495
Staff: Tamsen Schultz, Staff Assistant
Reports to: Secretary Andrew Natsios

PERSONAL INFORMATION:
Place of Birth: Washington, D.C.
Marital Status: married (Thomas Green) **Children:** 2
Education: University of Maryland (B.A., '75); Harvard University, JFK School of Government (M.P.A., '81); Georgetown University Law Center (J.D., '85)
Previous Employment: Office of the Governor (Deputy Legal Counsel); Goodwin, Procter and Hoar (Associate); U.S. Conference of Mayors
Years in Current Position: 3 **Years in State Service:** 7.5

JOB DESCRIPTION:
Responsible for overseeing and directing the Massachusetts Office of Dispute Resolution (MODR), which provides high-quality mediation and case evaluation services, dispute resolution skills training, meeting facilitation, and other alternative dispute resolution services. MODR provides these services to state and other public agencies, municipalities, the courts, and citizens of the Commonwealth using MODR staff and 65 private sector neutrals. These services provide a cost-effective and efficient means of resolving public policy disputes and often result in improved government responsiveness to the needs of the public. This office also trains state personnel in negotiation and mediation skills, so that problems can be efficiently addressed before they escalate into expensive and time-consuming disputes. MODR's programs and services include: Court Programs, Environmental Mediation,

Large-scale Mediations, Facilitation and Process Consulting, and the Training Program.

1999 PRIORITIES:
To expand the use of mediation for interagency disputes in particular, and to generally increase the use of alternative dispute resolution in the executive, judicial, and legislative branches of government, as well as in cit and towns.

ORGANIZATIONS:
Boston Bar Association; Massachusetts Bar Association; Women's Bar Association of Massachusetts; Society c Professionals in Dispute Resolution, New England Chapter

Dolores L. Mitchell

Executive Director

Group Insurance Commission
Address: 19 Staniford Street, Boston, MA 02114
Telephone: (617) 727-2310 ext. 3010
Fax: (617) 227-2681
Staff: Robert Johnson, Deputy Director and General Counsel
Reports to: Secretary Andrew Natsios

PERSONAL INFORMATION:
Marital Status: married (Marvin L. Mitchell, M.D.)
Children: 3
Education: Ohio State University; Harvard Graduate School of Arts & Sciences
Previous Employment: Katharine Gibbs School (Director, '80-'87); Abt Associates, Commonwealth of Massachusetts, Governor's Office
Years in Current Position: 11 **Years in State Service:** 15

JOB DESCRIPTION:
The provision of a broad range of benefits for state employees, retirees, and their families. The GIC designs, procures and monitors life and health insurance, long term disability insurance and dental and vision services. T agency strives to provide the highest quality services at fair and reasonable costs.

1999 PRIORITIES:
Continue to monitor cost and quality. Study the feasibility of moving to risk adjusted rates for health plans. See additional means of using the Commonwealth's purchasing power to keep health care affordable. Pay particular attention to pharmacy costs.

ORGANIZATIONS:
Health Data Consortium (Vice President); Mass Health Care Purchaser Group; National Steering Committee, National Women's Political Caucus; Director, Big Sister Assoc. of Greater Boston; Women's Economic Forum

Charles E. Walker, Jr.

Chairman

Massachusetts Commission Against Discrimination
Address: One Ashburton Place, Room 601, Boston, MA 02108
Telephone: (617) 727-3990 x201 **Fax:** (617)720-6053
Staff: Karen Charles, Executive Assistant
Reports to: Secretary Andrew Natsios

PERSONAL INFORMATION:
Born: May 1, 1951 **Place of Birth:** Alaska
Marital Status: married (Dorothy) **Children:** 2
Education: University of California at Santa Barbara (B.A., Political Science); Boston College Law School (J.D., '78)
Previous Employment: Executive Office of Elder Affairs (General Counsel); New England School of Law (Law Professor); Office of the Attorney General (Assistant Attorney General)
Years in Current Position: 4 **Years in State Service:** 15

JOB DESCRIPTION:
Serve as primary fact-finder and policy-maker on all the civil rights and antidiscrimination laws of the state. Sharing with two other commissioners the responsibility in overseeing and supervising five major departments under the MCAD's charter including: Legal, Administrative Operations, the Department of Investigations, Systematic Operations, and the Hearings Division.

1999 PRIORITIES:
Create new initiative to promote tolerance and to prevent discrimination from occurring.

ORGANIZATIONS:
Massachusetts, American and Boston Bar Associations; Massachusetts Black Lawyers Association (President, '93-'94)

Dorca I. Gomez

Commissioner

Massachusetts Commission Against Discrimination
Address: 436 Dwight Street, Springfield, MA 01105
Telephone: (413)739-2145 x104 **Fax:** (413)784-1056
Reports to: Secretary Andrew Natsios

PERSONAL INFORMATION:
Born: March 31 **Place of Birth:** New York
Marital Status: Single **Children:** 2
Education: University of Massachusetts - Amherst (B.A. '97)
Previous Employment: Executive Office of Elder Affairs (General Counsel); New England School of Law (Law Professor); Office of the Attorney General (Assistant Attorney General); MML Information Services, Inc. Registered Representative
Years in Current Position: 4 **Years in State Service:** 4

JOB DESCRIPTION:
Enforcement of civil rights laws in the Commonwealth.

1999 PRIORITIES:
Implementation of new regulations. Creation of a state-wide enforcement plan. Improve MCAD team to provide quality service to the state.

ORGANIZATIONS:
Board Member, Springfield Technical Community College

Douglas T. Schwarz

Commissioner

Massachusetts Commission Against Discrimination
Address: One Ashburton Place, Rm 601, Boston, MA 02108
Telephone: (617)727-3990 x202 **Fax:** (617)720-6053
Staff: Je'Lesia Jones
Reports to: Governor A. Paul Cellucci

PERSONAL INFORMATION:
Born: April 2, 1959 **Place of Birth:** Greenwich, CT
Marital Status: Married (Beth Marcus) **Children:** 2
Education: Dartmouth College, (A.B. '81); Harvard Law School (J.D. '86)
Previous Employment: Peckham Lobel, Casey, Prince & Tye, (partner); Mass. Office of Attorney General, (Assistant Attorney General); United States District Court, District of Vermont (law clerk).
Years in Current Position: 1 **Years in State Service:** 3

JOB DESCRIPTION:
Investigate and adjudicate claims of unlawful discrimination in employment, housing, public accommodations, and education. Share with two other commissioners responsibility for overseeing the three major departments of the MCAD: Legal, Enforcement, Hearings, and Administration. Educate the public regarding the law and the agency.

1999 PRIORITIES:
Target frequent violators of antidiscrimination laws; expand alternative dispute resolution program; improve investigator training; increase the number of public hearings.

Val Asbedian

Director Of Strategic Planning

Information Technology Division
Address: One Ashburton Place, Boston, MA 02108
Telephone: (617) 973-0762 **Fax:** (617) 727-3766
Staff: Marie Carpenito, Special Assistant to the Director; Jane Kauffman, Administrative Assistant
Reports to: Director of Information Technology

JOB DESCRIPTION:
The Office of Management Systems provides effective and reliable information technology and telecommunications (IT/TC) planning, design, implementation, and oversight to Commonwealth agencies.

1999 PRIORITIES:

Consolidation of major data centers to the Massachusetts Information Technology Center (MITC); work on implementation of the administration's reorganization plan; completion of the state's WAN network

James J. Hartnett, Jr.

Personnel Administrator

Human Resources Division
Address: One Ashburton Place, Room 307, Boston, MA 02108
Telephone: (617) 727-1556 **Fax:** (617) 727-3970
Staff: Four Bureau Directors; Anne Silva, Executive Assistant; Leslie Whidden, Administrative Secretary
Reports to: Secretary Andrew Natsios

PERSONAL INFORMATION:

Born: May 4, 1944
Marital Status: married (Joan) **Children:** 4
Education: Stonehill College (B.S., '66); Harvard University, JFK School of Government (Senior Executive Program, '82); Harvard Business School (Executives in State Government, '80)
Previous Employment: 26 years of public service in Human Resource field; titles include Deputy Commissioner for Personnel Management and Merit System Services; Deputy Commissioner for Management Services; Director, Bureau of Classification
Years in Current Position: 4 **Years in State Service:** 28

JOB DESCRIPTION:

Ensures consistent integration of Department of Personnel Administration goals and objectives. Manage merit system for city and state governments and assures that valid and equitable selection instruments are developed. Direct personnel management programs including management compensation program with a merit pay provision; manage human resource development and training activities.

ORGANIZATIONS:

American Society for Public Administrators (ASPA); Pre-Cana for engaged couples; Braintree Softball Association; Archbishop Williams High School Parents Executive Board; St. Vincent dePaul Society, Quincy; United Way Advisory Committee

James P. McDonagh

General Counsel

Human Resources Division
Address: One Ashburton Place, Room 307, Boston, MA 02108
Telephone: (617) 727-3555 **Fax:** (617) 727-1477
Staff: Desiree Rivera
Reports to: James J. Hartnett, Jr, Personnel Administrator

PERSONAL INFORMATION:

Born: March 1, 1959 **Place of Birth:** Boston
Marital Status: married (Marina) **Children:** 4
Education: College of the Holy Cross, (B.A. '81); Suffolk University Law School (J.D. '86)

Previous Employment: Massachusetts Organization of State Engineers and Scientists, General Counsel (1988-97)
Years in Current Position: 2 **Years in State Service:** 2

JOB DESCRIPTION:
Advising the Personnel Administrator and the Human Resources Division of the legal implications of policy determinations; supervising all labor arbitration and litigation before the Massachusetts Labor Relations Commission involving the Commonwealth; supervising all litigation before the Massachusetts Civil Service Commission involving the Personnel Administrator; assisting in the negotiation of labor agreements between the Commonwealth and public sector labor unions.

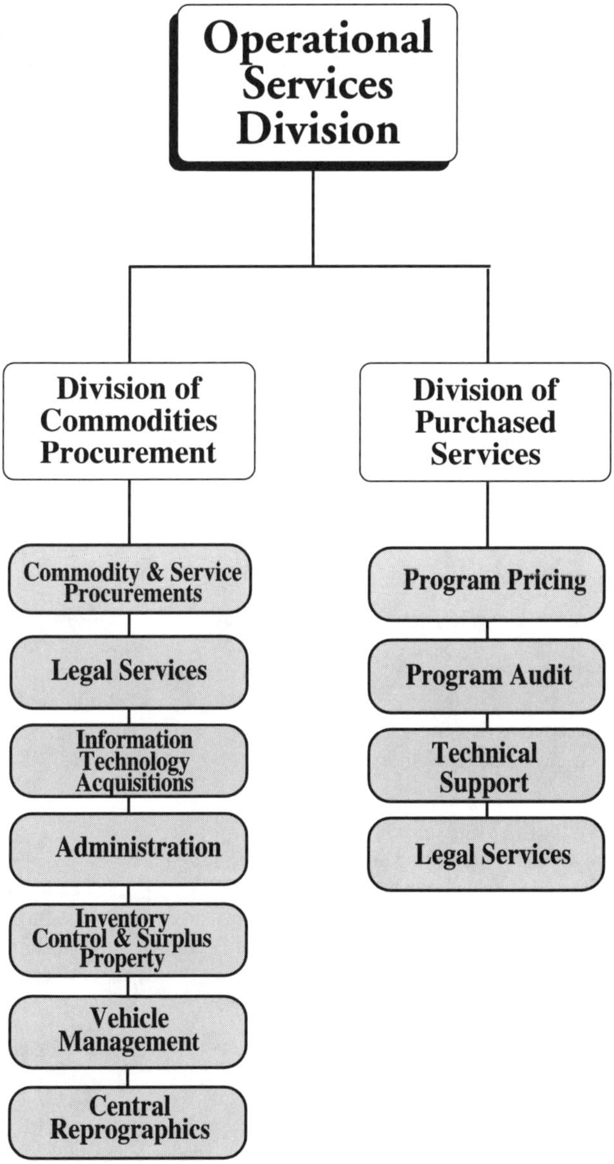
Operational Services Division
Division of Commodities Procurement
Division of Purchased Services
Commodity & Service Procurements
Legal Services
Information Technology Acquisitions
Administration
Inventory Control & Surplus Property
Vehicle Management
Central Reprographics
Program Pricing
Program Audit
Technical Support
Legal Services

Philmore Anderson III

State Purchasing Agent

Operational Services Division
Address: One Ashburton Place, 10th Floor, Boston, MA 02108
Telephone: (617) 727-7500
Staff: Vera Martin, Assistant
Fax: (617) 727-4527
Reports to: Secretary Andrew Natsios

PERSONAL INFORMATION:
Born: October 4, 1942
Place of Birth: Philadelphia, PA
Marital Status: married (Bertha)
Children: 1
Education: Central State University (B.S., '64)
Previous Employment: The Kendall Company (Manager of Office Services, Boston, '75-'91); Price Waterhouse Company (Senior Accountant, '71-'75); Federal Reserve Bank (Assistant Department Head, '65-'70)
Years in Current Position: 7
Years in State Service: 8

JOB DESCRIPTION:
Responsible for supervision, administration, and operation of the Operational Services Division. This division provides centralized purchasing to allow all agencies, departments, and commissions of the Commonwealth to acquire quality materials, supplies, and equipment at competitive prices in a manner consistent with Commonwealth laws, policy, and regulations. Enhance utilities to other state agencies by providing several retained revenue accounts offering printing, fleet management, and medical services.

Gary J. Lambert

Deputy Commissioner/Deputy Purchasing Agent

Operational Services Division
Address: One Ashburton Place, 10th Floor, Boston, MA 02108-1552
Telephone: (617) 727-7500
Staff: Donna Bonigli, Executive Assistant
Fax: (617) 727-6123
Reports to: State Purchasing Agent Philmore Anderson III

PERSONAL INFORMATION:
Education: Suffolk University (B.S., Government, '84)
Previous Employment: Division of Purchased Services (Deputy Assistant Commissioner, '90-'91); Executive Office for Administration and Finance (Deputy Assistant Secretary, '89-'90); Department of Personnel Administration (Director of Administrative Services, '86-'89); Executive Office of Human Services (Assistant Budget Director, '85-'86); Chief Financial Officer, '82-'85; Cost Control Analyst, '80-'81); Department of Public Health (Consultant, '80)
Years in Current Position: 7
Years in State Service: 20

JOB DESCRIPTION:
Oversee all commodity and general service procurements throughout the Commonwealth and offer effective and cost-competitive central support services.

1999 PRIORITIES:
Develop a uniform procurement process, rationalize commodity and supplier base, enhance electronic commerce in the procurement process.

ORGANIZATIONS:
National Association of State Purchasing Officials (Executive Committee, '93-'97; Information Technology Committee Chairperson, '94-'97; Finance Chairperson, '97); National Institute of Governmental Purchasing; National Association of Fleet Administrators

Cheryl L. Traina

Director of Professional & Institutional Services

Operational Services Division
Address: One Ashburton Place, Room 1017, Boston, MA 02108
Telephone: (617) 727-7500 ext. 207
Fax: (617) 727-4527 **E-mail:** Cheryl.Traina@osd.state.ma.us
Staff: Betty Fernandez, Bill Funk, Brian Putnam, Tess Francisco, Tricia McKim
Reports to: Deputy Purchasing Agent, Gary Lambert

PERSONAL INFORMATION:
Place of Birth: Framingham **Marital Status:** married (Joey)
Education: Stonehill (B.A.)
Previous Employment: Disability Determination Services (Director of Human Resources); State Street Business Group (Vice President Administration); The New England (Client Relations Manager); State Street Business Group (Asst. Treasurer, Client Relations)
Years in Current Position: 1 **Years in State Service:** 6

JOB DESCRIPTION:
Development and management of statewide contracts for the oversight of procurement team leaders responsible for medical supplies; services and equipment; human resources; legal supplies and services; financial services; clothing and toiletries; animals and animal supplies; public safety; law enforcement; trees; uniforms and apparel.

1999 PRIORITIES:
Enhancement and increased usage of Comm-PASS, the division's web site. Also, increased number of multi-state contracts.

ORGANIZATIONS:
Treasurer, Beachmont Neighborhood Association; Deacon - Maplewood Baptist Church

Tanja Ryden

Director of Technical Support

Operational Services Division
Address: One Ashburton Place, Room 1017, Boston, MA 02108
Telephone: (617) 727-7500 ext. 278
Fax: (617) 727-4527 **E-mail:** tryden@state.ma.us
Reports to: Assistant Commissioner

PERSONAL INFORMATION:
Education: Williams College (B.A., Biology, '81); Tufts University, School of Nutrition (M.S., Nutrition, '87)
Previous Employment: Department of Public Health, Purchase of Service Office (Director)
Years in Current Position: 6 **Years in State Service:** 10

JOB DESCRIPTION:
Oversee technical assistance for state agencies and contractors involved in the Purchase-of-Service system; coordinate procurement reform initiative for human/social service contracting.

ORGANIZATIONS:

Massachusetts Public Health Association; The Literacy Connection (TLC)

Robert F. Stalnaker

Executive Director

Public Employee Retirement Administration Commission
Address: 5 Middlesex Ave., 3rd Fl, Somerville, MA 02145
Telephone: (617) 666-4446 **Fax:** (617) 628-4002
E-mail: robert.f.stalnaker@state.ma.us
Reports to: Commissioners

PERSONAL INFORMATION:

Born: May 7, 1949 **Place of Birth:** Spencer, WV
Marital Status: married (Melissa) **Children:** 3
Education: University of Alaska (B.B.A. '83); Harvard (MPA '86)
Previous Employment: State of Alaska, Division of Retirement and Benefits, Executive Director.
Years in Current Position: 2 **Years in State Service:** 2

JOB DESCRIPTION:

Oversight and regulation of all aspects of pension administration and management of the 106 autonomous public pension systems in Massachusetts.

1999 PRIORITIES:

Implementation of Chapter 306, Disability Oversight and Fraud Intervention.

Department of Revenue

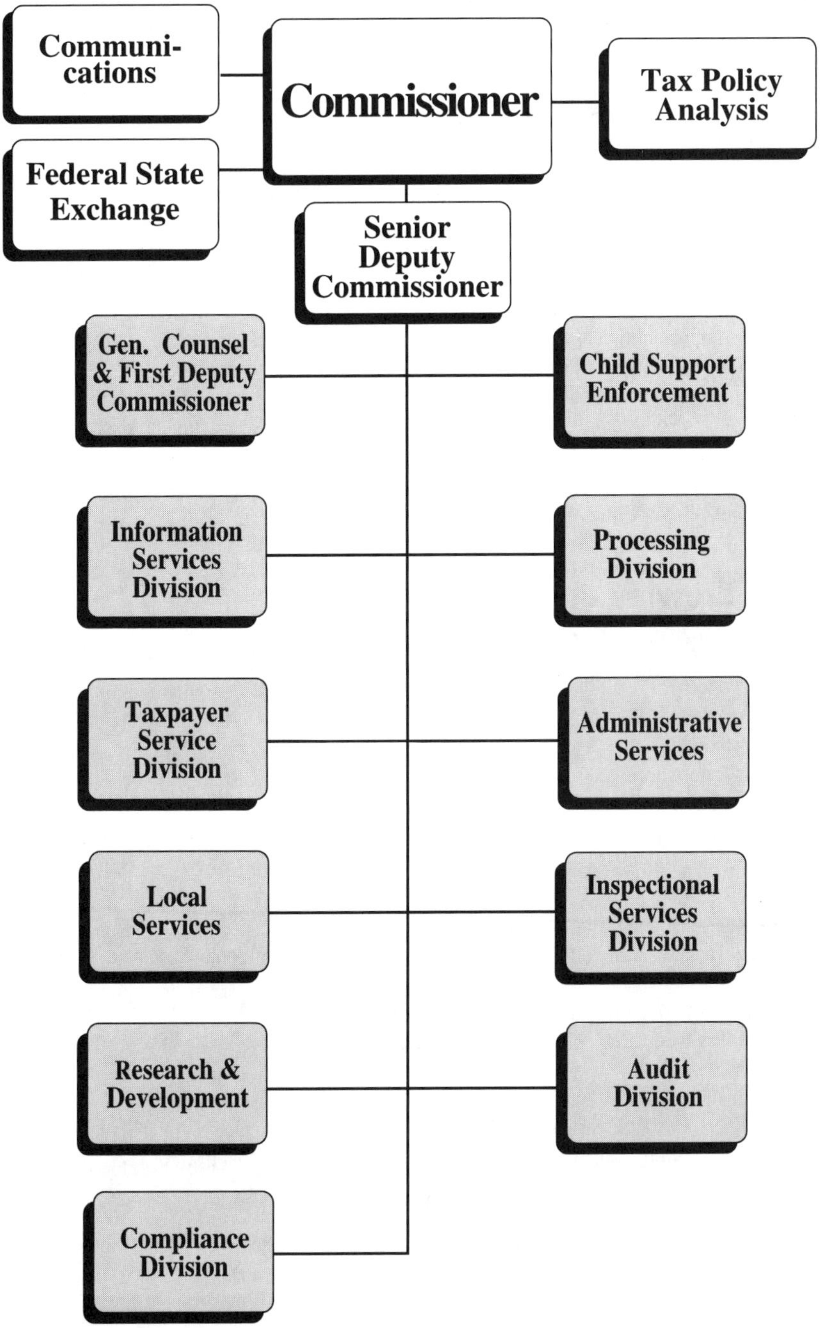

Frederick A. Laskey

Commissioner

Department of Revenue
Address: 100 Cambridge Street, P.O. Box 9681, Boston, MA 02114
Telephone: (617) 626-2201 **Fax:** (617) 626-2299
Staff: Jennifer Bates, Special Assistant
Reports to: Secretary Andrew Natsios

PERSONAL INFORMATION:
Born: March 25, 1957 **Place of Birth:** Everett
Marital Status: married (Donna) **Children:** 4
Education: University of Massachusetts at Boston (B.A., History/Political Science, '79)
Previous Employment: Department of Revenue, Assistant Commissioner
Years in Current Position: new **Years in State Service:** 19

JOB DESCRIPTION:
Responsible for the administration of the Commonwealth's tax laws through innovative use of technology; responsible for the Division of Local Services, which provides financial services to and approves the tax rates and budgets of the 351 cities and towns of the Commonwealth; responsible for management of the state's child support enforcement program, which is a national leader in ensuring children receive the support deserved.

ORGANIZATIONS:
Boy Scouts of America (Committee Chair)

Bernard F. Crowley, Jr.

Senior Deputy Commissioner

Department of Revenue
Address: P.O. Box 9478, Boston, MA 02205-9494
Telephone: (617) 626-2201 **Fax:** (617) 626-2299
E-mail: dorcomm@shore.net
Staff: Frances M. MacDonald, Administrative Assistant
Reports to: Secretary Frederick A. Laskey

PERSONAL INFORMATION:
Born: December 17, 1945 **Place of Birth:** Boston
Marital Status: married (Jane O'Hern) **Children:** 5
Education: Lowell Technological Institute (ABA. Accounting, '73); Harvard (Senior Executive Fellows Program Fall '86
Previous Employment: Department of Revenue, Assistant Commissioner
Years in Current Position: new **Years in State Service:** 19

JOB DESCRIPTION:
Chief Operating Officer for the Department of Revenue responsible for administering the Commonwealth's tax laws, child support enforcement program and providing financial services to cities an towns.

1999 PRIORITIES:
To resolve tax payer disputes quickly and fairly; to improve customer relation by providing timely and professional services; to develop internal training programs for tax professional employees.

Donald J. Evans

First Deputy Commissioner and General Counsel

Department of Revenue
Address: 100 Cambridge Street, Room 800S, Boston, MA 02114
Telephone: (617) 626-3200 **Fax:** (617) 626-3249
Staff: Catherine Gingola, Executive Assistan; Tanya Lewis-Richardson, Secretary
Reports to: Commissioner Frederick A. Laskey

PERSONAL INFORMATION:
Born: January 29, 1926 **Place of Birth:** Springfield
Marital Status: married **Children:** 3
Education: Dartmouth College (A.B., '47); Harvard Law School (J.D., '52)
Previous Employment: Goodwin, Procter & Hoar LLP (Senior Partner)
Years in Current Position: 2

JOB DESCRIPTION:
Serving as General Counsel for the Massachusetts Department of Revenue and related matters.

ORGANIZATIONS:
American Bar Association, Business Law Section and various committees; American College of Investment Counsel; American Law Institute; International Bar Association; Massachusetts Bar Association

Marie J. Parente

Trustee

State House Library
Address: State House, Room 134, Boston, MA 02133
Telephone: (617) 722-2400 **Fax:** (617) 722-2897
Staff: Lee Rogers, Research Director; Cheryl Sibley, Sr. Research Analyst

PERSONAL INFORMATION:
Born: May 22, 1928 **Place of Birth:** Springfield
Marital Status: married (Francis) **Children:** 2
Education: University of Massachusetts at Boston (B.A., '86; M.A., Human Services, '92)
Previous Employment: Presently in Massachusetts House of Representatives (10th Worcester District); Town of Milford (Selectman, '73-'81); County Commission Advisory Board; Worcester County Legislative Committee; Massachusetts Selectman's Association; Joint Labor-Management Committee; Seaver's Express, Inc. (Administrative Bookkeeper/Secretary, '56-'81)

ORGANIZATIONS:
Committee on Foster Care (Chair); Massachusetts Caucus of Women Legislators; Federation of Women's Clubs; State House Library (Trustee); Governor's Blue Ribbon Commission on Foster Care

Stephen A. Fulchino

Director

State House Library
Address: State House, Room 341, Boston, MA 02133
Telephone: (617) 727-2589 **Fax:** (617) 727-5819
E-mail: Stephen.Fulchino@state.ma.us
Reports to: Secretary Andrew Natsios and Library Board of Trustees

PERSONAL INFORMATION:
Born: Sept. 5, 1949 **Place of Birth:** Everett
Marital Status: married (Barbara) **Children:** 2
Education: Bowdoin College (A.B. '71); University of Chicago (M.A. '74)
Previous Employment: Swampscott Public Library, Director; Medford Public Library, Assistant Director.
Years in Current Position: 2 **Years in State Service:** 2

JOB DESCRIPTION:
To plan and administer a program of library and information services to the executive and legislative branches of state government. The director is responsible for the management of the State Library; duties include objectives, determining priorities, collection development, and promoting an awareness of the State Library as a government research center.

1999 PRIORITIES:
Upgrade technology, climate-control the vault, put on-line and Internet resources on the desktops of selected state employees.

ORGANIZATIONS:
Massachusetts Library Association, Board of Directors of Playwrights' Platform, Commissioner of Everett Housing Authority.

Veterans' Services

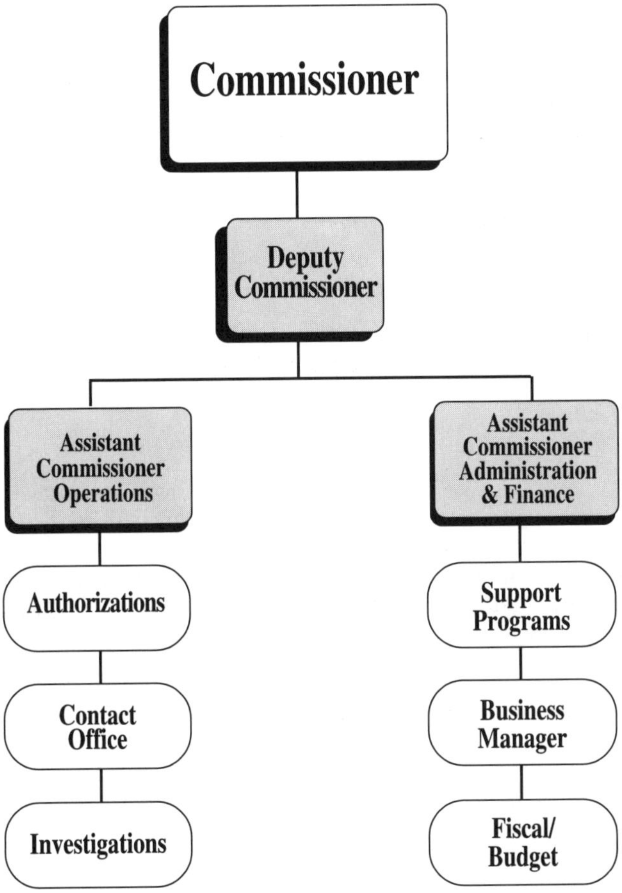

Thomas J. Hudner, Jr.

Commissioner

Veterans' Services
Address: 100 Cambridge Street, Room 1002, Boston, MA 02202
Telephone: (617) 727-3578 ext. 101
Fax: (617) 727-5903
E-mail: thomas.hudner@state.ma.us
Staff: Sharlene A. Queenan, Administrative Assistant
Reports to: Secretary Andrew Natsios

PERSONAL INFORMATION:

Born: August 31, 1924
Place of Birth: Fall River
Marital Status: married (Georgea)
Children: 3 stepchildren; 1 son
Education: U.S. Naval Academy (B.S.); George Washington University (M.A., International Affairs)
Previous Employment: Veterans' Services (Deputy Commissioner); The Discovery Foundation (Executive Director); U.S. Navy (30 years — retired Captain)
Years in Current Position: 8 **Years in State Service:** 11

JOB DESCRIPTION:

To establish policy, compose legislation, and author regulations for the proper administration of M.G.L. 115 (Veterans Benefits); to act as the agent for all departments, boards, and commissions of the Commonwealth in all matters before the federal Department of Veterans' Affairs involving any federal compensation, etc.; to advise the Governor and the Secretary for Administration and Finance relative to all programs and issues pertaining to veterans; to represent the interests of all veterans in matters coming before the Legislature, the Administration, and the public.

1999 PRIORITIES:

To ensure that all needy veterans and their dependents receive the benefits and services to which they are entitled in recognition of their sacrifices in time of war; to increase awareness by all eligible veterans and their families of the benefits provided by the Commonwealth; in this time of changing veterans' demographics and with more emphasis on municipal cost savings, to work closely with the Massachusetts Municipal Association to ensure that all veterans are properly served by the veterans agents throughout the Commonwealth; to establish state veterans' cemetery in central Massachusetts.

ORGANIZATIONS:

Member Congressional Medal of Honor Society; Legion of Valor, past President of the New England Chapter of the Chosen Few, Korean War Veterans Association, Ancient and Honorable Artillery Company of Massachusetts, First Corps of Cadets, American Legion, Veterans of Foreign Wars, Disabled American Veterans, Military Order of World Wars, Association of Naval Aviation, Tailhook Association, Order of the Daedalians, Navy League, Boston Marine Society, Reserve officers Association, The Retired Officers Association, and Past President of the New England Counsel of the USO

Walter F. Pero

Deputy Commissioner

Veterans' Services
Address: 100 Cambridge Street, Room 1002, Boston, MA 02202
Telephone: (617) 727-3578 ext. 209
Fax: (617) 727-5903
E-mail: walter.pero@state.ma.us
Staff: Sharlene A. Queenan, Administrative Assistant
Reports to: Commissioner Thomas J. Hudner, Jr.

PERSONAL INFORMATION:
Born: May 8, 1947 **Place of Birth:** Cambridge
Marital Status: married (Florence) **Children:** 2
Education: Boston State College (B.S. ;69); University of Southern California (M.Ed. '73); Worcester State College (C.A.G.S., '82)
Previous Employment: Somerville Public School, Supervisor Continuing Eduction (1974-95); Action for Boston Community Development (ABCD) Director of Education and Training (1995-97)
Years in Current Position: 1 **Years in State Service:** 1

JOB DESCRIPTION:
Work directly under the supervision of the Commissioner. Responsible for discharging all obligations of the agency, including establishment and execution of policy and operational oversight in the administration of the veterans' benefits program (Ch. 115 M.G.L.) and the Boston and Providence, R.I. contact offices (which assist in claims for Federal Veterans' benefits and pensions). Also, oversee the following non-profit support services: regional outreach counseling centers (9) and veterans' homeless shelters (6)

1999 PRIORITIES:
Increase collaboration and communication with various veterans groups and organizations. Establish state-wide training programs for veteran service providers.

ORGANIZATIONS:
Somerville Board of Alderman (President); American Legion, International Association of Approved Basketball Officials (IAABO)

Elder Affairs

The Executive Office of Elder Affairs is responsible for the planning and implementation of state programs that serve the needs of the state's elderly citizens. The secretariat works with a network of provider agencies and advocacy groups to develop delivery systems to elderly residents in their homes, institutions, and the community. It manages state and federally funded programs, offers technical assistance and oversight to community service agencies, and reviews other state agency programs related to service of the elderly.

The secretariat is divided into the following departments:

- *Office of Program Management*
- *Office of Administration and Finance*

The ***Office of Administration and Finance*** is responsible for budget policy and management information systems for the secretariat.

The ***Office of Program Management*** oversees the state's Home Care program, which accounts for the majority of the executive secretariat's annual funding. The Home Care program provides services that allow elderly citizens to remain in their own homes and avoid unnecessary institutionalization in nursing homes and hospitals. The administrative divisions of the Office of Program Management are as follows:

- *Home Care Division*
- *Nursing Home Liaison*
- *Nutritional Services Division*
- *Protective Services Division*
- *Health Policy*

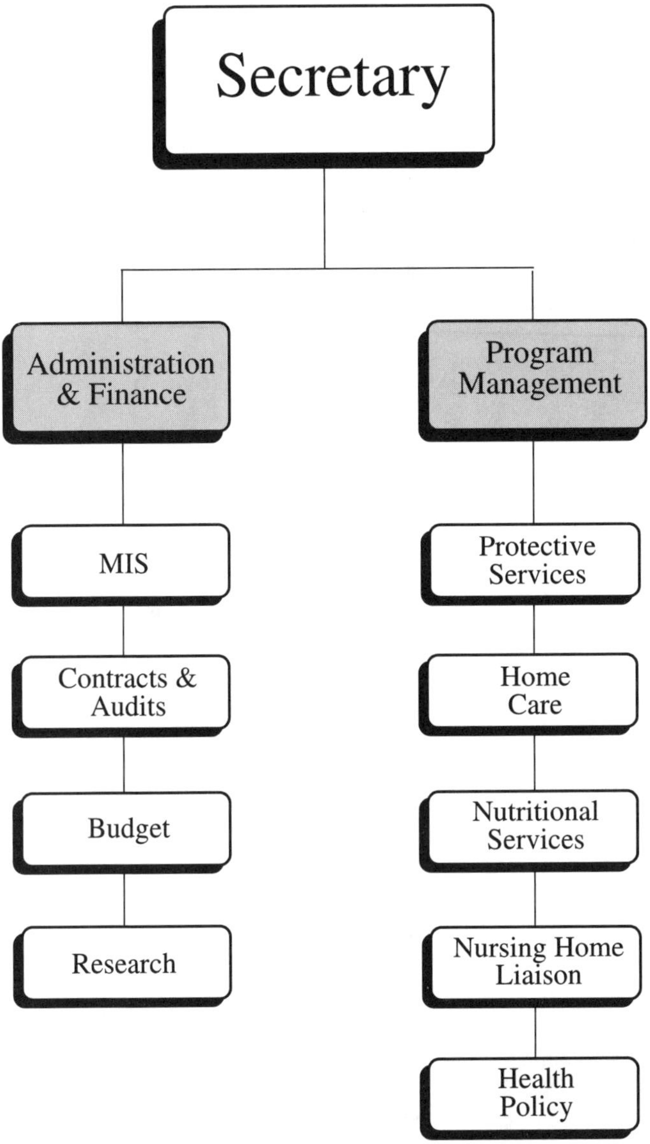
Secretary
Administration & Finance
Program Management
MIS
Contracts & Audits
Budget
Research
Protective Services
Home Care
Nutritional Services
Nursing Home Liaison
Health Policy

Secretary	**Lillian F. Glickman**	(617)727-7750

FINANCE AND ADMINISTRATION

Assistant Secretary	**Timothy Regan**	727-7750
Directors:		
Budget	**Randy Garten**	727-7750
MIS	**Norman Moy**	727-7750

POLICY AND PROGRAM DEVELOPMENT

Assistant Secretary	**Vacant**	727-7750
Directors:		
Community Services	**William Jackson**	727-7750
SHINE	**Mary Kaye Browne**	727-7750
Research	**Tom Lun-Nap Chung**	727-7750
Nursing Home Ombudsman	**Mary McKenna**	727-7750

PROGRAM MANAGEMENT

Assistant Secretary	**vacant**	727-7750
Directors:		
Home Care	**Patricia Rivard**	727-7750
Nutritional Services	**Shirley Chao**	727-7750
Protective Services	**Gregory Giuliano**	727-7750
Acting General Counsel	**Joel M. Semuels**	727-7750
Assistant General Counsel	**vacant**	727-7750
Human Resources	**Dean K. Denniston, Jr.**	727-7750
Information and Resource Services	**Peter D. Karg**	222-7442
Housing	**Naren Dhamodharan**	727-7750
Director of Communications	**Derrek Shulman**	222-7460

Lillian F. Glickman
Secretary

Executive Office of Elder Affairs
Address: One Ashburton Place, 5th Floor, Boston, MA 02108
Telephone: (617) 727-7750 **Fax:** (617) 727-9368
Reports to: Governor A. Paul Cellucci

PERSONAL INFORMATION:
Born: August 27, 1944 **Place of Birth:** Fall River
Marital Status: married (Ernest) **Children:** 1
Education: Harvard University (A.B. '66); Heller School, Brandeis University (M.S.W., '71; Ph.D., '80)
Previous Employment: University of Massachusetts at Boston Gerontology Institute (Senior Policy Analyst and Visiting Assistant Professor)
Years in Current Position: new **Years in State Service:** 12

JOB DESCRIPTION:
Responsible for developing and managing comprehensive community-based programs which help ensure the dignity and independence of the Commonwealth's 1.1 million elders. These programs include home, care protective services, nutrition, housing and health benefits education.

1999 PRIORITIES:
Enhancing services in elder housing to create a more "assisted living like" environment for low and moderate income elders; strengthening and expanding health benefits information and counseling to assist elders in decision making regarding their benefits; improving the quality of life in the Commonwealth's nursing homes; improving service delivery and support to persons with Alzheimers disease and their care givers; and enhancing care coordination activities of Aging Services Access Points.

Tom Lun-Nap Chung
Director of Research

Office of Policy and Program Development
Address: One Ashburton Place, 5th Floor, Boston, MA 02108
Telephone: (617) 727-7750 ext. 214 **Fax:** (617) 727-9368
Reports to: Assistant Secretary Timothy Regan

PERSONAL INFORMATION:
Education: The Chinese University of Hong Kong (B.S., '72; M.Ph., '74); Boston University (Ph.D., '82)
Previous Employment: Assistant Director of the Greater Boston Chinese Golden Age Center
Years in Current Position: 5 **Years in State Service:** 12

JOB DESCRIPTION:
Design and conduct surveys and other studies; develop and maintain computerized management information systems; review federal regulations; strategic planning; write grant proposals; process and disseminate demographic data; prepare RFP's and supervise projects contracted out.

ORGANIZATIONS:
American Gerontological Society

Mary Kaye Browne

SHINE Directors

Office of Program Management
Address: One Ashburton Place, 5th Floor, Boston, MA 02108
Telephone: (617) 727-7750 **Fax:** (617) 727-9368
Reports to: Secretary Lillian Glickman

Joel M. Semuels

Acting General Counsel

Executive Office of Elder Affairs
Address: One Ashburton Place, 5th Floor, Boston, MA 02108
Telephone: (617) 727-7750 **Fax:** (617) 727-9368
E-mail: jsemuels@state.ma.us
Reports to: Assistant Secretary

PERSONAL INFORMATION:
Years in Current Position: new **Years in State Service:** 20

JOB DESCRIPTION:
Provide legal counsel to agency secretary and staff in areas including legislation, regulations, contracts, privacy and confidentiality.

Dean K. Denniston, Jr.

Director of Human Resources

Office of Program Management
Address: One Ashburton Place, 5th Floor, Boston, MA 02108
Telephone: (617) 727-7750 **Fax:** (617) 727-9368
E-mail: Dean.Denniston@state.ma.us
Staff: Sheila Donahue King, Director of Staff Development; Christopher O'Brien, Personnel Analyst
Reports to: Secretary Lilian Glickman

PERSONAL INFORMATION:
Previous Employment: Department of Public Welfare (Assistant Commissioner for Personnel); Massachusetts Commission for the Blind (Regional Director); Department of Social Services (Senior Personnel Analyst)
Years in Current Position: 10 **Years in State Service:** 18

JOB DESCRIPTION:
Responsible for all human resources and information referral activities of cabinet level agency including staffing, payroll, benefits, staff development, labor relations, classification, Civil Service and Affirmative Action. Statewide liaison to personnel directors of all satellite agencies funded through the Executive Office.

ORGANIZATIONS:
Chairman, Executive Committee, WGBH Advisory Board.

Peter D. Karg

Director of Information and Resource Services

Executive Office of Elder Affairs
Address: One Ashburton Place, 5th Floor, Boston, MA 02108
Telephone: (617) 222-7442 **Fax:** (617) 727-9368
E-Mail: PeterKarg@state.ma.us
Reports to: Assistant Secretary

PERSONAL INFORMATION:
Education: Northeastern University (B.S., Political Science, '77; M.A., '92)
Years in Current Position: 3.5 **Years in State Service:** 20.5

JOB DESCRIPTION:
Responsible for the daily operations of the Information and Resource Services Unit.

1999 PRIORITIES:
Pursuing the development of a central, state-wide database that would lead to an enhanced and improved system of delivering I & R services.

Derrek Shulman

Director of Communications and Government Relations

Executive Office of Elder Affairs
Address: One Ashburton Place, 5th Floor, Boston, MA 02108
Telephone: (617) 222-7460 **Fax:** (617) 727-6944
E-Mail: derrek.shulman@state.ma.us
Reports to: Secretary Lillian Glickman

PERSONAL INFORMATION:
Born: July 11, 1968 **Place of Birth:** New Jersey
Marital Status: married (Beth)
Education: Clark University (B.A. '90); University of Massachusetts (M.A. Boston '96)
Previous Employment: Legislative aide in Massachusetts State Senate, Reporter/Columnist for The Daily Item
Years in Current Position: 4 **Years in State Service:** 7

JOB DESCRIPTION:
Developing and implementing communications and legislative strategies for the Secretariat

1999 PRIORITIES:
To expand visibility and support for the Cellucci/Swift Elder Affairs agenda.

ORGANIZATIONS:
The Ripon Society of New England (vice president)

Environmental Affairs

The Executive Office of Environmental Affairs is responsible for protection of the environment and enhancement of the Commonwealth's natural resources. The significant growth within the executive offices since its creation in 1975 reflects the heightened awareness of state officials and the general public toward environmental concerns.

The Executive Office of Environmental Affairs is charged with the management of the Commonwealth's environmental policy with respect to some of society's most troublesome and complex problems: solid waste disposal, low-level radioactive waste disposal, hazardous waste cleanup, clean water and air protection, and open space acquisition, preservation and development. The secretariat oversees state environmental laws and regulations as well as federal regulations promulgated by the U.S. Environmental Protection Agency. Several programs managed by the agency are the result of federal statutes. These include the Clean Water Act, Clean Air Act, Coastal Zone Management Act, and the Toxic Use Reduction Act.

The agency oversees the management and policy decisions of the six departments under its jurisdiction:

- *Department of Environmental Protection*
- *Department of Environmental Management*
- *Department of Fisheries, Wildlife and Environmental Law Enforcement*
- *Department of Food and Agriculture*
- *Metropolitan District Commission*
- *State Reclamation Board*

In addition to these functional departments, there are four divisions within the Office of the Secretary that assist in the development and implementation of state environmental policies:

- *Division of Conservation Services*
- *Coastal Zone Management Office*
- *Massachusetts Environmental Policy Act Office*
- *Office of Technical Assistance*

The ***Massachusetts Water Resources Authority***, an independent agency responsible for the sewer and waterworks systems of its member communities, is within, but not subject to, the control of the executive office.

Department of Environmental Protection

The Department of Environmental Protection administers the state's regulatory programs for air, water, solid waste, and land use controls. This department oversees solid waste management and recycling programs, hazardous waste cleanup, air quality monitoring, and wetlands management. It also awards grants and loans for the construction of water treatment and wastewater purification facilities. The department includes three functional divisions and several program bureaus:

- *Administration Division*
- *Operations and Programs Division*

  Bureau of Resource Protection

  Bureau of Waste Prevention

  Bureau of Waste Site Cleanup

  Regional Offices

- *Results and Strategic Priorities Division*

  Strategic Policy and Technology

  Environmental Results Program

  "One-Stop" Facility Reporting

  Information Technology Office

  Special Projects

Department of Environmental Management

The Department of Environmental Management is charged with land management, protection of the Commonwealth's natural resources, and administration of the state's parks, forests, and recreational facilities. It oversees the Heritage State Parks Program. Its responsibilities also include management of the state's water resources, waterways, and dams. The department is divided into three functional units:

- *Division of Administrative Services*

- *Division of Forests and Parks*
- *Division of Resource Conservation*

Department of Food and Agriculture

The Department of Food and Agriculture promotes the Commonwealth's agricultural industries and regulates the quality of certain products. Through its agricultural development programs, the agency promotes Massachusetts-grown products and encourages their sale at different venues. The department inspects poultry and livestock, regulates the use of pesticides, inspects for plant insects and diseases, and oversees mosquito control efforts. The agency is split into the following functional units:

- *Division of Administration*
- *Division of Agricultural Development*

  Bureau of Fairs

  Bureau of Markets
- *Division of Animal Health*
- *Division of Regulatory Services*

  Bureau of Dairying

  Bureau of Farm Products

  Bureau of Dairy Services

  Bureau of Plant Pest Control

Department of Fisheries, Wildlife and Environmental Law Enforcement

The Department of Fisheries, Wildlife and Environmental Law Enforcement oversees and maintains the quality and stock of the Commonwealth's fish, shellfish, game, and non-game wildlife species. It patrols the state's parklands, forests, and waterways and registers marine and recreational vehicles. The department enforces all of the rules and regulations promulgated by the Executive Office of Environmental Affairs, including those pertaining to pollution, hunting, fishing, and waste disposal. It manages wildlife habitats, stocks game and fish species, and issues fishing, hunting, and gaming licenses. It also licenses, regulates, and protects the state's commercial fishing industries. The department is organized into the following administrative divisions:

- *Division of Law Enforcement*
- *Division of Fisheries and Wildlife*
- *Division of Marine Fisheries*
- *Public Access Board*

Metropolitan District Commission

The Metropolitan District Commission provides water, park, recreation, and other environmental services to the Greater Boston area. Its jurisdiction includes Boston and 35 surrounding cities and towns. The commission operates an extensive flood control and dam network on the Charles, Mystic, and Neponset Rivers and is responsible for the management of pools, rinks, beaches, stadia, nature preserves, and band shells. The MDC also oversees the Commonwealth Zoological Corporation, which manages the Franklin Park and Stone Zoos.

Massachusetts Water Resources Authority

An independent authority responsible for the delivery of drinking water and/or the conveyance and treatment of wastewater on a bulk or wholesale basis for approximately sixty cities and towns, mostly in the greater Boston area. The population of its service area is approximately 2.5 million. MWRA operates the new Deer Island Wastewater Treatment Plant and numerous pipelines, pumping stations and other treatment works. MWRA is governed by an 11-member board of directors, variously appointed by the governor, the Mayor of the City of Boston, and the elected Advisory Board on behalf of other service area communities. The Secretary of Environmental Affairs is, ex officio, the chairperson of the board of directors.

The MWRA is divided into the following functional units:

- *Engineering and Construction*
- *Finance*
- *Program Management*
- *Law*
- *Sewerage*
- *Waterworks*

Executive Office

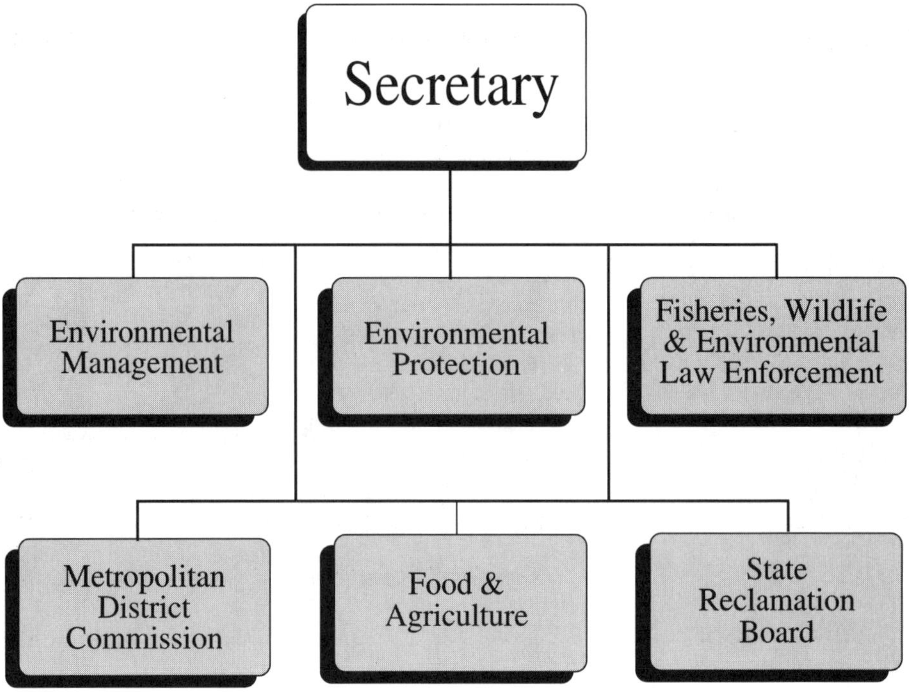
Secretary
Environmental Management
Environmental Protection
Fisheries, Wildlife & Environmental Law Enforcement
Metropolitan District Commission
Food & Agriculture
State Reclamation Board

Office of Environmental Affairs

Secretary	**Robert A. Durand**	(617) 727-9800
Asst. Secretary for External Relations	**John Rodman**	727-9800
Chief of Staff	**Chuck Anastas**	727-9800
General Counsel	**Arthur Bergeron**	727-9800

COASTAL ZONE MANAGEMENT

Director	**Margaret M. Brady**	727-9530

MASSACHUSETTS ENVIRONMENTAL POLICY ACT

Director, Assistant Secretary for Environmental Impact Review	**Jay Wickersham**	727-5830

DEPARTMENT OF ENVIRONMENTAL MANAGEMENT

Commissioner	**Peter C. Webber**	727-3180
Chief of Legal Services	**Katharine E. Lewis**	727-3180
Diector of Public Information	**Susan Fairbanks Hamilton**	727-3180
Chief of Staff	**Susan Whalen Frechette**	727-3180
Director of Forests and Parks	**Todd A. Frederick**	727-3180

Deputy Commissioners:

Resource Conservation	**Martin Suuberg**	727-3180
Chief Engineer	**Raul Silva**	727-3160
Chief Fire Warden	**Michael Tirrell**	727-3180
Chief Forester	**Warren Archey**	727-3180
Chief Planner	**Richard Thibedeau**	727-3160
Recreation Chief	**Gary Briere**	727-3180
Waterways	**Eugene F. Cavanaugh**	(781) 740-1600
Chief Ranger	**Curt Rudge**	727-3180
Chief of Interpretive Service	**John Nove**	727-3180
Dam Safety Director	**David Clarke**	(508)792-7716

DEPARTMENT OF ENVIRONMENTAL PROTECTION

Commissioner	**vacant**	292-5856
Chief of Staff	**Gary Moran**	292-5536
Deputy Commissioners:		
Operations and Programs	**Edward P. Kunce**	292-5915
Administration	**Daniel McGuillicuddy**	292-6831
Environmental Results & Strategic Priorities	**Madeline Snow, Acting**	292-5509
Assistant Commissioners:		
Resource Protection	**Arleen O'Donnell**	292-5850
Waste Prevention	**James C. Colman**	292-5664
General Counsel	**Ralph A. Child**	574-6824
Waste Site Cleanup	**Deirdre C. Menoyo**	292-5648
Strategic Policy and Technology	**Philip Griffiths, Acting**	292-5675

DEPARTMENT OF FISHERIES, WILDLIFE & ENVIRONMENTAL LAW ENFORCEMENT

Commissioner	**David M. Peters**	727-1614
Assistant Commissioner	**Robert W. Austin**	727-1614
General Counsel	**David C. Hoover**	727-1614
Legislative Liaison	**Priscilla E. Geigis**	727-1614
Director, Public Access Board	**John P. Sheppard**	727-1843
Division of Marine Fisheries:		
Director	**Philip G. Coates**	727-3193
Assistant Director	**W. Leigh Bridges**	727-3193
Assistant Director	**James Fair, Jr.**	727-3193
Assistant Director	**Michael G. Henry**	727-3193

Office of Environmental Affairs

Division of Fish and Wildlife:

Director	**Wayne F. MacCallum**	*727-3155*
Assistant Director	**John L. Buckley**	*727-3151*
Deputy Director	**Carl S. Prescott**	*(508)792-7270*

Division of Law Enforcement:

Director	**Richard A. Murray**	*727-3905*
Deputy Director	**William H. McKeon**	*727-3905*
Deputy Director	**Alban Landry**	*727-3905*

DEPARTMENT OF FOOD AND AGRICULTURE

Commissioner	**Jonathan L. Healy**	*727-3000*
Assistant Commissioner	**Richard K. Hubbard**	*727-3000*
General Counsel	**Lawrence E. McCormick**	*727-3000*
Chief, Animal Health	**vacant**	*727-3000*
Chief of Markets	**Susan Allen**	*727-3000*
Chief of Fairs	**Stephen F. Quinn**	*727-3000*
Chief, Regulatory Services	**Brad Mitchell**	*727-3000*
Chief, Farm Products & Plant Ind.	**George Porter**	*727-3000*
Chief, Education & Outreach	**Janet Christensen**	*727-3000*

Directors:

Agricultural Development	**Mary Jordan**	*727-3000*
Regulatory Services	**David Sheldon**	*727-3000*
Dairy Services	**Jim Hines**	*727-3000*

MASSACHUSETTS WATER RESOURCES AUTHORITY

Executive Director	**Douglas B. MacDonald**	*242-6000*

Directors:

Managing Director	**Kate Murray**	*242-6000*
Deputy Director	**Thomas Powers**	*242-6000*

Finance	**Barbara Gottschalk**	*242-6000*
Human Resources	**Leroy Walker**	*242-6000*
Internal Audit	**Peter Babachicos**	*242-6000*
Program Management	**Walter Armstrong**	*242-6000*
Public Affairs	**Mike Ralph**	*242-6000*
Sewerage Division	**John Fitzgerald**	*242-6000*
Waterworks Division	**William Brutsch**	*242-6000*
General Counsel	**Mary Jeka**	*242-6000*
Affirmative Action	**Neal Anderson**	*242-6000*

METROPOLITAN DISTRICT COMMISSION

Commissioner	**David B. Balfour, Jr.**	*727-5114*
Deputy Commissioner, Administration and Finance	**Andrew Iovanna**	*727-5228*
Deputy Commissioner, Operations	**Brian W. Kerins**	*727-5114*
Deputy Commissioner, Policy	**Samantha M. Overton**	*727-5114*
Deputy Commissioner for Engineering	**Francis Faucher**	*727-5264*
Secretary	**William F. Chisholm**	*727-5204*

Operations Directors:

Recreation	**Gary Doak**	*727-9547*
Reservations and Historic Sites	**Brian T. Broderick**	*727-5250*
Watershed Management	**Joseph M. McGinn**	*727-5274*
Director of the Zoological Corporation	**Saunders Lewallen**	*442-4896*

Robert A. Durand
Secretary

Executive Office of Environmental Affairs
Address: 100 Cambridge Street, Room 2000, Boston, MA 02202
Telephone: (617) 727-9800 x260 **Fax:** (617) 727-2754
Staff: Chuck Anastas, Chief of Staff ; Executive Assistant Meredith Hultgren
Reports to: Governor A. Paul Cellucci

PERSONAL INFORMATION:
Born: February 28, 1953 **Place of Birth:** Marlboro
Education: Boston College (B.A. '75)
Marital Status: married (Brenda) **Children:** 3
Previous Employment: Senator State of Massachusetts
Years in Current Position: new

JOB DESCRIPTION:
The Secretary of Environmental Affairs is a cabinet-level appointee responsible for implementing and overseeing state policies aimed at preserving, protecting, and regulating the natural resources and environmental integrity of Massachusetts. This executive office oversees five agencies: Metropolitan District Commission; Department of Environmental Protection; Department of Environmental Management; Department of Fisheries, Wildlife and Environmental Law Enforcement; and Department of Food and Agriculture. The Secretary also chairs the Massachusetts Water Resources Authority. Five units within the executive office report directly to the Secretary: Division of Conservation Services; Massachusetts Environmental Policy Act Office; Coastal Zone Management Office; Hazardous Waste Facility Site Safety Council; and the Low-Level Radioactive Waste Board.

ORGANIZATIONS:
Marlboro Fish and Game (Past Board); Marlboro Boys Club; Marlboro Hospital (Trustee)

Margaret M. Brady
Director

Massachusetts Office of Coastal Zone Management
Address: 100 Cambridge Street, Boston, MA 02202
Telephone: (617) 727-9530 ext. 400 **Fax:** (617) 727-2754
E-mail: peg.brady@state.ma.us
Staff: Deirdre Buckley, Program Coordinator
Reports to: Secretary Robert A. Durand

PERSONAL INFORMATION:
Born: December 29, 1954 **Place of Birth:** New York
Marital Status: married (Capt. David Condino)
Education: University of Rhode Island (B.S., '77; M.S., '82)
Previous Employment: Massachusetts Department of Environmental Protection, Division of Wetlands & Waterways (Deputy Director)
Years in Current Position: 4 **Years in State Service:** 8

JOB DESCRIPTION:
Manage Coastal Planning Agency responsible for federal consistency, research and policy development, technical assistance for private/public activities within the Massachusetts coastal zone.

1999 PRIORITIES:
Implement a statewide port/harbor revitalization plan; coordinate the development and implementation of a comprehensive coastal monitoring program for Massachusetts; and improve technical assistance to coastal communities.

ORGANIZATIONS:
Coastal States Organization (MA Delegate); Sea Education Association (Corp. Member)

Jay Wickersham

Assistant Secretary of Environmental Affairs/MEPA Director

Executive Office of Environmental Affairs
Address: 100 Cambridge Street, 20th Floor, Boston, MA 02202
Telephone: (617) 727-5830 **Fax:** (617) 727-1598
E-mail: jay.wickersham@state.ma.us
Reports to: Secretary Robert A. Durand

PERSONAL INFORMATIO:
Born: Feb. 25, 1956
Place of Birth: Schenectady, NY
Marital Status: married (Joan) **Children:** 2
Education: Yale (B.A. '78); Harvard Law (J.D. '94)
Previous Employment: Hill & Barlow
Years in Current Position: 1 **Years in State Service:** 1

JOB DESCRIPTION:
Overseeing the state environmental impact review program for public and private development projects.

1999 PRIORITIES:
Implementation of the new MEPA regulations, integrating the goals of Executive Order 385 (Planning for Growth) into the MEPA review process.

ORGANIZATIONS:
American Institute of Architects, Boston Society of Architects, Urban Land Institute, National Trust for Historic Preservation

Department of Environmental Management

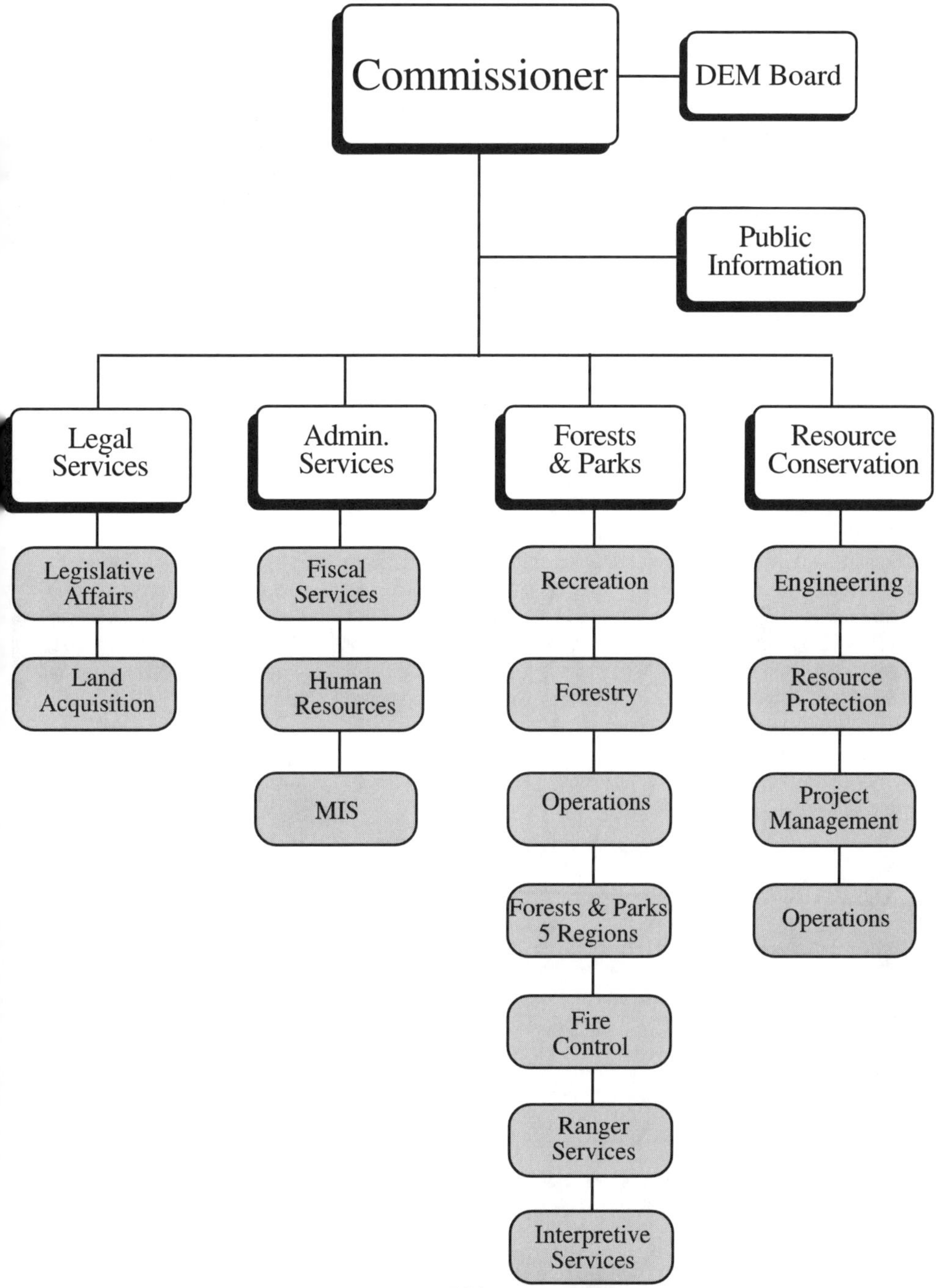

Peter C. Webber

Commissioner

Department of Environmental Management
Address: 100 Cambridge Street, 19th Floor, Boston, MA 02202
Telephone: (617) 727-3180 ext. 600 **Fax:** (617) 727-9402
Staff: Susan Frechette, Chief of Staff; Todd Frederick, Director of Forests and Parks; Kate Lewis, Chief of Legal Services; Martin Suuberg, Deputy Commissioner of Resource Conservation; Susan Hamilton, Director of Public Information
Reports to: Secretary Robert A. Durand

PERSONAL INFORMATION:
Born: May 12, 1952
Marital Status: married (Karen) **Children:** 2
Education: Amherst College (B.A., American Studies, '74)
Previous Employment: Massachusetts State Senator representing Berkshire, Franklin, Hampden and Hampshire Senatorial Districts ('81-'91)
Years in Current Position: 8 **Years in State Service:** 22

JOB DESCRIPTION:
The Commissioner is responsible for the stewardship of an 285,000 acre state forests and parks system, the ninth largest in the nation. The Department of Environmental Management cares for and oversees the management and conservation of the natural, cultural, scenic and historic resources of Massachusetts. It provides public recreationa opportunities which are environmentally sound, affordable and accessible to all. Its responsibilities include the management of the state's forests and parks system, water resources, waterways and dams. Oversight includes system-wide renovations and improvements of the state forests and parks system; the acquisition of protected ope space; grant programs to assist communities with projects such as historic landscape preservation; improved coastal access, water quality and other issues regarding lakes and ponds, enhancement of greenways and trails, and urban forestry; other programs include Forest Stewardship and Historic Curatorship.

ORGANIZATIONS:
Blackstone River Valley National Heritage Corridor Commission; Advisory Council on Travel and Tourism; Chair, Boston Harbor Island Partnership

Todd A. Frederick

Director of Forests and Parks

Department of Environmental Management, Division of Forests and Parks
Address: 100 Cambridge Street, 19th Floor, Boston, MA 02202
Telephone: (617) 727-3180 **Fax:** (617) 727-9402
E-mail: Todd.Frederick@state.ma.us
Staff: Lynne E. Worrell, Executive Assistant
Reports to: Commissioner Peter C. Webber

PERSONAL INFORMATION:
Born: December 16, 1961 **Place of Birth:** North Adams
Marital Status: single
Education: North Adams State College (B.A., '84)

Years in Current Position: 5 **Years in State Service:** 15

JOB DESCRIPTION:

Provide leadership for the Division of Forests and Parks.

ORGANIZATIONS:

National Association of State Park Directors; Northeast State Park Directors Association (President); Massachusetts Junior Conservation Camp (Trustee)

Susan Whalen Frechette

Chief of Staff

Department of Environmental Management
Address: 100 Cambridge Street, 19th Floor, Boston, MA 02202
Telephone: (617) 727-3180 ext. 620 **Fax:** (617) 727-9402
Staff: Robin Barbozar, Administrative Assistant
Reports to: Commissioner Peter Webber

Martin Suuberg

Deputy Commissioner of Resource Conservation

Department of Environmental Management
Address: 100 Cambridge Street, 19th Floor, Boston, MA 02202
Telephone: (617) 727-3160 ext. 535 **Fax:** (617) 727-2630
Staff: Barbara Black, Administrative Assistant
Reports to: Commissioner Peter Webber

Susan Fairbanks Hamilton

Director, Public Information

Department of Environmental Management
Address: 100 Cambridge Street, 19th Floor, Boston, MA 02202
Telephone: (617) 727-3180 ext. 602 **Fax:** (617) 727-9402
Reports to: Commissioner Peter Webber

PERSONAL INFORMATION:

Born: May 8, 1965 **Place of Birth:** Chicago
Marital Status: married (William)
Education: St. Lawrence University, (B.A.)
Years in Current Position: 5 **Years in State Service:** 10

JOB DESCRIPTION:

Articulating and communicating the Department's mission and goals both to an external and internal audience. Activities include coordinating all agency communication with the media, event planning, development and production of the department's printed material, management of the department's marketing and merchandising activities, and maintaining photo archives library.

Katharine E. Lewis
Chief of Legal Services

Department of Environmental Management
Address: 100 Cambridge Street, 19th Floor, Boston, MA 02202
Telephone: (617) 727-3180 ext .503 **Fax:** (617) 727-9402
Reports to: Commissioner Peter Webber
Education: Harvard ('84); Harvard Law ('87)

Warren Archey
Chief Forester

Department of Environmental Management
Address: 100 Cambridge Street, 19th Floor, Boston, MA 02202
Telephone: (617) 727-3180 ext. 685 **Fax:** (617) 727-9402
Reports to: Director Todd Frederick

PERSONAL INFORMATION:
Education: University of Massachusetts at Amherst (B.S., Forestry, '63; M.S. and Ph. D., Forestry, '69 and '82)
Previous Employment: University of Massachusetts at Amherst (Regional Community Development Specialist, Cooperative Extension)
Years in Current Position: 6 **Years in State Service:** 28

JOB DESCRIPTION:
Provide leadership in the conduct of forestry programs on public and private forest land in Massachusetts.

ORGANIZATIONS:
Society of American Foresters; Massachusetts Association of Professional Foresters; Massachusetts Forestry Association; Massachusetts Wood Producers Association; National Association of State Foresters

Eugene F. Cavanaugh
Director

Department of Environmental Management, Office of Waterways
Address: 345 Lincoln St., Bldg. 45, Hingham, MA 02043
Telephone: (781) 740-1600 **Fax:** (617) 727-2950
Staff: Kevin Maguire, Construction Engineer; Kevin Mooney, Design Engineering, Julie Chochrek, Administration Assistant
Reports to: Martin Suuberg, Deputy Commmssioner

PERSONAL INFORMATION:
Born: May 29, 1939 **Place of Birth:** Boston
Marital Status: married (Susan) **Children:** 3
Education: University of Lowell (BCE '74); Northeastern University, (ACE '96)
Years in Current Position: 12 **Years in State Service:** 36

JOB DESCRIPTION:
Oversees the Rivers and Harbors Program for the Department including fiscal management, design and construction scheduling and long-term coordination.

1999 PRIORITIES:
Provide contract services and funding to maintain the navigable waterways and public access.

ORGANIZATIONS
Society of Military Engineers, Knights of Columbus.

Department of Environmental Protection

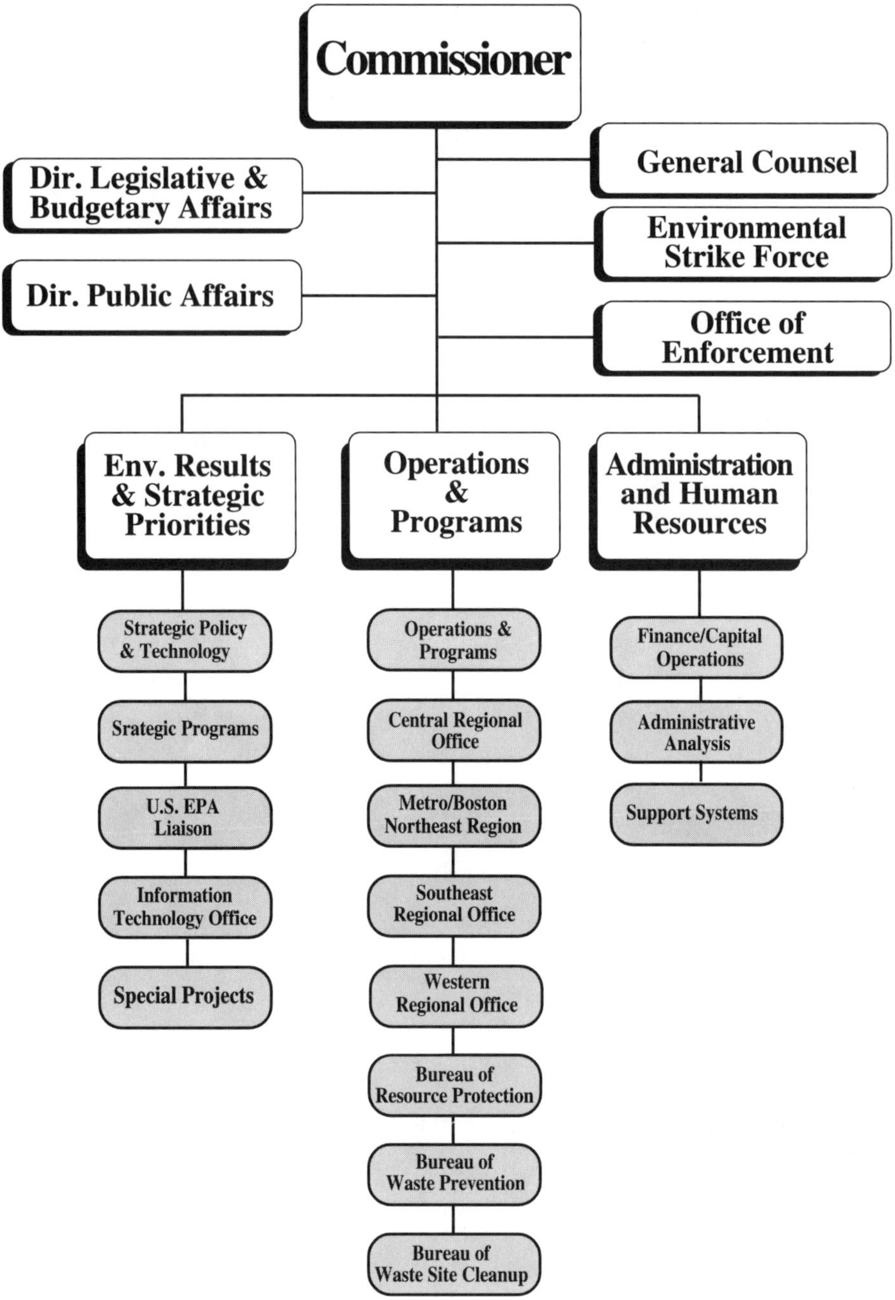
Commissioner
Dir. Legislative & Budgetary Affairs
Dir. Public Affairs
General Counsel
Environmental Strike Force
Office of Enforcement
Env. Results & Strategic Priorities
Operations & Programs
Administration and Human Resources
Strategic Policy & Technology
Srategic Programs
U.S. EPA Liaison
Information Technology Office
Special Projects
Operations & Programs
Central Regional Office
Metro/Boston Northeast Region
Southeast Regional Office
Western Regional Office
Bureau of Resource Protection
Bureau of Waste Prevention
Bureau of Waste Site Cleanup
Finance/Capital Operations
Administrative Analysis
Support Systems

Edward P. Kunce

Deputy Commissioner of Operations

Department of Environmental Protection
Address: One Winter Street, Boston, MA 02108
Telephone: (617) 292-5915 **Fax:** (617) 574-6880
Staff: Willa Kuk, Lou Gitto, Dave Murphy, Steve Lipman, Myles Brown
Reports to: Commissioners

PERSONAL INFORMATION:
Born: December 16, 1951
Marital Status: married (Nancy Ellen) **Children:** 2
Education: University of Rhode Island (B.S., '73); Boston University (M.S., '76); Harvard University (M.A., '90)
Previous Employment: Camp, Dresser and McKee, Inc. (Project Manager, Team Leader); General Dynamics, Electric Boat Division (Production Manager); U.S. Army Corps of Engineers (Army Officer)
Years in Current Position: 7 **Years in State Service:** 13

JOB DESCRIPTION:
Responsible for all the permitting, compliance and enforcement, as well as all the hazardous waste site remediation activities for the Department of Environmental Protection's four regional offices. Responsible for coordinating key operational activities in the Department of Environmental Protection's Boston office related to permitting, compliance, enforcement, and site remediation. Also responsible for all programs, policy, and regulatory development as well as grants and SRF loans.

1999 PRIORITIES:
Compliance and enforcement; Watershed Program, Environmental Results Program; complete Department of Environmental Protection realignment.

ORGANIZATIONS:
Massachusetts Health Officer Association; New England Waterworks Association

Arleen O'Donnell

Assistant Commissioner, Bureau of Resource Protection

Department of Environmental Protection
Address: One Winter Street, Boston, MA 02108 **Telephone:** (617) 292-5975
Fax: (617) 292-5850 **E-mail:** arleen.odonnell@state.ma.us
Staff: Julianne E. Turé, Administrative Assistant
Reports to: Deputy Commissioner Edward Kunce

PERSONAL INFORMATION:
Marital Status: married (Howard Woolf) **Children:** 1
Education: University of Massachusetts at Amherst (B.S., Zoology/Environmental Science, '76); Tufts University (M.S., Civil Engineering/Urban Environmental Policy)
Previous Employment: Massachusetts Audubon Society

Years in Current Position: 10 **Years in State Service:** 10

JOB DESCRIPTION:
Direct the agency's programs in water supply, water pollution control and wetlands and waterways regulations.

James C. Colman

Assistant Commissioner, Waste Prevention

Department of Environmental Protection
Address: One Winter Street, Boston, MA 02108
Telephone: (617) 292-5664
Fax: (617) 292-5530 **E-mail:** jcolman@state.ma.us
Reports to: Deputy Commissioner Edward Kunce

PERSONAL INFORMATION:

Education: Brandeis University (B.A., '67); University of Massachusetts at Amherst (M.A., Regional Planning)
Previous Employment: Office of Incident Response in the Division of Hazardous Waste (Director); Division of Hazardous Waste (Deputy Director); Hazardous Waste Regulatory Task Force (Director); Division of Wetland Protection (Director); Wetlands Project, Massachusetts Audubon Society (Co-Director)
Years in Current Position: 9 **Years in State Service:** 20

Ralph A. Child

General Counsel

Department of Environmental Protection
Address: One Winter Street, Boston, MA 02108
Telephone: (617) 574-6824 **Fax:** (617) 338-5511
E-mail: ralph.child@state.ma.us
Reports to: Commissioner

PERSONAL INFORMATION:

Marital Status: married **Children:** 2
Education: Dartmouth ('72); Harvard Law School ('76)
Previous Employment: Palmer and Dodge
Years in Current Position: 2.5 **Years in State Service:** 2.5

JOB DESCRIPTION:

Manage the Department of Environmental Protection's Office of General Counsel, Office of Enforcement, Environmental Strike Force, and Office of Administrative Appeals.

Deirdre C. Menoyo

Assistant Commissioner, Waste Site Cleanup

Department of Environmental Protection
Address: One Winter Street, Boston, MA 02108
Telephone: (617) 292-5648 **Fax:** (617) 292-5530
E-mail: deidre.menoyo@ma.state.us
Reports to: Deputy Commissioner Edward P. Kunce

PERSONAL INFORMATION:

Born: June 20, 1945 **Place of Birth:** New York City
Marital Status: married (Eric) **Children:** 2
Education: Trinity College (B.A. '67); George Washington University (M.A. '71)
Previous Employment: Conservation Law Foundation (Director of Brownfields Initiatives)
Years in Current Position: new **Years in State Service:** new

JOB DESCRIPTION:

Responsible for response and remediation of releases of oil or hazardous materials

1999 PRIORITIES:

Reduce risks associated with toxic releases in the environment

David M. Peters

Commissioner

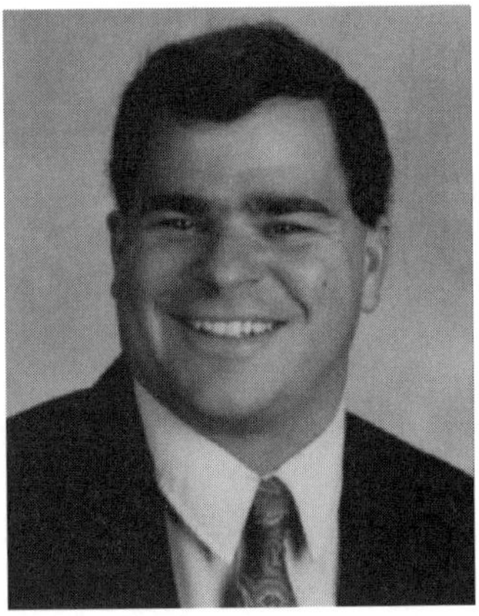

Department of Fisheries, Wildlife & Environmental Law Enforcement
Address: 100 Cambridge Street, Room 1901, Boston, MA 02202
Telephone: (617) 727-1614 **Fax:** (617) 727-2566
Staff: Aimee Barrette, Assistant
Reports to: Secretary Robert A. Durand

PERSONAL INFORMATION:

Born: March 1, 1954 **Place of Birth:** Hartford, CT
Marital Status: married (Donna) **Children:** 2
Education: Bryant College (B.S., B.A., '76)
Previous Employment: Massachusetts House of Representatives (4 terms)
Years in Current Position: new

JOB DESCRIPTION:

Coordinate activities associated with the assessment, protection, and management of our inland resources of fish and wildlife, coastal shellfish and fin fish and inland and coastal waters for boating. In charge of the Divisions of Fisheries and Wildlife, Marine Fisheries and Environmental Law Enforcement and the Public Access Board.

ORGANIZATIONS:

Governor's Commission on Domestic Violence (Co-Chair); Conservation of Public Safety Caucus; National Wildlife Federation; Massachusetts Bowhunters Association; Corporator Harrington Memorial Hospital

David C. Hoover

General Counsel

Department of Fisheries, Wildlife & Environmental Law Enforcement
Address: 100 Cambridge Street, Room 1901, Boston, MA 02202
Telephone: (617) 727-1614 ext. 365 **Fax:** (617) 727-2566
Reports to: Commissioner David M. Peters

PERSONAL INFORMATION:

Born: April 22, 1950 **Place of Birth:** Waterville, ME
Marital Status: Married (Kathleen Delia Powell) **Children:** 2
Education: University of New Hampshire (B.A., '72); Suffolk University School of Law (J.D., '76)
Previous Employment: Attorney-Advisor, Office of General Counsel, National Oceanic and Atmospheric Administration, U.S. Department of Commerce.
Years in Current Position: 15 **Years in State Service:** 18

JOB DESCRIPTION:

Chief legal advisor to the Commissioner of the Department and to the Directors of the Division of Marine Fisheries, Division of Fisheries and Wildlife and Division of Environmental Law Enforcement. Special Assistant Attorney General responsible for prosecuting specified environmental crimes; Administrative Law Magistrate responsible for adjudicatory practice and procedure before the Department and Divisions.

ORGANIZATIONS:

Territorial Sea Journal, Marine Law Institute, University of Maine (Board of Editors); Law Related Education Committee, Massachusetts Bar Association (Attorney/Advisor to Mock Trial Tournament); Who's Who in American Law; Lawyers Concerned for Lawyers

John P. Sheppard

Director, Public Access Board

Department of Fisheries, Wildlife & Environmental Law Enforcement
Address: 1440 Soldiers Field Road, Brighton, MA 02135
Telephone: (617) 727-1843 **Fax:** (617) 727-7214
Reports to: Commissioner David Peters

PERSONAL INFORMATION:

Born: January 23, 1944 **Place of Birth:** Boston
Marital Status: married (Jeanne M.) **Children:** 4
Education: Northeastern University (B.S., '70)
Previous Employment: Massachusetts Division of Fisheries and Wildlife, Engineering and Development (Chief); Fay, Spofford and Thorndike, Inc. (Civil Engineer)
Years in Current Position: 11 **Years in State Service:** 26

JOB DESCRIPTION:

General administration of Public Access Board, the construction agency within the Department.

ORGANIZATIONS:

American Society of Civil Engineers, Boston section; Association of Conservation Engineers; Northeast Society of Conservation Engineers (Board of Directors, past President)

Philip G. Coates
Director, Division of Marine Fisheries

Department of Fisheries, Wildlife & Environmental Law Enforcement
Address: 100 Cambridge Street, Room 1901, Boston, MA 02202
Telephone: (617) 727-3193 **Fax:** (617) 727-7988
Staff: W. Leigh Bridges, Assistant Director, Research; James Fair, Assistant Director, Commercial Fisheries; Michael Henry, Assistant Director, Administration, Paul Diodati, Recreetional Fisheries Chief
Reports to: Commissioner David Peters

PERSONAL INFORMATION:
Years in Current Position: 19 **Years in State Service:** 34

JOB DESCRIPTION:
Responsible for managing, monitoring, and enhancing the Commonwealth's marine resources.

Wayne F. MacCallum
Director of Fish and Wildlife

Department of Fisheries, Wildlife & Environmental Law Enforcement
Address: 100 Cambridge Street, Room 1901, Boston, MA 02202
Telephone: (617) 727-3151 **Fax:** (617) 727-7288
Staff: Julie Delaney, Administrative Assistant
Reports to: Commissioner David M. Peters

PERSONAL INFORMATION:
Education: University of Massachusetts at Amherst (B.S., '68); Pennsylvania State University (M.S., '71)
Previous Employment: Woodward Clyde Consultants, Environmental Systems Division (Associate)
Years in Current Position: 9 **Years in State Service:** 15

JOB DESCRIPTION:
Oversee all Division of Fisheries and Wildlife operations associated with protection, management, and perpetuation of inland floral and faunal resources.

Carl S. Prescott
Deputy Director of Fish and Wildlife

Department of Fisheries, Wildlife & Environmental Law Enforcement
Address: 100 Cambridge Street, Room 1901, Boston, MA 02202
Telephone: 508-792-7270
Reports to: Director Wayne F. MacCallum

PERSONAL INFORMATION:
Education: Nichols College (A.B.A., '63); University of Massachusetts at Amherst (B.S., '67)
Years in Current Position: 17 **Years in State Service:** 30

JOB DESCRIPTION:
In charge of all field operations, 16 installations, 130 employees, $4,500,000 budget.

Richard A. Murray

Director

Dept. of Fisheries, Wildlife and Environmental Law Enforcement
Address: 175 Portland St., Boston, MA 02193
Telephone: (617) 727-3950 **Fax:** (617) 727-8551
E-mail: rmurray@state.ma.us
Staff: William McKeon, Lt. Col, Law Enforcement; Alban Landry, Dep. Director, Administration; Nadine Walkowski, Confidential Secretary.
Reports to: CommissionerDavid M. Peters

PERSONAL INFORMATION:

Born: March 15, 1939 **Place of Birth:** Boston
Marital Status: Married (Marlene) **Children:** 2
Education: Northeastern University, (B.S. '80)
Previous Employment: Private enterprise.
Years in Current Position: 8 **Years in State Service:** 8

JOB DESCRIPTION:

Statewide enforcement of all Fish & Wildlife regulations, commercial fishing regulations, recreation boating and recreation vehicle enforcement, marine theft, all environmental laws, hunter and boating safety educational programs.

1999 JOB PRIORITIES:

Strict enforcement of Marine Fisheries regulation, reorganization of hunter education program, increased effort in boating education.

ORGANIZATIONS:

President, National Conservation Law Enforcement Chiefs Association; President; Mass. Chiefs of Police Association; Boating Law Administrator for Commonwealth.

Jonathan L. Healy

Commissioner

Department of Food and Agriculture
Address: 100 Cambridge Street, Room 2103, Boston, MA 02202
Telephone: (617) 727-3000 ext. 100 **Fax:** (617) 727-7235
E-mail: Jhealy_dfa_boston@state.ma.us
Staff: Janet H. Lafond, Chief of Staff; Maureen M. Martel, Confidential Secretary
Reports to: Secretary Robert A. Durand

PERSONAL INFORMATION:
Born: October 10, 1945
Place of Birth: Greenfield
Marital Status: married (Elizabeth [Bunny]) **Children:** 2
Education: Williams College (B.A., '68); Suffolk University School of Law (L.L.B., '81)
Previous Employment: Massachusetts House of Representatives; Hall Tavern Farm (Manager)
Years in Current Position: 5 **Years in State Service:** 26

JOB DESCRIPTION:
Preserving open space through agricultural economic development, regulating animal health and use of pesticides.

1999 PRIORITIES:
Creating jobs and preserving open space by encouraging economically sound agricultural businesses and farms.

ORGANIZATIONS:
Academy at Charlemont (Board of Trustees); Massachusetts 4-H Clubs; Franklin Land Trust

Lawrence E. McCormick

General Counsel

Department of Food and Agriculture
Address: 100 Cambridge Street, Room 2103, Boston, MA 02202
Telephone: (617) 727-3000 ext. 125 **Fax:** (617) 727-7235
E-mail: LarryMcCormick@administration@DFABoston
Reports to: Commissioner Jonathan L. Healy

PERSONAL INFORMATION:
Place of Birth: Cambridge
Marital Status: married (Mary) **Children:** 3
Education: Univ. of Massachusetts (B.B.A. '65); Boston College Law School (J.D. '68) Northeastern University (M.B.A. '89)
Years in Current Position: 1 **Years in State Service:** 12

Massachusetts Water Resources Authority

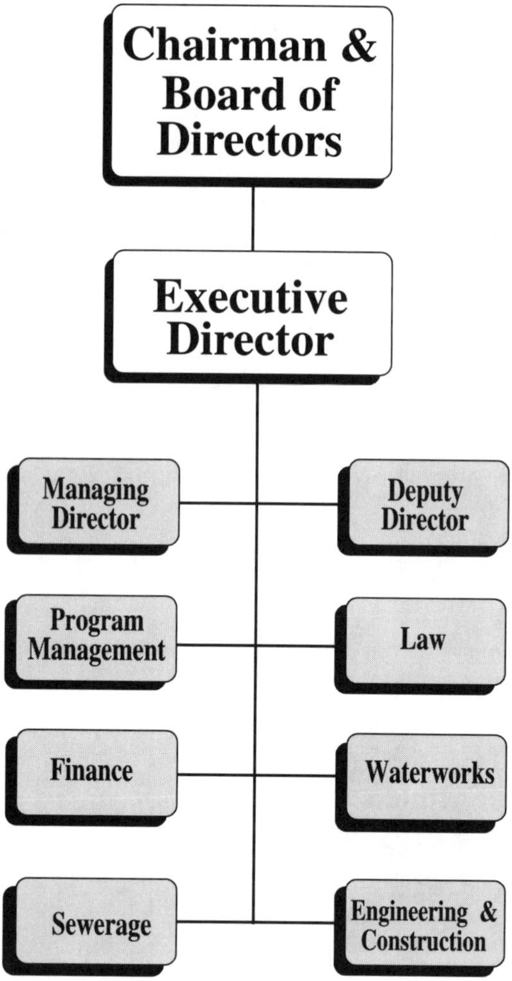

Douglas B. MacDonald
Executive Director

Massachusetts Water Resources Authority
Address: Charlestown Navy Yard, 100 First Avenue, Boston, MA 02129
Telephone: (617) 242-6000 **Fax:** (617) 241-6175
Staff: Tom Powers, Deputy Director; Kate Murray, Managing Director
Reports to: MWRA Board of Directors

PERSONAL INFORMATION:
Born: April 17, 1945 **Place of Birth:** Boston
Marital Status: single **Children:** 2
Education: Harvard (A.B., '67); Harvard Law School (J.D., '73)
Previous Employment: Palmer and Dodge (Partner)
Years in Current Position: 7

Kate Murray
Managing Director

Massachusetts Water Resources Authority
Address: Charlestown Navy Yard, 100 First Avenue, Boston, MA 02129
Telephone: (617) 788-1104 **Fax:** (617) 788-4893
Staff: Mary Shaw, Executive Secretary
Reports to: Douglas MacDonald, Executive Director

PERSONAL INFORMATION:
Place of Birth: Manchester, CT
Education: Simmons College Graduate School of Management (M.B.A. '82)
Previous Employment: Mass. General Hospital, Special Assistant to the director
Years in Current Position: 4 **Years in State Service:** 12

JOB DESCRIPTION:
Human Resources/Labor Relations; Procurement, Management Information Systems, Facilities Management; Vehicle Maintenance; Internal Audit, Affirmative Action; Emergency Response

David B. Balfour, Jr.
Commissioner

Metropolitan District Commission
Address: 20 Somerset Street, Boston, MA 02108
Telephone: (617) 727-5114 **Fax:** (617) 727-0891
E-mail: www.state.ma.us/mdc
Staff: Andrew Iovanna, Dep. Commissioner for Admin. and Finance; Brian Kerins, Dep. Commissioner for Operations; Samantha Overton, Dep. Commissioner for Policy; Conan French, Chief of Staff; Francis D. Faucher, P.E., Dep. Commmsioner for Engineering & Construction.
Reports to: Secretary Robert A. Durand

PERSONAL INFORMATION:

Born: April 2, 1953 **Place of Birth:** Medford
Education: North Shore Community College; Central Texas College
Previous Employment: Office of the Governor (Director of Special Projects); Bureau of State Office Buildings (Superintendent); The White House, Office of the Vice President (Special Assistant & Lead Advance Representative)
Years in Current Position: 4 **Years in State Service:** 14

JOB DESCRIPTION:

Oversee the Metropolitan District Commission, which consists of a 17,000-acre urban parks system, a 330,000-acre watershed and reservoir system that provides drinking water for 2.5 million people in the metropolitan area, and one of the largest flood control operations in the Northeast. The MDC has care, custody and control of 700 lane miles of scenic parkways. MDC provides recreational and environmental opportunities to an ethnically diverse, multicultural clientele in the Greater Metropolitan area. In addition, MDC owns and operates 22 skating rinks, 19 swimming pools, 2 golf courses (54 holes), 1 ski area, 33 miles of coastline and beaches, numerous ballfields, tot lots and stadia, 3 Boston Harbor islands and numerous historic sites.

1999 PRIORITIES:

To create a stronger and more effective agency with a user-friendly approach; provide better recreational and educational services for the citizens of the Commonwealth of Massachusetts.

ORGANIZATIONS:

Massachusetts Film Bureau (Advisory Member); Governor's Blue Ribbon Commission on State House Renovations; Commonwealth Zoological Corporation (Board of Directors); Museum of Science Trustees; Ancient and Honorable Artillery Company

Brian W. Kerins

Deputy Commissioner for Operations

Metropolitan District Commission
Address: 20 Somerset Street, Boston, MA 02108
Telephone: (617) 727-5114 **Fax:** (617) 727-4763
Staff: Marty Glavin, Deputy Director of Operations; James Griffin, Deputy Director for Administration; Edward Pontremoli, District Superintendent
Reports to: Commissioner David B. Balfour, Jr.

PERSONAL INFORMATION:

Born: May 14, 1954 **Place of Birth:** Boston
Marital Status: married (Mary Ellen) **Children:** 3
Previous Employment: M.D.C., Central Services (Laborer, Skilled Laborer, Supervisor of Motor Pools, Head Administrative Assistant, Deputy Director)
Years in Current Position: 1.5 **Years in State Service:** 24

JOB DESCRIPTION:

Oversee field activities including the maintenance and programming of facilities, parkways, reservations, parks and beaches.

1999 PRIORITIES:

Have clean and safe properties for visitors and constituents to enjoy.

William F. Chisholm
Secretary

Metropolitan District Commission
Address: 20 Somerset Street, Boston, MA 02108
Telephone: (617) 727-5204 **Fax:** (617) 727-7333
Staff: Jane McCarthy, Elaine Rowan, Administrative Assistants
Reports to: Commissioner David B. Balfour, Jr.

PERSONAL INFORMATION:
Marital Status: married (Judith B.) **Children:** 3
Education: Suffolk University (B.S.B.A., '63)
Previous Employment: United States Air Force
Years in Current Position: 16 **Years in State Service:** 42

JOB DESCRIPTION:
Executive Secretary of the Metropolitan District Commission.

Samantha M. Overton
Deputy Commissioner for Policy

Metropolitan District Commission
Address: 20 Somerset Street, Boston, MA 02108
Telephone: (617) 727-5114 **Fax:** (617) 727-0891
Staff: Andrea Lichty, Special Program Coordinator.
Reports to: Commissioner David B. Balfour, Jr.

PERSONAL INFORMATION:
Born: Sept. 2, 1966 **Place of Birth:** Newton, NJ
Marital Status: single
Education: Smith College, (B.A., M.A.)
Previous Employment: Chief of Staff, Metropolitan District Commission; Director, Executive Secretariat for Office of Governor Weld.
Years in Current Position: 3 **Years in State Service:** 7

JOB DESCRIPTION:
Oversight and coordination of the agency's environmental policy and planning functions, direct MDC's Back to the Beaches initiative and agency's clean state compliance program.

1999 PRIORITIES:
Implementation of good environmental practices. Implementation of restoration of Constitution Beach and other beaches.

ORGANIZATIONS:
Past president of Massachusetts Women's Political Caucus, Co-chair Mass Action for Women, Emerald Necklace Conservancy Board.

Brian T. Broderick

Director of Reservations and Historic Sites

Metropolitan District Commission
Address: 20 Somerset Street, Boston, MA 02108
Telephone: (617) 727-5250 **Fax:** (617) 727-9905
Staff: Kay Cassell, Administrative Assistant; Peter Church, Chief Ranger; Pat Flynn, South Region Supervisor; Karl Pastore, North Region Supervisor; Don Fraser, Harbor Region Supervisor
Reports to: Commissioner David B. Balfour, Jr.

PERSONAL INFORMATION:
Born: December 23, 1941 **Place of Birth:** Boston
Marital Status: married (H. Louise [Lisa])
Education: Babson College (Business Administration, '63)
Previous Employment: M.D.C., Reservations and Historic Sites Division (Deputy Director, '87-'91); M.D.C., Central Services Director (Deputy Director, '72-'87); State Street Bank and Trust Company (Senior Methods and Systems Analyst, '65-'71)
Years in Current Position: 7 **Years in State Service:** 25

JOB DESCRIPTION:
Supervise the management of the large parks, reservations and historic sites within the 17,000-acre Metropolitan Park System.

1999 PRIORITIES:
Continue current program of upgrading and improving the quantity and quality of cultural and natural resource management and protection for the park system.

ORGANIZATIONS:
Fire Chiefs Association of Massachusetts; New England Association of Fire Chiefs; National Fire Protection Association (Wildland Fire Management Section)

Joseph M. McGinn

Director of Watershed Management

Metropolitan District Commission
Address: 20 Somerset Street, Boston, MA 02108
Telephone: (617) 727-5274 ext. 272 **Fax:** (617) 727-8301
Staff: Dennis Kane, Director of Engineering; Patricia Austin, P.E., Director of Environmental Quality; Robert O'Conner, Director of Natural Resources; Jeanne Wildman, Regional Planner
Reports to: Commissioner David B. Balfour, Jr.

PERSONAL INFORMATION:
Born: October 31, 1952 **Place of Birth:** Worcester
Marital Status: married (Debbie) **Children:** 4
Education: Worcester Polytechnical Institute (B.S., Sanitary Engineering, '74); Massachusetts School of Law (J.D., '91)
Previous Employment: MDC-DWM (Director of Environmental Quality); Maguire Group, Inc. (Senior Engineer); DEQE-QPPM (Principal Investigator); Metropolitan Area Planning Council (Water Quality Program Director)
Years in Current Position: 8 **Years in State Service:** 9

Executive Office of Environmental Affairs

JOB DESCRIPTION:
Direct and manage a diverse staff of 160 people including civil and environmental engineers, regional planners, foresters, interpreters, skilled tradesmen and laborers; protect and preserve the watershed system, which provides 300 million gallons per day of safe drinking water to over 2.5 million citizens; territory includes Quabbin, Ware River, Wachusett and Sudbury Reservoir watersheds, including over 400 square miles.

ORGANIZATIONS:
Worcester County Bar Association; Worcester Planning Board; Worcester Open Space Advisory Committee; Worcester Chapter, Society for the Preservation and Encouragement of Barbershop Quartet Singing in America (SPEBSQSA); Massachusetts Water Works Association; New England Water Works Association; American Water Works Association; Regional Environmental Council; Attorney admitted to practice in Massachusetts and Federal District Court, Massachusetts District

Health & Human Services

The Executive Office of Health and Human Services is responsible, through its member agencies, for the provision of essential health care, rehabilitation, social, correctional, and family services to the citizens of the Commonwealth. The numerous programs administered by this executive secretariat provide financial aid, residential services, counseling and placement to persons in need of public assistance. The various agencies are funded through a combination of state and federal resources. The role of the central executive office consists of the coordination, management, and fiscal oversight of the 15 departments and agencies under its jurisdiction. The agencies that make up the secretariat are as follows:

- *Department of Public Health*
- *Department of Mental Health*
- *Department of Mental Retardation*
- *Department of Youth Services*
- *Office of Child Care Services*
- *Department of Transitional Assistance*
- *Division of Medical Assistance*
- *Department of Social Services*
- *Health Care Finance and Policy*
- *Massachusetts Office for Refugees and Immigrants*
- *Holyoke Soldiers' Home*
- *Chelsea Soldiers' Home*
- *Massachusetts Rehabilitation Commission*
- *Massachusetts Commission for the Blind*
- *Massachusetts Commission for the Deaf and Hard of Hearing*

Department of Public Health

The Department of Public Health is charged with numerous responsibilities, including the provision of health care through the state's public hospitals, the prevention and control of communicable diseases, health promotion and education. The public hospitals overseen by the department provide health care services for patients with financial constraints and special medical needs. The department investigates outbreaks of infectious diseases and works with local boards of health to develop and implement strategies to combat them. It provides AIDS education programs and HIV counseling and testing sites. It monitors medical services and health care quality and serves as an advocate for patients in health care facilities. The department inspects and licenses producers and purveyors of food, pharmaceutical drugs, medical devices, pesticides, and other consumer products. It administers health programs for parents, children, and adolescents and provides substance abuse treatment options for individuals unable to receive other treatment. In addition, the department collects, analyzes, interprets, and publishes Massachusetts public health data in order to assess the impact of programs and set development goals.

The Department of Public Health is organized into the following units:

- *Bureau of Public Health Hospitals*
- *Bureau of Communicable Disease Control*
- *HIV/AIDS Bureau*
- *Bureau of Health Care Systems*
- *Bureau of Food and Drugs*
- *Bureau of Family and Community Health*
- *Bureau of Community Health Services*
- *Bureau of Health Statistics, Research, and Evaluation*
- *Bureau of Laboratory and Environmental Sciences*

Department of Mental Health

The Department of Mental Health provides a comprehensive array of mental health services to adults with serious mental illness and to adolescents and children who are seriously mentally ill or severely emotionally disturbed. The Department operates four psychiatric hospitals, nine community mental health centers, and 33 local service sites, and oversees 812 purchase of service contracts with 184 providers of community based services. The Department provides continuing care, case management, residential clubhouses and social clubs, rehabilitation and employment opportunities for mental health clients as well as specialty forensic and children's services.

Department of Mental Retardation

The Department of Mental Retardation oversees the delivery of state services to persons with mental retardation and their families. Through its programs and services, the department strives to help retarded individuals lead full and independent lives. It provides funding for daytime programs, operates residential units, and administers emergency services throughout the Commonwealth. In addition, the department offers respite care and family support services.

Department of Youth Services

The Department of Youth Services is a juvenile corrections agency responsible for the provision of services to delinquent youngsters between the ages of 7 and 21. The department seeks to protect the public from juvenile offenders and to rehabilitate those youths who have been committed to its care through a comprehensive network of programs, services, and treatment options. It provides pretrial detention for youths pending court action in addition to long-term programs for youths adjudicated delinquent. These programs include educational and psychological counseling, substance abuse treatment, and vocational training. The agency operates a gradual integration model in an attempt to provide juvenile offenders with a smooth transition back into the community.

Office of Child Care Services

The Office of Child Care Services (OCCS), formerly the Office for Children, seeks to advance high quality childcare for children and families. In pursuit of this goal, OCCS has several main areas of responsibility: license, regulate, and monitor child care facilities and residential and detention programs for children and youth; refer parents to appropriate child care; train child care workers through support of the statewide Child Care Resource and Referral Network; purchase subsidized child care for eligible low-income families, authorized welfare-to-work participants, families moving off of welfare, teen parents, and Department of Social Services family support consumers; and support child abuse prevention programs through budgetary support of the nursery schools, private kindergartens, day care centers, day care homes, residential facilities for troubled children, as well as foster care and adoption placement agencies.

Department of Transitional Assistance

The Department of Transitional Assistance administers programs that provide financial and medical benefits to elderly, and low-income individuals and families. The department makes eligibility determinations and disburses payments for a variety of state and federally funded assistance programs, including Emergency Aid to the Elderly, Disabled, and Children (EAEDC, formerly General Relief); Aid to Families with Dependent Children (AFDC); MassJOBS; Supplemental Security Income; and the United States Department of Agriculture's food stamps program. In addition the agency oversees a shelter resource unit for homeless individuals and assists these individuals and families in obtaining permanent housing. The department handles client appeals, but investigations of welfare fraud complaints and subsequent hearings are conducted by the Bureau of Special Investigations, which is part of the Executive Office for Administration and Finance.

Department of Social Services

The Department of Social Services is the state's child and family protection agency. Its role is to protect children from abuse and neglect while strengthening family units. The agency is responsible for the enforcement and oversight of laws regarding the reporting, investigation, evaluation, and supervision of cases of alleged child abuse. It receives and responds to initial reports of child abuse and handles the casework arising from reports through a network of 26 area offices. The department administers a number of social service programs intended to ameliorate the plight of abused children and their families. These include counseling, referral, day care, respite, emergency shelter, family planning, foster care, and adoption. Potential foster care and adoptive families are recruited and assessed by the department, which also prepares children for placement. Financial assistance, training, and orientation services for participating families are provided as well.

Health Care Finance & Policy

The Health Care Finance & Policy office is responsible for establishing payment rates for health services purchased by the Commonwealth, oversight of the hospital payment system, analysis and publication of health cost and utilization for use by state officials in the formulation of public policy, the purchase of health care services, and management of the uncompensated care pool. The Commissioners oversee the design, implementation, and evaluation of financing and pricing mechanisms for a wide variety of health care services, including long-term, intermediate, non-acute, and ambulatory providers. Rates for these services are subject to public hearings and promulgated through regulations. Under recently enacted hospital payment legislation, the Commission is also responsible for evaluation of the new system, studying the cost of health insurance, monitoring hospital revenue limitations, and setting payment rates for hospitals providing services under the Freecare Program.

Massachusetts Office for Refugees and Immigrants

The Massachusetts Office for Refugees and Immigrants is a federally funded program established to assist refugees in adjusting to life in this country. The office acts as public advocate to new immigrants, coordinates state services to ensure cultural and linguistic accessibility, and provides employment and welfare services in order to promote self-sufficiency as soon as possible. The agency conducts outreach programs in ethnic communities, provides a statewide information and referral service, and offers educational programs with respect to employment discrimination on the basis of citizenship or national origin.

Soldiers' Homes

The two state Soldiers' Homes in Chelsea and Holyoke strive to maintain quality health care for Massachusetts veterans. These facilities offer full-service residential care and comprehensive outpatient clinic services in order to meet the medical distribution requirements of veterans in need.

Massachusetts Rehabilitation Commission

The Massachusetts Rehabilitation Commission provides a variety of educational, vocational, residential, and medical services to physically and mentally disabled persons in order to assist them in securing employment and prevent institutionalization. Vocational rehabilitation services provided by the Commission include specialized training, placement, evaluation, counseling, and adaptive technology. The Commission provides residential and technical assistance to persons in private homes. It also provides medical evaluations, aptitude testing, disability determinations, and prosthetic devices for those who need such services.

Massachusetts Commission for the Blind

The Massachusetts Commission for the Blind provides rehabilitative services as well as financial and medical assistance to many of the Commonwealth's 31,000 legally blind residents. The Commission administers a variety of federal and state programs which provide services to blind and multi-handicapped blind residents.

Massachusetts Commission for the Deaf and Hard ofHearing

The Massachusetts Commission for the Deaf and Hard of Hearing provides advocacy, services, and communication access for the estimated 292,000 hearing impaired persons in the Commonwealth, of whom approximately 29,000 are deaf. Among the services provided by the Commission are interpreter referral, bilingual case management and advocacy, independent living training services, and peer support. In its advocacy capacity, the Commission assists the hearing impaired in obtaining the public services they require and assists agency providers in making service communication accessible.

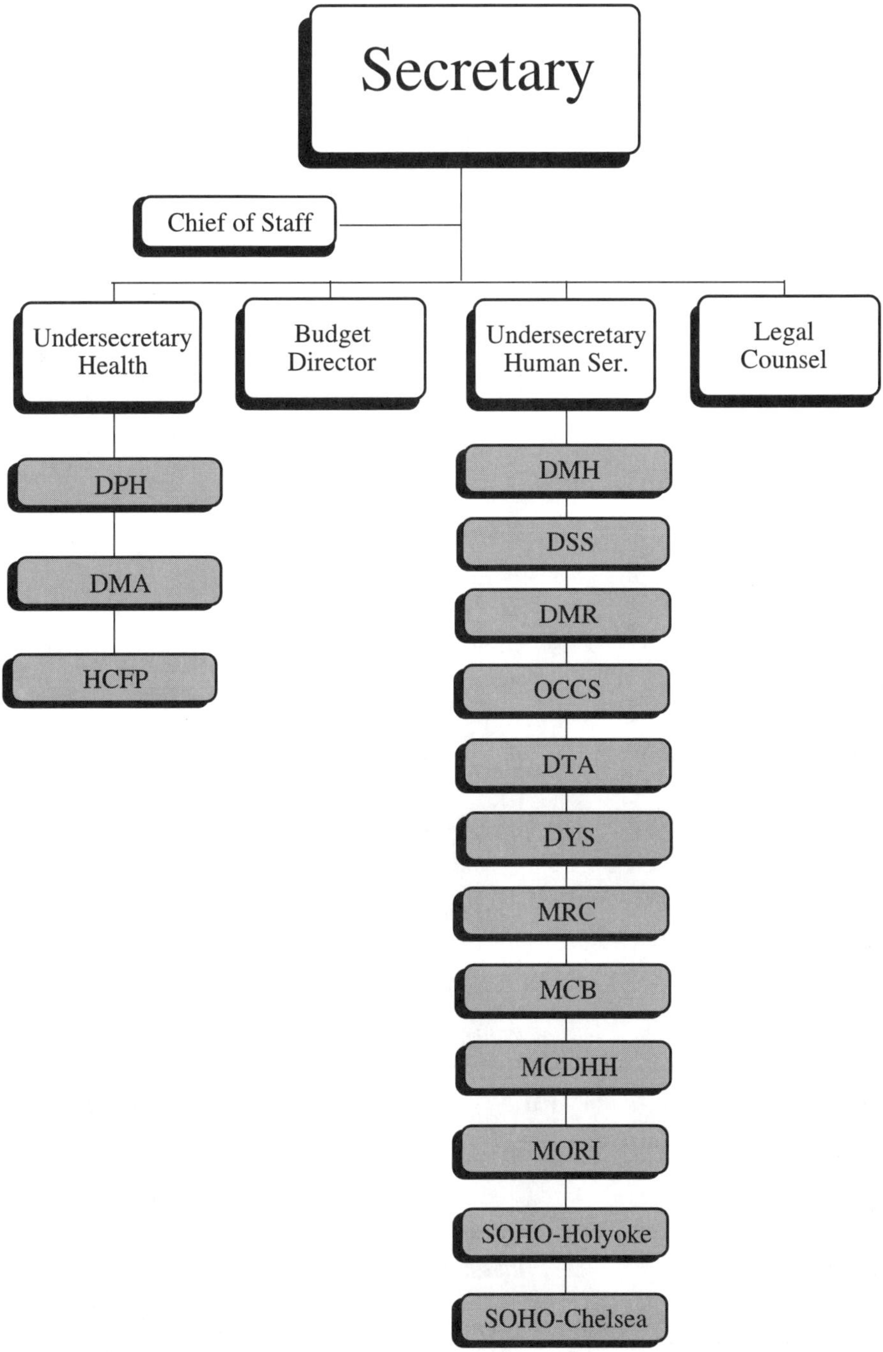
Secretary
Chief of Staff
Undersecretary Health
Budget Director
Undersecretary Human Ser.
Legal Counsel
DPH
DMA
HCFP
DMH
DSS
DMR
OCCS
DTA
DYS
MRC
MCB
MCDHH
MORI
SOHO-Holyoke
SOHO-Chelsea

Secretary	**William O'Leary**	*(617) 727-0077*
Chief of Staff	**Mary McGeown**	*727-0077*
Undersecretary/Health	**John R. Ford**	*727-7600*
Undersecretary/Human Services	**Daniel Nakamoto**	*727-7600*
Administration and Finance	**Henry Swiniarski**	*727-7600*
General Counsel	**Stuart A. Kaufman**	*727-7600*

Directors:

Affirmative Action	**A. Victoria Mederos**	*727-7600*
Systems	**Jack Hornfeldt**	*727-7600*
Contracts	**Carin Kale**	*727-7600*
Human Resources	**Diane Boulanger-Prescott**	*727-7600*
Communications	**David A. Ball**	*727-0077*
Client Services	**Betty Anne Ritcey**	*727-7600*

Deputy Commissioners:

Administration and Finance	**William Brouillard**	*727-5550*

COMMISSION FOR THE DEAF AND HARD OF HEARING

Commissioner	**Barbara Jean Wood**	*695-7500*

Directors:

Interpretive Services	**Irma Kahle**	*695-7500*
Administration and Finance	**Kimberly S. Egan**	*695-7500*
Case Management Services	**Elizabeth Banta**	*695-7500*

Policy and Programs	**vacant**	695-7500
Communication Access, Training and Technology Services	**Andrea Galvin**	695-7500
General Counsel	**Jeanne Dusombre**	727-7600

COMMISSION FOR THE BLIND

Commissioner	**David Govostes**	727-5550

Deputy Commissioners:

Administration and Finance	**William Brouillard**	727-5550
Services	**Robert Dowling**	727-5550
General Counsel	**Susan Herz**	727-5550

Directors:

Information Services	**Philip Oliver**	727-5550
Policy and Medicaid	**vacant**	727-5550

DEPARTMENT OF PUBLIC HEALTH

Commissioner	**Howard K. Koh**	624-5200
Assoc. Commissioner	**James Hill**	624-5260

Directors:

Bureau of Environmental Health Assessment	**Suzanne K. Condon**	624-5757
Bureau of Substance Abuse	**Mayra Rodriguez-Howard**	624-5151
Communicable Disease Control	**Alfred DeMaria**	983-6550
Community Health Programs	**Deborah Klein Walker**	624-6090
Health Statistics/ Research	**Dan Friedman**	624-5600
Laboratory/ Environmental	**Ralph Timperi**	983-6201
Hospital Management	**Mary E. Hardiman**	624-5256
Health Quality Management	**Nancy T. Ridley**	624-5280

DEPARTMENT OF MENTAL RETARDATION

Commissioner	**Gerald J. Morrissey, Jr.**	727-5608
Chief of Staff	**Mary Ann Brennen**	727-5608
Assistant Commissioners:		
Quality Management	**Dorothy Mullen**	727-5608
Field Operations	**Lawrence Tummino**	727-5608
Management and Finance	**William Hetherington**	727-5608
Children's Services & Policy Planning	**Janet L. George**	727-5608
General Counsel	**Margaret Chow-Menzer**	727-5608

DEPARTMENT OF TRANSITIONAL ASSISTANCE

Commissioner	**Claire McIntire**	348-8410
Deputy Commissioner	**Todd H. Maio**	348-8493
Director of Equal Opportunity	**Judith Subanny**	348-8490
General Counsel	**Thomas E. Noonan**	348-8526
Assistant Commissioners:		
Field Operations	**Joyce Sampson**	348-8415
Policy & Program Management	**Edward Sanders-Bey**	348-8412
Management Info. Systems (Acting)	**James Reen**	348-8408
Administration and Finance	**William Bell**	348-8431

DIVISION OF MEDICAL ASSISTANCE

Commissioner	**Bruce M. Bullen**	210-5690
Deputy Commissioner	**Mark E. Reynolds**	210-5670
Clinical Director	**Annette Hanson**	210-5683
General Counsel	**Jean Sullivan**	210-5361
Assistant Commissioners:		
Administration and Finance	**Louise Povall**	210-5094

Member Services	**Russell Kulp**	*210-5311*

DEPARTMENT OF MENTAL HEALTH

Commissioner	**Marylou Sudders**	*727-5500*
Dep. Comm. for Program Operations	**Carolyn Schlaepfer**	*727-5500*
Dep. Comm. for Management & Budget	**Jeff McCue**	*727-5500*
Dep. Comm. for Clinical & Prof. Services	**Paul Barreira**	*727-5500*
General Counsel	**Jennifer Wilcox**	*727-5500*
Chief of Staff	**Marilyn E. Berner**	*727-5500*
Dir. of Constituent & Legislative Affairs	**Stephen M. Cidlevich**	*727-5500*
Director of Public Affiars	**John Widdison**	*727-5500*
Asst. Comm. for Forensic Mental Health	**Deborah Scott**	*727-5500*
Asst. Comm. for Child/ Adolescent Services	**Joan Mikula**	*727-5500*

DEPARTMENT OF YOUTH SERVICES

Commissioner	**Robert P. Gittens**	*727-7575*
Deputy Commissioner	**Edward J. Dolan**	*727-7575*
General Counsel	**Lawrence J. Feeney**	*727-7575*
Director of Public Affairs	**Glenn E. Daly**	*727-7575*

OFFICE FOR CHILD CARE SERVICES

Commissioner	**Ardith A. Wieworka**	*626-2000*
Dep. Commissioner, Field Operations	**Fran Barrett**	*626-2000*
Asst. Comm. Admin. & Finance	**Jan Avallone**	*626-2000*
Chief of Staff	**vacant**	*626-2000*
General Counsel	**Katherine Clark**	*626-2000*
Dir. of Communications/ Legislative Liaison	**Douglas Pizzi**	*626-2000*

Director of Investigations	**Carol Randolph**	626-2000
Asst. Commissioner, Information Systems	**Joan Clark**	626-2000

OFFICE FOR REFUGEES AND IMMIGRANTS

Acting Executive Director	**Phuac Cao**	727-7888
Deputy Director	**vacant**	727-7888
Director, Communications	**Claire McDonough**	727-7888
Director, Family Independence	**Emel Hadzipasic**	727-7888
Director, Community Building	**Carol Chandler**	727-7888
Assistant General Counsel	**Vivie Hengst**	727-7888

HEALTH CARE FINANCE AND POLICY

Commissioner	**vacant**	988-3120
Acting Commissioner	**Louis I. Freedman**	988-3120
Executive Secretary	**John A. Daley**	988-3120
General Counsel	**Kathleen Connors**	988-3138
Directors:		
Audit Compliance & Evaluation Group	**Michael Berolini (Acting)**	988-3228
Communications	**Harry A. Lohr, Jr.**	988-3125
Health Data Policy Group	**Gerald O'Keefe**	988-3140
Pricing Policy & Financial Analysis Group	**Stephen McCabe**	988-3198
Information Technology Group	**David Wessmann**	988-3272
Health Systems Measurement and Improvement Group	**Amy M. Lischko**	988-3158

MASSACHUSETTS REHABILITATION COMMISSION

Commissioner	**Elmer C. Bartels**	204-3600
General Counsel	**Richard F. Arcangeli**	204-3616
Chief of Staff	**Janna Z. Jacobs**	204-3608

Deputy Commissioners:

Disability Determination Services	**Kasper M. Goshgarian**	654-7400
Independent Living	**John A. Chappell, Jr.**	204-3620
Vocational Rehabilitation	**Warren McManus**	204-3613

SOLDIER'S HOME

Commandant, Chelsea	**William D. Thompson**	884-5660
Deputy Superintendent	**Richard J. Palazzi**	(413)532-9475
Superintendent, Holyoke	**Paul A. Morin**	(413)532-9475

DEPARTMENT OF SOCIAL SERVICES

Commissioner	**Linda K. Carlisle**	748-2325
General Counsel	**Kristen Apgar**	748-2011
Agency Ombudsman	**Margaret E. Connors**	748-2360

Deputy Commissioners:

Administration and Finance	**Teresa Kinsella**	748-2062
Field Operations	**John T. Farley III**	748-2348

Assistant Commissioners:

Office of Human Resources	**David Young**	748-2071
Placement & Family Based Services	**Joan Louden-Black**	748-2365
Clinical Services and Intergovernmental Affairs	**Susan I. Pederzoli**	748-2257
Information Technology	**Craig Burlingame**	748-2222

Directors:

Public Affairs	**Lorraine Carli**	748-2367
Constituent Affairs	**Michael D. Donovan**	748-2329
Management Planning & Analysis	**Peter Watson**	748-2353
Foster Care/Adoption Services	**Mary Gambog**	748-2248

William O'Leary

Secretary

Executive Office of Health and Human Services
Address: One Ashburton Place, Room 1109, Boston, MA 02108
Telephone: (617)727-0077 **Fax:** (617) 727-5134
Reports to: Governor A. Paul Cellucci

PERSONAL INFORMATION:
Born: Feb. 15, 1954 **Place of Birth:** Pittsfield
Marital Status: married (Deborah) **Children:** 2
Education: University of Massachusetts at Amherst (B.A. '76); State University of New York at Albany (M.A. '77); Western New England College School of Law (J.D. '84);
Previous Employment: Commissioner, Department of Youth Services; Department of Mental Health (Assistant Commissioner, Division of Forensic Mental Health); Crime and Justice Foundation (Deputy Director)
Years in Current Position: new

JOB DESCRIPTION:
Oversee 15 departments and agencies employing 24,000 people with a budget of nearly $8 billion. The Secretary manages the following agencies: Youth Services, Social Services, Public Health, Mental Health, Mental Retardation, Commission for the Blind, Commission for the Deaf, Office for Childcare Services, Medicaid, Refugees, Soldiers' Homes, and Rehabilitation Commission.

1999 PRIORITIES:
Expand access to health care. Target juvenile delinquency and child abuse prevention. Oversee consolidation and expansion of childcare services. Manage continued implementation of welfare reform.

Mary McGeown

Chief of Staff

Executive Office of Health and Human Services
Address: One Ashburton Place, Boston, MA 02108
Telephone: (617) 727-0077 **Fax:** (617) 727-5134
Reports to: Secretary William O'Leary

PERSONAL INFORMATION:
Date of Birth: March 21, 1962 **Place of Birth:** Chelmsford
Education: Boston University (B.S. '84)
Previous Employment: Department of Mental Health (Director of Public Affairs); Department of Correction (Deputy Director of Public Affairs)
Years in Current Position: new **Years in State Service:** 19

John R. Ford

Undersecretary/Health

Executive Office of Health and Human Services
Address: One Ashburton Place, Boston, MA 02108
Telephone: (617) 727-7600 **Fax:** (617) 727-5134
E-mail: johnford@state.ma.us
Reports to: Secretary William O'Leary

PERSONAL INFORMATION:
Education: Boston College (B.S., Finance, '54; M.S.W., '61)
Previous Employment: Department of Mental Health (Deputy Commissioner)
Years in Current Position: 2 **Years in State Service:** 18

Stuart A. Kaufman

General Counsel

Executive Office of Health and Human Services
Address: One Ashburton Place, Boston, MA 02108
Telephone: (617) 727-7600 **Fax:** (617) 727-5134
Staff: Dee Bernier, Legal Assistant
Reports to: Secretary William O'Leary

PERSONAL INFORMATION:
Date of Birth: Feb. 22, 1946 **Place of Birth:** Boston
Marital Status: married (Deborah Shilkoff) **Children:** 2
Education: New York University (B.A. '68); Boston College Law School (J.D. '71)
Previous Employment: State Ethics Commission, General Counsel; Public Service Committee, Counsel; Northeastern University School of Law, adjunct professor
Years in Current Position: 7 **Years in State Service:** 27

JOB DESCRIPTION:
Legal advice and policy direction to Secretary and Secretariat staff; legislation; tort claims; litigation and environmental compliance.

ORGANIZATIONS:
Newton Choral Society; MBA Mock Trial Program

Betty Anne Ritcey

Director of the Bureau of Transitional Planning;
Director of Client Services; Coordinator for Health and Disability

Executive Office of Health and Human Services
Address: One Ashburton Place, Boston, MA 02108
Telephone: (617) 727-7600 ext. 410 **Fax:** (617) 727-1396
Staff: Shirley Arnold, Coordinator of the Bureau of Transitional Planning; Karen O'Leary, Assistant Director of Client Services
Reports to: Undersecretary John Ford

PERSONAL INFORMATION:

Born: March 10, 1948 **Place of Birth:** Newton

Marital Status: single

Education: Laboure College (A.D., Nursing, '74); Emmanuel College (B.S., Psychology, '77); American Nurses Association (Certification, Gerontology, '88); University of Massachusetts (M.S., Human Services, '96)

Previous Employment: Department of Public Welfare, Medicaid Division (Relocation Advisor); Maristhill Nursing Home (Nursing Supervisor)

Years in Current Position: 6.5 **Years in State Service:** 11.5

JOB DESCRIPTION:

Chairperson for Interagency "Special Populations" Committee for the Secretary; liaison between Governor's Office and other human service agencies concerning client service issues; participate with our agencies around program design; assist agencies with closure, consolidation, and privatizing planning and implementation; coordinate at Secretariat level issues concerning our health or disability agencies.

David A. Ball

Director of Communications

Executive Office of Health and Human Services

Address: One Ashburton Place, Boston, Rm 1109, MA 02108

Telephone: (617) 727-0077 **Fax:** (617) 727-5134

E-Mail: dball@state.ma.us

Staff: Rich Copp, Deputy Director of Communications

Reports to: Secretary William D. O'Leary

PERSONAL INFORMATION:

Born: June 10, 1964 **Place of Birth:** Boston

Marital Status: single

Education: UMASS/Amherst (B.A. '86); UMASS/Boston (Senior Executive Program, '98); JFK School Government, Harvard

Previous Employment: Director of External Affairs, Division of Medical Assistance

Years in Current Position: 3 **Years in State Service:** 12

JOB DESCRIPTION:

Manager of internal and external communications for the Secretariat; overseeing media relations and serving as spokesman on Health and Human Services issues.

Barbara Jean Wood
Commissioner

Massachusetts Commission for the Deaf and Hard of Hearing
Address: 210 South Street, 5th Floor, Boston, MA 02111
Telephone: (617) 695-7500 **TTY:** (617) 695-7600
Fax: (617) 695-7599 **E-mail:** BWood@state.ma.us
Staff: Kim Egan, Deputy Commissioner for Administration and Finance
Reports to: Secretary William O'Leary

PERSONAL INFORMATION:
Born: September 22, 1950 **Place of Birth:** Elizabeth, NJ
Education: Rochester Institute of Technology (B.A., Social Work, '75)
Previous Employment: Office of Handicapped Affairs (Dep. Director)
Years in Current Position: 11 **Years in State Service:** 16

JOB DESCRIPTION:
To provide, assure, and advocate for appropriate services, programs, and communication access for the estimated 292,000 hearing-impaired individuals in the state, of which an estimated 29,000 are deaf. The Commissioner manages and directs the Commission, to provide the following: formulating the policy; planning and developing programs; assessing the needs of the deaf and hard of hearing; implementing and maintaining programs and policies; financial management of the agency (including budget, contracts, and expenditures); personnel; administration; liaison with other agencies and the public; and relating to potential sources for federal resources.

1999 PRIORITIES:
To deliver and/or assure the delivery of quality, appropriate, special services and programs to enable deaf and hard of hearing persons to enjoy them; to increase and maintain the competency and availability of special, communication-related professionals and paraprofessionals working with deaf and hard of hearing people; to create a public awareness about special communication situations, special needs, and capabilities of deaf and hard of hearing people to facilitate creation of generally accessible daily environment for deaf and hard of hearing individuals; to access for special populations services from state and community agencies; to increase communication access in community and state services; to increase and maintain consumer information access and skills for independence.

ORGANIZATIONS:
Massachusetts State Association for the Deaf; National Association for the Deaf; Massachusetts Deaf Professional Group; National Registry of Interpreters; National Self Help for the Hard of Hearing

Kimberly S. Egan
Deputy Commissioner for Administration and Finance

Massachusetts Commission for the Deaf and Hard of Hearing
Address: 210 South Street, 5th Floor, Boston, MA 02111
Telephone: (617) 695-7500 **TTY:** (617) 695-7600
Fax: (617) 695-7599 **E-mail:** Kimberly.Egan@state.ma.us
Reports to: Commissioner Barbara Jean Wood

PERSONAL INFORMATION:

Education: Massasoit Community College (Architecture, '94); Boston Architectural Center (Architectural Design, '88); Chamberlayne Junior College (Advertising/Design, '83)

Previous Employment: Disabled Persons Protection Commission (Director, Human Resources); Massachusetts Commission for the Deaf and Hard of Hearing (Deputy Commissioner for Administration and Finance, '90-'92); Executive Office of Health and Human Services (Personnel Coordinator)

Years in Current Position: 3 **Years in State Service:** 15

JOB DESCRIPTION:

Executive staff position responsible for the fiscal and administrative affairs of the agency, including budget, revenue, federal grant management, contracts, procurement, personnel, payroll, labor relations, training, affirmative action, benefits coordination, and recruitment.

Philip Oliver

Director of Office Information Services

Massachusetts Commission for the Blind

Address: 88 Kingston Street, Boston, MA 02111

Telephone: (617) 727-5550 **Fax:** (617) 727-5960

E-mail: POliver@state.ma.us

Reports to: Commissioner David Govostes

PERSONAL INFORMATION:

Years in Current Position: 6 **Years in State Service:** 13

JOB DESCRIPTION:

Direct and oversee the office of information services.

Department of Public Health

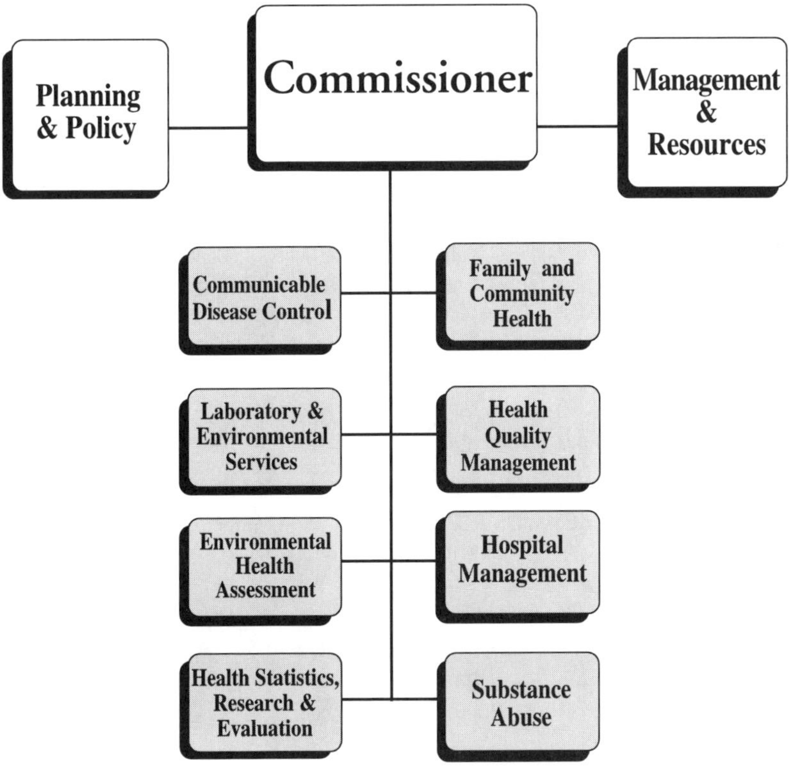

Howard K. Koh, M.D.

Commissioner

Department of Public Health
Address: 250 Washington Street, Boston, MA 02108
Telephone: (617) 624-5200 **Fax:** (617) 624-5206
E-mail: Howard.Koh@state.ma.us
Staff: Kathy Collin, Chief of Staff; Mark Leccesse, Public Relations
Reports to: Secretary William D. O'Leary

Years in Current Position: 1

JOB DESCRIPTION:
To oversee a wide range of public health programs and services for the Commonwealth. These include AIDS, substance abuse, and maternal and child health programs and services. The Department operates public health hospitals and the State Laboratory Institute, and has regulatory responsibility for the Commonwealth's health care facilities. Responsible to chair the Public Health Council, the Commonwealth's senior health care policy committee.

Nancy T. Ridley

Director, Health Quality Management

Department of Public Health
Address: 250 Washington Street, Boston, MA 02108
Telephone: (617) 624-5280 **Fax:** (617) 624-5046
E-mail: Nancy.Ridley@state.ma.us
Staff: Karen Flanagan, Administrative Assistant
Reports to: Commissioner Howard K. Koh.

PERSONAL INFORMATION:
Born: November 21, 1944 **Place of Birth:** Woburn
Marital Status: married (Stephen)
Education: Northeastern University (B.A., Biology; M.S., Medical Laboratory Science)
Previous Employment: Lahey Clinic Foundation
Years in Current Position: 4 **Years in State Service:** 19

JOB DESCRIPTION:
Responsible for Divisions of Food and Drugs, Radiation Control, Community Sanitation, Health Care Quality, Emergency Medical Services, Determination of Need Program and Childhood Lead Poisoning Prevention Program.

ORGANIZATIONS:
U.S. Food and Drug Commissioned Officer

Suzanne K. Condon

Director, Bureau of Environmental Health Assessment

Department of Public Health
Address: 250 Washington Street, Boston, MA 02108
Telephone: (617) 624-5757 **Fax:** (617) 624-5777
Reports to: Commissioner Howard Koh, M.D.

Education: Bridgewater State College (B.S., '79); Emmanuel College (MSM '98)
Years in Current Position: 8 **Years in State Service:** 17

JOB DESCRIPTION:
Direct the Bureau of Environmental Health Assessment, which has an annual state and federal budget of $3.5 million and consists of six programs: Environmental Epidemiology, Community Assessment, Environmental Toxicology, Emergency Response/Right to Know, Environmental Education and Indoor Air.

ORGANIZATIONS:
American Public Health Association; National Environmental Health Association; Massachusetts Environmental Health Association

Mayra Rodriguez-Howard

Director, Bureau of Substance Abuse Services

Department of Public Health
Address: 250 Washington Street, 3rd Fl, Boston, MA 02108
Telephone: (617) 624-5151 **Fax:** (617) 624-5185
E-mail: mayra.rodriguez-howard@state.ma.us
Staff: Lucille I. Nunes, Administrative Assistant; Margaret Dougher, Special Assistant
Reports to: Commissioner Howard Koh

PERSONAL INFORMATION:
Born: October 4, 1950
Place of Birth: Santurce, Puerto Rico
Marital Status: married (William C. Howard) **Children:** 2
Education: University of Puerto Rico; State University of New York (B.A., '72); Boston College Graduate School of Social Work (M.S.W.)
Previous Employment: Center for Addictive Behaviors (Director of Prevention Services)
Years in Current Position: 3 **Years in State Service:** 11

JOB DESCRIPTION:
Direct the Bureau of Substance Abuse Services services the state's single state agency for substance abuse and its $80 million purchase of service contracts for the prevention and treatment of alcoholism and other substance abuse.

Deborah Klein Walker

Assistant Commissioner, Bureau of Family and Community Health

Department of Public Health
Address: 250 Washington Street, Boston, MA 02108
Telephone: (617) 624-6090 **Fax:** (617) 624-6062
E-mail: debbie.walker@state.ma.us
Reports to: Commissioner Howard Koh

PERSONAL INFORMATION:
Education: Mount Holyoke College (B.A., '65); Harvard Graduate School of Education (Ed.M., '75; Ed.D., '78)
Previous Employment: Harvard School of Public Health (Associate

Professor of Human Development)
Years in Current Position: 10 **Years in State Service:** 10

JOB DESCRIPTION:

Responsible for developing systems of health care through family and community health activities; responsible for Title V MCH Block Grant, (Healthy Start), WIC, Early Intervention (Part C of IDEA), Prevention Block Grant, Women's Health, Tobacco Control Program, Primary Care and Chronic Disease Programs.

ORGANIZATIONS:

Association of Maternal and Child Health Programs (President); American Public Health Association (past Chair, Maternal and Child Health Section); Massachusetts Public Health Association; American Psychological Society, Society for Research in Child Development

Mary E. Hardiman

Director of Hospital Management

Department of Public Health
Address: 250 Washington Street, Boston, MA 02108
Telephone: (617) 624-5256 **Fax:** (617) 624-5261
Reports to: Commissioner Howard Koh

PERSONAL INFORMATION:

Born: November 15, 1954 **Place of Birth:** Boston
Marital Status: married (James)
Education: Salem State College (B.S., Nursing, '76); Boston College (M.S., Nursing, '78)
Previous Employment: DPH (Hospital Management, '88-'95); Massachusetts Bay Community College (Nursing Faculty, '82-'88)
Years in Current Position: 6 **Years in State Service:** 15

JOB DESCRIPTION:

Responsible for management of four public health hospitals.

ORGANIZATIONS:

Massachusetts Nurses Association; Salem State Board of Friends of Nursing; Massachusetts Public Health Association

Gerald J. Morrissey, Jr.

Commissioner

Department of Mental Retardation
Address: 160 North Washington Street, Boston, MA 02114
Telephone: (617) 727-5608 **Fax:** (617) 624-7577
E-mail: Gerry.Morrissey@DMR.state.ma.us
Staff: Mary Ann Brennen, Chief of Staff; Bernadette Davis, Executive Assistant
Reports to: Secretary William O'Leary

PERSONAL INFORMATION:

Born: November 9, 1952 **Place of Birth:** Boston
Marital Status: married (Joanne)

Education: University of Massachusetts at Amherst (B.A., Education, '76); Antioch University (M.Ed., '80); Harvard University, JFK School of Government (M.D.A, '94)
Previous Employment: Department of Mental Health (Area Director)
Years in Current Position: 2 **Years in State Service:** 24

JOB DESCRIPTION:
Serving the Commonwealth's families and individuals with mental retardation.

1999 PRIORITIES:
Addressing the Commonwealth's wait list, strengthening community partnerships, develop well trained and effective workforce.

ORGANIZATIONS:
Colonel Daniel F. Marr, Jr., Boys & Girls Club

Mary Ann Brennen

Chief of Staff

Department of Mental Retardation
Address: 160 North Washington Street, Boston, MA 02114
Telephone: (617) 727- 5608 **Fax:** (617) 624-7577
Staff: Joanne Carney, Executive Assistant
Reports to: Commissioner Gerald J. Morrissey, Jr.

PERSONAL INFORMATION:
Education: University of Massachusetts at Amherst (B.A. '87)
Years in Current Position: new **Years in State Service:** 25

JOB DESCRIPTION:
Carry out and execute the Commissioner's management plan for the agency.

Janet L. George

Assistant Commissioner, Policy Planning and Children's Services

Department of Mental Retardation
Address: 160 North Washington Street, Boston, MA 02114
Telephone: (617) 727-5608 **Fax:** (617) 624-7577
Reports to: Commissioner Gerald J. Morrissey, Jr.

PERSONAL INFORMATION:
Born: May 8, 1948 **Place of Birth:** Cambridge
Marital Status: married (Edward) **Children:** 3
Education: Connecticut College (B.A., '70); University of Hartford (M.A., '73); Boston University (Ed.D., '83)
Previous Employment: Undersecretary of Human Services; Lutheran Service Association (Vice President, Coordinator of Residential Services, Program Director, Clinical Director, Staff Psychologist, Foster Care Worker)
Years in Current Position: 7 **Years in State Service:** 7

Department of Transitional Assistance

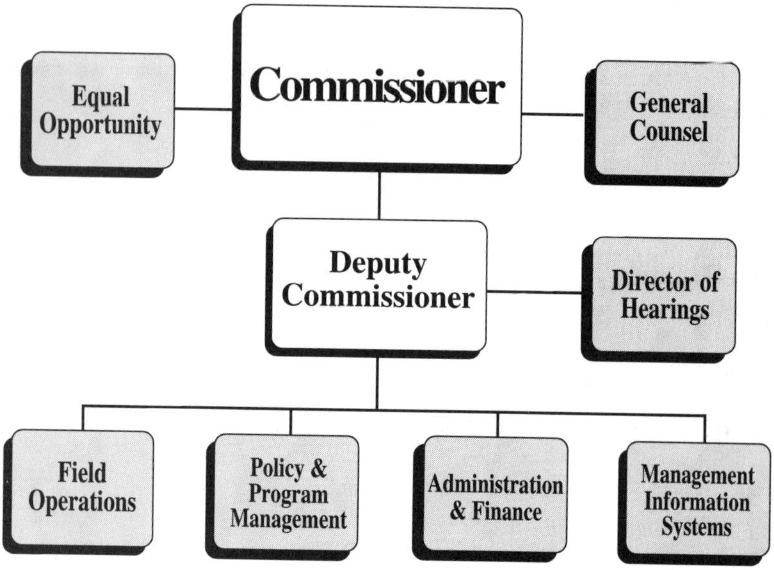

Claire McIntire

Commissioner

Department of Transitional Assistance
Address: 600 Washington Street, Boston, MA 02151
Telephone: (617) 348-8410 **Fax:** (617) 348-8575
Reports to: Secretary William D. O'Leary

PERSONAL INFORMATION:
Education: Stonehill College (B.A., '66)
Years in Current Position: 1.5 **Years in State Service:** 29

JOB DESCRIPTION:
To manage one of the largest agencies (annual budget $955 million) in state government. The Department of Transitional Assistance has about 2,500 employees in 40 offices statewide, providing cash assistance to 400,000 poor residents of Massachusetts. Specific programs include Transitional Aid to Families with Dependent Children, Food Stamps, MassJOBS, Emergency Aid for Elderly, Disabled, and Children.

Todd H. Maio

Deputy Commissioner

Department of Transitional Assistance
Address: 600 Washington Street, Boston, MA 02111
Telephone: (617) 348-8493 **Fax:** (617) 348-8575 **E-mail:** Todd_Maio@DTA.state.ma.us
Reports to: Commissioner Claire McIntire

PERSONAL INFORMATION:
Born: Nov. 10, 1964 **Place of Birth:** Brockton
Education: Brandeis University (B.A. '87)
Years in Current Position: 1 **Years in State Service:** 10

JOB DESCRIPTION:
To provide financial assistance and services to more than 400,000 recipients each month through a network of 40 local offices. Specific programs administered by DTA include: Transitional Aid to Families with Dependent Children (TAFDC), Food Stamps, Employment Service Program, Emergency Aid to Elderly, Disabled and Children.

Joyce Sampson

Assistant Commissioner, Field Operations

Department of Transitional Assistance
Address: 600 Washington Street, Boston, MA 02111
Telephone: (617) 348-8415 **Fax:** (617) 348-8575
Reports to: Commissioner Claire McIntire

PERSONAL INFORMATION:
Education: College of St. Elizabeth (B.A., '65)
Years in Current Position: 7 **Years in State Service:** 30

JOB DESCRIPTION:
Responsible for managing over 2,100 employees assigned to 40 local offices across the Commonwealth, providing benefits valued at over $1 billion to 400,000 people.

Edward Sanders-Bey

Assistant Commissioner for Policy and Program Management

Department of Transitional Assistance
Address: 600 Washington Street, Boston, MA 02111
Telephone: (617) 348-8412 **Fax:** (617) 348-8575
Staff: Jean Marino, Administrative Assistant
Reports to: Commissioner Claire McIntire

PERSONAL INFORMATION:
Born: May 18, 1949 **Place of Birth:** Philadelphia, PA
Marital Status: married (Catherine Ann Flaherty)
Education: Harvard University (B.A., '72); Newton College Sacred Heart/ Boston College (M.A., '73)
Previous Employment: Department of Transitional Assistance (Area Office Director); City of Boston (Project Manager)
Years in Current Position: 7 **Years in State Service:** 18

JOB DESCRIPTION:
Responsible for the supervision and evaluation of the Offices of Policy and Procedure, Housing Services, Program Assessment and Employment Services.

1999 PRIORITIES:
Welfare reform implementation.

ORGANIZATIONS:
Children's Trust Fund

Thomas E. Noonan

General Counsel

Department of Transitional Assistance
Address: 600 Washington Street, Boston, MA 02111
Telephone: (617) 348-8526 **Fax:** (617) 348-5108
Reports to: Commissioner Claire McIntire

PERSONAL INFORMATION:
Education: Boston College (B.A., '70); Suffolk University School of Law (J.D., '76)
Years in Current Position: 8 **Years in State Service:** 24

Bruce M. Bullen
Commissioner

Division of Medical Assistance
Address: 600 Washington Street, 5th Fl, Boston, MA 02111
Telephone: (617) 210-5690 **Fax:** (617) 210-5697
E-mail: bbullen@nt.dma.state.ma.us
Staff: Laura Basso, Administrative Assistant; Sharon Torgerson, Director of External Affairs
Reports to: Secretary William D. O'Leary

PERSONAL INFORMATION:
Born: April 15, 1947 **Place of Birth:** Boston
Marital Status: married (Marie)
Education: Williams College, (B.A. '70); Harvard University, JFK School of Government (M.P.A. '88)
Previous Employment: Department of Public Welfare/Deputy Commissioner
Years in Current Position: 5 **Years in State Service:** 24

JOB DESCRIPTION:
Responsible for the administration of the MassHealth program, a low-income health insurance program serving 700,000 members.

1999 PRIORITIES:
To implement an expansion of MassHealth to cover families with incomes below 200% of official poverty levels.

ORGANIZATIONS:
Chair, National Association of State Medicaid Directors and Vice President/Executive Committee, American Public Welfare Association.

Mark E. Reynolds
Deputy Commissioner

Division of Medical Assistance
Address: 600 Washington Street, 5th Fl, Boston, MA 02111
Telephone: (617) 210-5670 **Fax:** (617) 210-5697
Staff: Cynthia Cheek, Administrative Assistant
Reports to: Commissioner Bruce Bullen

PERSONAL INFORMATION:
Born: December 18, 1962 **Place of Birth:** Washington, D.C.
Marital Status: single
Education: Swarthmore, (B.A. '84)
Previous Employment: Exec. Office of Health and Human Services, Budget Director; Budget Bureau, Assistant Director
Years in Current Position: 3 **Years in State Service:** 10

JOB DESCRIPTION:
Chief Operating Officer of the agency. Responsible for agency goal setting and project management. Direct special high priority projects such as the health care reform expansion efforts.

1999 PRIORITIES:
Implementing the last two phases of the health care reform expansions.

Department of Mental Health

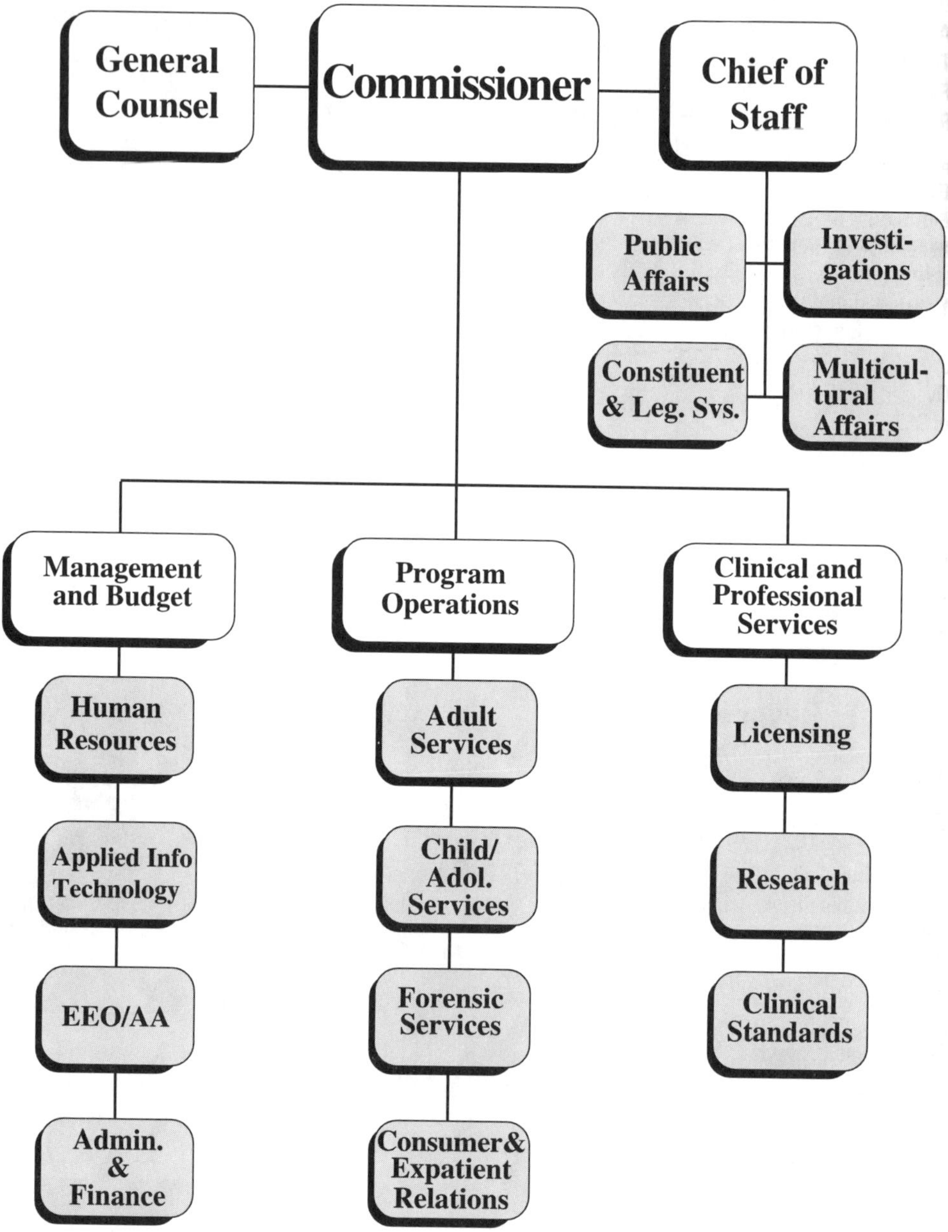

Marylou Sudders
Commissioner

Department of Mental Health
Address: 25 Staniford Street, Boston, MA 02114
Telephone: (617) 727-5500 ext. 448
Fax: (617) 727-4350 **E-mail:** marylou.sudders@state.ma.us
Reports to: Secretary William D. O'Leary

PERSONAL INFORMATION:
Born: July 22, 1954 **Place of Birth:** Ellenville, NY
Education: Boston University (A.B., Psychology, '76; M.S.W., '78)
Previous Employment: State of New Hampshire, Division of Mental Health and Developmental Services (Deputy Director)
Years in Current Position: 2 **Years in State Service:** 19

JOB DESCRIPTION:
Oversee a public mental health system that provides services to an estimated 80,000 residents on an annual budget of $537.7 million.

1999 PRIORITIES:
Direct the Department of Mental Health in a manner that instills public confidence. Manage the Department of Mental Health's resources to ensure positive clinical outcomes and cost effectiveness. Reframe the DMH regulatory authority in the new health care environment. Promote consumer rights, responsibilities, and recovery opportunities.

ORGANIZATIONS:
Academy of Certified Social Workers; National Association of Social Workers; National Association of State Mental Health Program Directors

Carolyn Schlaepfer
Deputy Commissioner of Program Operations

Department of Mental Health
Address: 25 Staniford Street, Boston, MA 02114
Telephone: (617) 727-5500 ext. 367
Fax: (617) 727-1538 **E-mail:** carolyn.schlaepfer@state.ma.us
Staff: Deborah Scott, Assistant Commissioner Forensic Mental Health Services, Joan Mikula, Assistant Commissioner Child/Adolescent Services, (tbd) Assistant Commissioner for Field Operations, 6 Area Directors.
Reports to: Secretary Marylou Sudders

PERSONAL INFORMATION:
Education: Boston College, Graduate School of Social Work (M.S.P.)
Years in Current Position: 2 **Years in State Service:** 22

JOB DESCRIPTION:
Oversees and directs the day to day operations of all programs and services provided or purchased by the Department through supervision of six Area Directors and three Assistant Commissioners. Serves as the Department's liaison with DMA for the purpose of planning, oversight and coordination of services provided by the Massachusetts Behavioral Health Partnership under the Division's Mental Health/Substance Abuse Program.

1999 PRIORITIES:
Reorganization of the programs and services of the Department, as needed, to foster greater flexibility and more appropriate utilization of inpatient resources. Coordination with DMA to implement a reasonable, high quality, integrated system of managed care for persons requiring behavioral health services.

Jeff McCue

Deputy Commissioner of Management and Budget

Department of Mental Health
Address: 25 Staniford Street, Boston, MA 02114
Telephone: (617) 727-5500 ext. 401 **Fax:** (617) 727-1538
E-mail: jeff.mccue@state.ma.us
Staff: Perry Trilling, Assistant Commissioner of Administration and Finance; Michael Coughlin, Assistant Commissioner of Human Resources; Larry Hookey, Assistant Commissioner, A.I.T.; Marilyn Carrington, Director of Affirmative Action/Equal Opportunity Employment
Reports to: Commissioner Marylou Sudders

PERSONAL INFORMATION:
Born: May 27, 1957 **Place of Birth:** Quincy
Marital Status: married **Children:** 6
Education: Merrimack College (B.A., '79); Suffolk University (M.P.A., '81)
Previous Employment: Massachusetts Department of Mental Health (Assistant Commissioner of Human Resources)
Years in Current Position: 4 **Years in State Service:** 17

JOB DESCRIPTION:
Responsible for the direction of department's budgeting, contracting, fiscal, human resource, EEO/Affirmative Action, and Information Technology.

1999 PRIORITIES:
Introduction of state-of-the-art information systems, reconstruction of DMH in-service training infrastructure, enhanced diversification of workforce.

ORGANIZATIONS:
Executive Director, The Friends of Sandy McCue.

Paul Barreira

Deputy Commissioner of Clinical and Professional Services

Department of Mental Health
Address: 25 Staniford Street, Boston, MA 02114
Telephone: (617) 727-5500 ext. 435 **Fax:** (617) 727-5622
E-mail: paul.barriera@state.ma.us
Staff: Gary Pastva, Assistant Commissioner Clinical and Professional Services, Joan Kerzner, Director of Policy Development, Michael Weeks, Director of Licensing, Robert Goldstein, Director of Data Analysis, Raymond Flannery, Jr., Director of Training
Reports to: Commissioner Marylou Sudders

PERSONAL INFORMATION:

Born: March 1, 1947 **Place of Birth:** Boston
Marital Status: married **Children:** 1
Education: Boston College (B.S. '70); Georgetown University Medical School (M.D. '74)
Previous Employment: Director, Psychiatric Residency Training Program; U-Mass Medical Center, Worcester.
Years in Current Position: 3 **Years in State Service:** 14

JOB DESCRIPTION:

The Office of Clinical and Professional Services is responsible for establishing a pro-active system of clinical accountability for the provision of effective, high quality and efficient multi-disciplinary mental health services throughout the Commonwealth. The Office is committed to carrying out this primary responsibility following the principles of Utilization Management, Quality Management Accountability and Partnership.

1999 PRIORITIES:

Integration of medical care and mental health services; the development of a plan for the implementation of a single model of care for patients suffering with dual diagnosis-mental illness and substance abuse.

Marilyn E. Berner

Chief of Staff

Department of Mental Health
Address: 25 Staniford Street, Boston, MA 02114
Telephone: (617) 727-5500 ext. 443 **Fax:** (617) 727-4350
E-mail: marilyn.berner@state.ma.us
Staff: Peter Morin, Director of Internal Affairs; John Widdison, Director of Public Affairs; Stephen Cidlevich, Director of Constituent and Legislative Affairs; Ed Wong, Director of Multicultural Affairs
Reports to: Commissioner Marylou Sudders

PERSONAL INFORMATION:

Born: November 21, 1942 **Place of Birth:** New York
Marital Status: married (Robert Belvery) **Children:** 2
Education: University of Hartford (B.A., '74); Northeastern University (J.D., '76); Simmons College of Social Work (M.S.W., '86)
Previous Employment: Private practice (psychotherapy for adults); Consultation to individuals and to public and private agencies on clinical, systems, and forensic issues; Cambridge Forensic Associates (Founder and Principal, Director of Adult Services, Central Middlesex); Director, Homeless Evaluation Unit, Massachusetts Mental Health Center, Private practice of law; Assistant Director, Legal Assistance Corp. of Central Mass.
Years in Current Position: 2 **Years in State Service:** 34

JOB DESCRIPTION:

Advise the Commissioner in managing strategic operational activities affecting the Department of Mental Health.

1999 PRIORITIES:

Develop (independently and with the Commissioner) strategies and guidelines for operation that promote the agency's mission.

ORGANIZATIONS:

National Association of Social Workers; Massachusetts Bar Association; Massachusetts Association for Psychoanalytic Psychology

Stephen M. Cidlevich

Director of Constituent and Legislative Affairs

Department of Mental Health
Address: 25 Staniford Street, Boston, MA 02114
Telephone: (617) 727-5500 ext. 302 **Fax:** (617) 727-4350
E-mail: stephen.cidlevich@state.ma.us
Reports to: Chief of Staff Marilyn Berner

PERSONAL INFORMATION:
Born: August 19, 1957 **Place of Birth:** Boston
Marital Status: married (Theresa) **Children:** 2
Education: Boston College (B.A., '79)
Previous Employment: Office of State Representative James T. Brett (Chief of Staff, '85-'96); Department of Public Welfare (Director, '81-'84)
Years in Current Position: 1 **Years in State Service:** 20

JOB DESCRIPTION:
Develop and present the Department's legislative agenda to the General Court. Monitor the progress of legislation that is of interest to the Department; meet with and educate legislators on the needs of the Department and its clients. Research and resolve requests of legislators who contact the Department on behalf of their constituents. Assist the executive staff and the Commissioner in interactions with the General Court and maintain a close relationship with legislative staff and other human service agencies. The Director also interacts with advocacy groups working on behalf of the mentally ill to ensure that lobbying efforts achieve their desired effects.

1999 PRIORITIES:
To develop a coordinated legislative approach that involves the various advocacy groups and providers in meeting the goals and mission of the Department; part of that approach will involve a proactive presence on Beacon Hill and a realistic strategy to achieve the goals of the Department.

ORGANIZATIONS:
St. Joseph Nursing Care Center, Dorchester (Member, Board of Trustees); House Council Advisory Board, Kit Clark Senior Services, Dorchester; Harbor Health Services, Inc., Dorchester (Corporate Member)

Robert P. Gittens

Commissioner

Department of Youth Services
Address: 27-43 Wormwood Street, Boston, MA 02210
Telephone: (617) 727-7575 x304 **Fax:** (617) 727-0696
Staff: Edward J. Dolan, Deputy Commissioner; Lawrence J. Feeney, General Counsel
Reports to: Secretary William D. O'Leary

PERSONAL INFORMATION:
Born: June 26, 1952
Marital Status: married **Children:** 2
Education: Northeastern University (B.A. '75; J.D. '78)
Previous Employment: First Assistant to Suffolk County DA Ralph Martin; Chairman of the MA Parole Board; Deputy Chief Legal Counsel in the Governor's Office. Served on the Boston School Committee and as Chairman.
Years in Current Position: 1

JOB DESCRIPTION:

Operate a juvenile justice system that provides for the public safety, accountability, and prevention of future criminal activities of juvenile offenders. Specifically, the Commissioner oversees a $100 million operating budget and provides secure and residential support services to more than 5,000 juveniles per year, with an average daily caseload of more than 3,000. Departmental priorities includes a) protecting the public through partnerships with the criminal justice system, law enforcement, public officials, local schools, the private sector, community organizations and families; b) promoting positive opportunities for juvenile offenders

Edward J. Dolan

Deputy Commissioner

Department of Youth Services
Address: 27-43 Wormwood Street, Boston, MA 02210
Telephone: (617) 727-7575 **Fax:** (617)727-0696
Reports to: Commissioner Robert P. Gittens

PERSONAL INFORMATION:

Born: May 16, 1953 **Place of Birth:** Chelsea
Marital Status: married **Children:** 3
Education: University of Massachusetts (B.A. '75); Syracuse University (M.P.A. '77)
Previous Employment: Chief Operating Officer, MA Half-Way Houses, Inc.; Forensic Manager, Division of Forensic Mental Health, MA Dept. of Mental Health; Executive Director, MA Parole Board.
Years in Current Position: 1 **Years in State Service:** 18

JOB DESCRIPTION:

Overall responsibility for DYS operations, which includes four areas and central office administration.

Lawrence J. Feeney

General Counsel

Department of Youth Services
Address: 27-43 Wormwood Street, Boston, MA 02210
Telephone: (617) 727-7575 **Fax:** (617) 727-0696 **E-mail:** lawrence.feeney@state.ma.us
Reports to: Commissioner Robert P. Gittens

PERSONAL INFORMATION:

Born: November 18, 1944 **Place of Birth:** Boston
Marital Status: married (Maureen) **Children:** 2
Education: Boston College (B.A. '66); Suffolk University Law School (J.D. '73)
Previous Employment: Massachusetts Dept. of Youth Services, Asst. Regional Director; Assistant Commissioner; Director of Legal Services
Years in Current Position: 1 **Years in State Service:** 25

JOB DESCRIPTION:

Overall responsibility for department's legal operations, including litigation, hearings, policy review, and investigations.

ORGANIZATIONS:

Massachusetts Bar Association; Carney Hospital Foundation

Glenn E. Daly

Director of Public Affairs

Department of Youth Services
Address: 27-43 Wormwood Street, Boston, MA 02210
Telephone: (617) 727-7575 **Fax:** (617) 727-0696
Reports to: Commissioner Robert P. Gittens

PERSONAL INFORMATION:
Born: July 6, 1960 **Place of Birth:** Lawrence
Marital Status: married **Children:** 1
Education: University of Massachusetts (B.S. '83)
Previous Experience: Department of Social Services (Asst. Dir. of Public Affairs, Foster Care Review Unit, Social Worker); Westside Food Bank (Program Director)
Years in Current Position: 3 **Years in State Service:** 12

JOB DESCRIPTION:
Receive and respond to all media inquiries. Oversee response to all requests for public information. Coordinate agency events, develop all agency publications.

Ardith A. Wieworka

Commissioner

Office of Child Care Services (formerly the Office for Children)
Address: One Ashburton Place, 11th Floor, Boston, MA 02108
Telephone: (617) 626-2000 **Fax:** (617) 626-2028
E-mail: AWieworka@state.ma.us
Staff: Jessica Hanley, Administrative Assistant
Reports to: Secretary William D. O'Leary

PERSONAL INFORMATION:
Education: Northeastern University School of Law (J.D.); State University of New York, Albany (B.A.)
Previous Employment: Department of Transitional Assistance (First Deputy General Counsel, Legal Division, '88-'96); State Ethics Commission (Staff Counsel, Legal Division, '86-'88); Goodwin, Procter & Hoar (Associate, Litigation Department, '84-'86)
Years in Current Position: 2 **Years in State Service:** 12

JOB DESCRIPTION:
The Office of Child Care Services (OCCS), formerly the Office for Children, seeks to advance high quality child care for children and families. The office has several main areas of responsibility in pursuit of this goal. They are to: license, regulate and monitor child care facilities and residential and detention programs for children and youth; refer parents to appropriate child care; train child care workers through support of the statewide Child Care Resource and Referral Network; purchase subsidized child care for eligible low income families, authorized welfare to work participants, families moving off of welfare, teen parents and Department of Social Services family support consumers; and, support child abuse prevention programs through budgetary support of The Children's Trust Fund. Programs under the jurisdiction of OCCS include private nursery schools, private kindergartens, day care centers,

day care homes, residential facilities for troubled children as well as foster care and adoption placement agencies.

1999 PRIORITIES:

Create an integrated system that ensures the seamless delivery of quality, accessible and affordable child care services for children birth through school age and their families. Maximize resources through public-private partnerships and other collaborations to encourage further investment in the expansion of the Commonwealth's child care services. Administer consistent procurement and payment policies and procedures for the purchasing of child care services through vouchers and contracts. Ensure quality child care through both consumer education and professional development and training opportunities for child care providers. Coordinate child care services with the Department of Education and other state agencies involved in early care and education.

Claire McDonough

Communications Director

Office for Refugees and Immigrants
Address: 18 Tremont Street, Suite 600, Boston, MA 02108
Telephone: (617) 727-7888 **Fax:** (617) 727-1822
Staff: Nina Nguyen, Information Officer; Thelma Dixon, Civil Rights Officer
Reports to: Acting Director Nam Van Pham
Years in Current Position: 11 **Years in State Service:** 18

PERSONAL INFORMATION:

Born: Feb. 15, 1933 **Place of Birth:** Boston
Education: Emmanuel College (B.A., English, '54)
Previous Employment: Governor's Correspondence Office (Deputy Director); Department of Employment Services (Policy Manager)

JOB DESCRIPTION:

Develop and implement public information and education campaigns; serve as liaison to Governor's Advisory Council; respond to requests for information from public and media; organize special events, public hearings and public presentations.

1999 JOB PRIORITIES:

Increased outreach to immigrants and refugees regarding citizenship eligibility

Health Care Finance & Policy

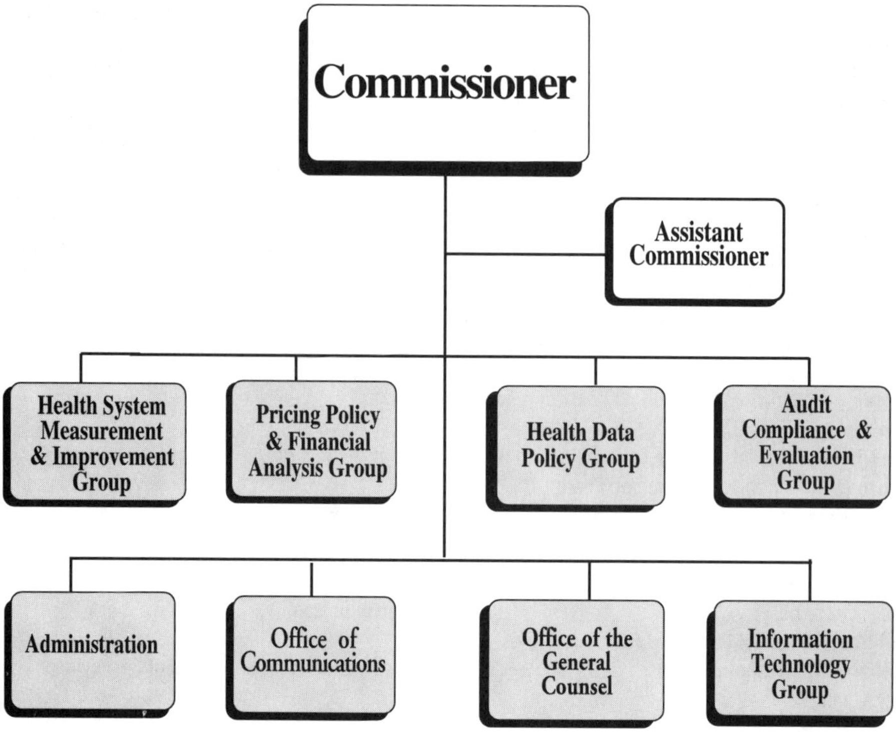
Commissioner
Assistant Commissioner
Health System Measurement & Improvement Group
Pricing Policy & Financial Analysis Group
Health Data Policy Group
Audit Compliance & Evaluation Group
Administration
Office of Communications
Office of the General Counsel
Information Technology Group

Louis I. Freedman

Acting Commissioner

Division of Health Care Finance and Policy
Address: 2 Boylston Street, Boston, MA 02116
Telephone: (617) 988-3120 **E-mail:** lfreedman@state.ma.us
Fax: (617)727-7662
Staff: Linda M. Carroll, Administrative Assistant
Reports to: Secretary William O'Leary

PERSONAL INFORMATION:
Born: October 18, 1940 **Place of Birth:** Ft. Bragg, NC
Marital Status: married (Jane) **Children:** 2
Education: Centre College of Kentucky (B.A., '62); University of Kentucky (M.S.P.H., '65); Columbia University (M.S.H.A., '68)
Previous Employment: Bureau of Parent, Child and Adolescent Health, Department of Public Health (Director of Operations); Services for Children with Special Health Care Needs, Massachusetts Public Health
Years in Current Position: 6 **Years in State Service:** 25

ORGANIZATIONS:
Town of Plymouth Capital Outlay Committee; National Association of Health Data Organizations

Elmer C. Bartels

Commissioner

Rehabilitation Commission
Address: Fort Point Place, 27-43 Wormwood Street, Boston, MA 02210
Telephone: (617) 204-3600 **Fax:** (617) 727-1354
E-mail: elmer.bartels@mrc.state.ma.us
Staff: Warren McManus, Deputy Commissioner VR; John Chappell, Deputy Commissioner, IL; Kasper Goshgarian, Deputy Commissioner, DDS; Janna Jacobs, Chief of Staff
Reports to: Secretary William D. O'Leary

PERSONAL INFORMATION:
Born: June 10, 1938 **Place of Birth:** Boston
Marital Status: married (Mary) **Children:** 2

Education: Colby College (B.S., '62); Tufts University (M.S., '64)
Previous Employment: Honeywell Information Systems ('68-'77)
Years in Current Position: 22 **Years in State Service:** 22

JOB DESCRIPTION:
As Commissioner of the Massachusetts Rehabilitation Commission I am responsible for a $100 million budget and 950 staff focussed on services for individuals with severe disabilities.

1999 PRIORITIES:

Provide quality vocational rehabilitation, Independent Living, and Disability Determination services to more than 150,000 Massachusetts citizens with disabilities.

ORGANIZATIONS:

Corporation for Business Work and Learning; Wang Center for the Performing Arts, (Board Member); Massachusetts Health Council (Board Member); American Red Cross of Mass. (Board Member)

Janna Z. Jacobs

Chief of Staff

Massachusetts Rehabilitation Commission
Address: Fort Point Place, 27-43 Wormwood Street, Boston, MA 02210
Telephone: (617) 204-3608 **Fax:** (617) 727-1354
E-mail: Janna.Jacobs@mrc.state.ma.us
Reports to: Commissioner Elmer C. Bartels

PERSONAL INFORMATION:

Date of Birth: October 18, 1955 **Place of Birth:** Atlanta, GA
Marital Status: single
Education: Brandeis University (B.A. '77); Arkansas State University (M.R.C. '82)
Previous Employment: Consultant, 1994-96 National Spinal Cord Injury Association, Executive Director 1987-94
Years in Current Position: 2 **Years in State Service:** 2

JOB DESCRIPTION:

Oversight, human resources administration and coordination of the activities of MRC's three divisions - DDS, VR and IL on behalf of the Commissioner.

Richard F. Arcangeli

Acting General Counsel

Rehabilitation Commission
Address: Fort Point Place, 27-43 Wormwood Street, Boston, MA 02210
Telephone: (617) 204-3616 **Fax:** (617) 727-1354
Reports to: Commissioner Elmer C. Bartels

PERSONAL INFORMATION:

Education: Brandeis University (B.A.); Suffolk University Law School (J.D., '85)
Previous Employment: Massachusetts Rehabilitation Commission (Deputy General Counsel)
Years in Current Position: 3 **Years in State Service:** 18

JOB DESCRIPTION:

Responsible for legal policy and support for the Massachusetts Rehabilitation Commission.

Kasper M. Goshgarian

Deputy Commissioner /Disability Determination

Rehabilitation Commission
Address: 110 Chauncy Street, Boston, MA 02111
Telephone: (617) 654-7400 **Fax:** (617) 654-7859
Reports to: Commissioner Elmer C. Bartels

PERSONAL INFORMATION:
Education: Northeastern University (B.A., '72); Northeastern University (M.Ed., '74); Suffolk University (M.B.A., '84)
Years in Current Position: 15 **Years in State Service:** 27

JOB DESCRIPTION:
Responsible for the management and direction of the Disability Determination Services division. Provide disability determination decisions for individuals applying for Social Security Disability Insurance (SSDI) and/or Supplemental Security Income (SSI) benefits.

John A. Chappell, Jr.

Deputy Commissioner, Independent Living

Rehabilitation Commission
Address: Fort Point Place, 27-43 Wormwood Street, Boston, MA 02210
Telephone: (617) 204-3850 **Fax:** (617) 727-1354 **E-mail:** John_Chappell@Prodigy.net
Reports to: Commissioner Elmer C. Bartels

PERSONAL INFORMATION:
Education: Florida Institute of Technology (B.S., Electronic Engineering, '70)
Years in Current Position: 12 **Years in State Service:** 13

JOB DESCRIPTION:
Responsible for directing the Division for Independent Living and Consumer Involvement, which includes Statewide Head Injury Program; Homecare Services Program; Work Personal Care Assistance Program; Consumer Involvement Program; Independent Living Center/Services Program; Turning 22 Program; Protective Services Program; Housing/ Supported Living Program; and Housing Registry.

William D. Thompson

Commandant

Chelsea Soldiers' Home
Address: 91 Crest Avenue, Chelsea, MA 02150
Telephone: (617) 884-5660 **Fax:** (617) 884-1162
Staff: Linda Sullivan, Margy Deroche, Assistants
Reports to: Secretary William O'Leary

PERSONAL INFORMATION:
Born: July 16, 1945 **Place of Birth:** Boston
Marital Status: married (Patricia) **Children:** 2

Education: University of Pennsylvania (B.A., '67); George Washington University (M.H.A., '73)
Previous Employment: Rutland Heights Hospital (Executive Director, '83-'88); Huntington General Hospital (Executive Director, '78-'83)
Years in Current Position: 11 **Years in State Service:** 16

JOB DESCRIPTION:
To serve as chief administrative officer of the Chelsea Soldiers' Home, Quigley Hospital; responsible for planning, directing, and coordinating all services and activities at the Home, including the full supervision of a large number of medical and non-medical employees; responsible for preparing the budget and controlling expenditures, formulating policy, and representing the Home at legislative hearings and various forums.

1999 PRIORITIES:
Renovation of the nursing units in the Quigley Memorial Hospital and expansion of clinical data processing capabilities.

ORGANIZATIONS:
Scituate Federal Savings Bank (Board of Directors); National Association of State Veterans' Homes; Massachusetts State Health Care Professionals Dental Fund (Vice-Chair); Bunker Hill Community College Foundation

Paul A. Morin

Superintendent

Soldiers' Home in Holyoke
Address: 110 Cherry Street, Holyoke, MA 01040
Telephone: (413) 532-9475 **Fax:** (413) 538-7968
Staff: Richard J. Palazzi, Deputy Superintendent; Joanne M. Kovalski, Administrative Assistant.
Reports to: Secretary William D. O'Leary

PERSONAL INFORMATION:
Born: October 14, 1952 **Place of Birth:** Springfield
Marital Status: single **Children:** 4
Eduction: Springfield Technical Community College
Previous Employment: Soldiers' Home in Holyoke, Assistant Superintendent of Operations; Department of Welfare, Department of Veterans Services.
Years in Current Position: new **Years in State Service:** 10

JOB DESCRIPTION:
To serve as chief executive officer and administrator of a 3311-bed facility. The superintendent administers a comprehensive outpatient clinic that provides 16,000 outpatient visits annually. Through the services of 20 medical specialists the superintendent is responsible for all non-service matters for veterans in the four western counties and a large portion of Worcester County. The superintendent is responsible for 317 employees and is totally responsible for a $13 million budget.

1999 PRIORITIES:
Maintain quality care for our Massachusetts veterans.

ORGANIZATIONS:
American Legion; Knights of Columbus, Regional Employment Board.

Department of Social Services

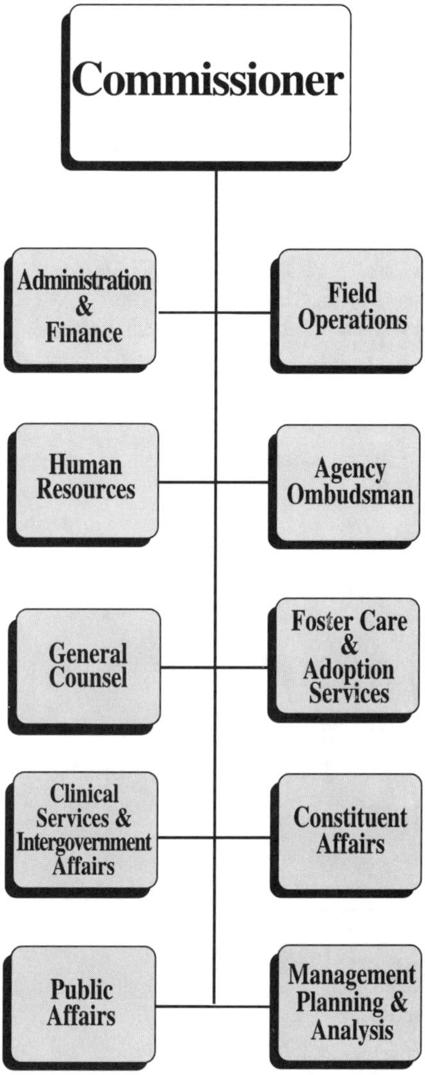

Linda K. Carlisle

Commissioner

Department of Social Services
Address: 24 Farnsworth Street, Boston, MA 02210
Telephone: (617)748-2325
Fax: (617) 439-4482 **E-mail:** Linda.Carlisle@state.ma.us
Reports to: Secretary William O'Leary

PERSONAL INFORMATION:

Born: February 11, 1954 **Place of Birth:** Lewiston, ID
Marital Status: married
Education: Washington State University (B.S., Political Science, '76); Columbia University (M.A., '81)
Previous Employment: New York City Welfare Administration/HRA (Assistant Deputy Commissioner, Policy and Planning); Columbia University (Adjunct Professor); Institute of Public Administration, NY (Senior Staff and Director, Management Programs)
Years in Current Position: 6 **Years in State Service:** 6

JOB DESCRIPTION:

Executive responsibility for overall strategic planning, policy setting and organizational leadership for the Commonwealth's Child Welfare Agency.

1999 PRIORITIES:

Improved foster care and residential service system, adoption, multidisciplinary assessments, case practice/quality assurance, worker safety, and caseload reduction.

ORGANIZATIONS:

Green Chimney's Children's Services (Board of Directors); Columbia University School of Public and International Affairs (Alumni Advisory Committee)

Margaret E. Connors

Agency Ombudsman

Department of Social Services
Address: 24 Farnsworth Street, Boston, MA 02210
Telephone: (617) 748-2360 **Fax:** (617) 439-4482
Staff: Richard Manning, David Coughlin, Fran Sceppa, Bernice Rodriguez
Reports to: Commissioner Linda K. Carlisle

PERSONAL INFORMATION:

Born: September 13, 1951 **Place of Birth:** Winchester, MA
Education: Emmanuel College (B.A.,, '73); Suffolk University (M.P.A., '80); Emmanuel College (M.A. Pastoral Ministry, '90; Certificate in Pastoral Counseling, '93)
Previous Employment: Massachusetts Commission for the Blind (Public Information Officer); Massachusetts Rehabilitation Commission (Administrative Assistant to Commissioner)
Years in State Service: 24

JOB DESCRIPTION:

Responsibilities include mediating and resolving questions and complaints of clients, foster and adoptive parents, and advocates concerning policies, programs, and services of the agency.

John T. Farley III

Deputy Commissioner for Field Operations

Department of Social Services
Address: 24 Farnsworth Street, Boston, MA 02210
Telephone: (617) 748-2348 **Fax:** (617) 946-2707
Staff: Beryl Domingo, Director of Field Support; Joan Louden-Black, Assistant Commissioner; Michael MacCormack, Deputy Interstate Compact Administrator
Reports to: Commissioner Linda K. Carlisle

PERSONAL INFORMATION:

Born: July 8, 1946 **Place of Birth:** New York, NY
Marital Status: married (Kathleen) **Children:** 2
Education: St. John's University (B.A., '68); Fordham University (M.S.W., '92)
Previous Employment: NYC Child Welfare Administration (Brooklyn Borough Director, Coordinator of Substance Abuse Services, Director of Court Services)
Years in Current Position: 5.5 **Years in State Service:** 5.5

JOB DESCRIPTION:

Responsibility for daily operations; input/consultation on full agency planning and budgeting for 6 regional and 28 area offices.

ORGANIZATIONS:

N.A.S.W.

Susan I. Pederzoli

Clinical Services and Intergovernmental Affairs

Department of Social Services
Address: 24 Farnsworth Street, Boston, MA 02210
Telephone: (617) 748-2257 **Fax:** (617) 261-7437
Staff: Kate May, Director of Foster Care Review; Jean Wilson, Director of Case Investigations; Scott Chapman, Director of Special Investigations; Mary Gambon, Director of Adoption Support Services; Liz Skinner-Reilly, Assistant Director of Community and Intergovernmental Affairs; Kathy Bettes, Medicaid/Managed Care Specialist
Reports to: Deputy Commissioner John Farley III

PERSONAL INFORMATION:

Born: December 31, 1949 **Place of Birth:** Milford
Education: Regis College (B.A., '71); Boston College School of Social Work (M.S.W., '78); Licensed Independent Clinical Social Worker
Previous Employment: DSS (Director of Professional Standards, Office of Policy and Programs; Regional Program Manager, Northeast; Area Program Manager, Coastal Office; Regional Adoption/Family Resource Manager, Northeast)
Years in Current Position: 4 **Years in State Service:** 26

JOB DESCRIPTION:

Management and supervisory responsibility for agency's Foster Care Review System, Adoption Support and Case Investigation Units, as well as special investigations in intergovernmental and interagency cases.

ORGANIZATIONS:
National Association of Social Workers; Newton Community Service Centers, Inc. (Advisory Board); Young Parents Program

Lorraine Carli
Director of Public Affairs

Department of Social Services
Address: 24 Farnsworth Street, Boston, MA 02210
Telephone: (617) 748-2367 **Fax:** (617) 261-7435
Reports to: Commissioner Linda K. Carlisle

PERSONAL INFORMATION:
Education: Northeastern University (B.A., Journalism, '84); University of Massachusetts at Boston (M.Ed, '88)
Previous Employment: Department of Social Services (Assistant Director of Public Affairs); Massachusetts Parole Board (Public Information Officer); Department of Correction (Assistant Public Information Officer)
Years in Current Position: 10 **Years in State Service:** 15

JOB DESCRIPTION:
Direct all media and public affairs activities for the agency. Chief spokesperson, oversee all publications, manage all public education campaigns including foster and adoptive parent recruitment, child abuse prevention and child abuse reporting.

Michael D. Donovan
Director of Constituent Affairs

Department of Social Services
Address: 24 Farnsworth Street, Boston, MA 02210
Telephone: (617) 748-2329 **Fax:** (617) 439-4482
Staff: Martin R. Grossman, Human Resource Planner
Reports to: Commissioner Linda K. Carlisle

PERSONAL INFORMATION:
Education: Boston College (B.S., '66); Lyndon B. Johnson School of Public Affairs, University of Texas (M.A., Public Affairs, '73)
Previous Employment: Boston Rent Equity Board (Administrator); Boston Housing Inspection Department (Commissioner); Boston Police Department (Executive Assistant)
Years in Current Position: 11 **Years in State Service:** 11

JOB DESCRIPTION:
Oversee the Department of Social Services' Legislative Agenda, advise the Commissioner on legislative matters, provide assistance to legislators regarding DSS issues and requests from constituents.

Public Safety

The Executive Office of Public Safety is responsible for the oversight of a number of boards and agencies concerned with the physical safety of Massachusetts citizens. The secretariat is involved primarily with law enforcement, corrections, public protection, and safety monitoring. The agencies that fall under its aegis serve support and enforcement functions. These agencies are as follows:

- *Department of State Police*
- *Department of Public Safety*
- *Department of Correction*
- *Criminal Justice Training Council*
- *Committee on Criminal Justice*
- *Criminal History Systems Board*
- *Massachusetts Emergency Management Agency*
- *State Medical Examiner*
- *Registry of Motor Vehicles*
- *Statewide Emergency Telecommunications Board*
- *Governor's Alliance Against Drugs*
- *Massachusetts Parole Board*
- *Military Division (Massachusetts National Guard)*
- *Governor's Highway Safety Bureau*
- *Merit Rating Board*
- *Department of Fire Services*
- *Automobile Theft Strike Force*
- *Police Accreditation Commission*

Department of State Police

Chapter 412 of the Acts of 1991 consolidated the former divisions of the State Police, Registry of Motor Vehicles Police, Metropolitan Police, and Capitol Police into a single Department of State Police comprising over 2,400 sworn police officers. The new department, headquartered in Framingham, is responsible for extensive patrol functions that range from a major international airport to rural communities. It provides patrol coverage to the state highway system, state properties, and rural areas where such services cannot be provided at the local level. The department is organized into the following divisions:

- *Division of Support Services*
- *Bureau of Administrative Services*
- *Bureau of Technical Services*
- *Division of Field Services*
- *Bureau of Eastern Field Services*
- *Bureau of Western Field Services*
- *Division of Investigations and Intelligence*
- *Bureau of Investigative Services–Eastern Field*
- *Bureau of Investigative Services–Western Field*
- *Division of Special Police*
- *Bureau of Metropolitan Operations Services*
- *Bureau of Motor Vehicle Enforcement*
- *Bureau of Facility Security*
- *Office of the Superintendent*
- *Bureau of Department Operations*

Department of Public Safety

The Department of Public Safety oversees a number of divisions and boards responsible for protection of lives and property within the Commonwealth. The functional units that fall under the jurisdiction of the department are as follows:

Major Statutory Functions:

- *Bureau of Special Investigations*
- *Division of Inspections*
- *Special Licensing Section*
- *Administrative Services Section*

Boards and Commissions:

- *State Boxing Commission*
- *Board of Elevator Examiners*
- *Board of Elevator Appeals*
- *Bureau of Pipe-Fitters and Refrigeration Technicians*
- *Board of Elevator Regulation*
- *Board of Boiler Rules*

Department of Correction

The Department of Correction is responsible for the oversight and custody of the over 19,000 criminal and civil offenders committed to the state correctional system. It oversees the state's 21 correctional facilities, which range from maximum to pre-release security levels. In addressing its goal of public protection, the department isolates offenders from society while providing educational, vocational, recreational, and psychiatric services in anticipation of their eventual release and reintegration.

Criminal Justice Training Council

The Criminal Justice Training Council, which is made up of leading state officials in the realm of criminal justice, approves training curricula for related agencies, including local police departments and correctional facilities. The council also offers programs on sensitive public safety programs such as rape investigation, suicide prevention, and hate crimes.

Committee on Criminal Justice

The Committee on Criminal Justice advises the Governor on law enforcement policy. It is the state planning agency responsible for obtaining and administering assistance grants from the Federal Bureau of Justice Administration. Such grants fund five main areas of law enforcement: juvenile justice, narcotics control, statistical analysis, domestic violence, and in-depth research.

Criminal History Systems Board

The Criminal History Systems Board maintains an extensive database containing record information on every convicted adult in the Commonwealth. This information is available on-line to police departments throughout the state. Additionally, the board can interface with a national criminal record service and the Registry of Motor Vehicles computer network.

Massachusetts Emergency Management Agency

The Massachusetts Emergency Management Agency is responsible for planning and administering state response to emergencies in order to preserve lives and property of citizens. The Agency coordinates the activities of all federal, state, and local organizations engaged in emergency preparedness, response, and hazard mitigation within the Commonwealth. It conducts local assistance programs and trains emergency management personnel. Its aim is to prepare citizens to cope with man-made and natural disasters such as floods, hurricanes, nuclear accidents, and hazardous waste spills.

Sate Medical Examiner

The State Medical Examiner is responsible for determining the cause and manner of death in all suspected homicides, suicides, accidents, and unexpected natural deaths. The office oversees the activities of all local and state medical examiners and maintains records of all medical investigations and autopsies.

Registry of Motor Vehicles

The Massachusetts RMV, while largely a driver-licensing and motor vehicle registration and titling regulatory agency, provides many additional services. These include maintenance of accurate and secure information relating to individual identification, driver records and vehicles, suspension of driving privileges for unsafe drivers and vehicles, education outreach to youth and senior populations, licensing and certification of vehicle inspection stations, school buses and other school pupil vehicles, certification of driving schools and regulation of driver retraining programs monitoring of registrations for compliance with mandatory motor vehicle liability insurance requirements, motor registration, generation of excise tax bills, assistance with the collection of overdue excise tax, parking tickets, child support payments, fees and the resolution of outstanding warrants, and the collection of sales tax.

Statewide Emergency Telecommunications Board

The Statewide Emergency Telecommunications Board is responsible for development and implementation of enhanced 911 statewide emergency telephone systems. Enhanced 911 will automatically route emergency calls to the nearest police station, order incoming calls according to emergency priority, and provide emergency response personnel with automatic caller number and location identification. The Board assists local government with development of 911 municipal plans and coordinates statewide implementation.

Governor's Alliance Against Drugs

The Governor's Alliance Against Drugs sets statewide policy on drug prevention education and intervention programs. The Alliance advises the Governor on demand reduction prevention methods for the state.

Massachusetts Parole Board

The State Parole Board is responsible for monitoring the statutorily established parole eligibility system. It monitors offenders' eligibility dates, prepares case files for consideration, and supervises release through its regional offices. It also acts as an advisory board for the Governor with respect to pardon applications.

Military Division

The Military Division is the state militia organized for state and national defense and other emergencies. It consists of the Massachusetts National Guard and Air National Guard. The Military Division also participates in drug enforcement activities, disaster assistance, infrastructure repair, and community outreach. Additionally, the Military Division maintains a state facility that houses records of all state residents who have served in armed conflict.

Automobile Theft Strike Force

The Automobile Theft Strike Force conducts investigations to combat the theft of automobiles and parts and to recover stolen vehicles.

Department of Fire Services

The Department of Fire Services' primary mission and responsibility is to preserve life and property from fire, explosion, electrical and related hazards through public education, investigation, regulation, law enforcement, and technical assistance to fire departments, the public, and regulated trades and industries.

Motor Vehicle Insurance Merit Rating Board

The Motor Vehicle Insurance Merit Rating Board is the statistical agency responsible for administering the Insurance Commissioner's Safe Driving Plan. The board maintains a database of motor vehicle violations and accident claim records. This information is disseminated to insurance carriers who utilize it to adjust automobile insurance premiums based on the driving record of the operator. The board is the sole repository for automobile citations issued by the state.

Police Accreditation Commission

On October 17, 1996, an Executive Order of the Governor authorized the Secretary of Public Safety to establish a nine-member commission to oversee a statewide law enforcement accreditation program. Accreditation involves an evaluation of an agency's performance against standards established by the commission for the law enforcement profession. The Commission represents the law enforcement community, governmental officials and the general public. Agencies demonstrating compliance with law enforcement standards during its on-site assessment are awarded accreditation for a three-year period. Participation in the program is voluntary.

Executive Office of Public Safety

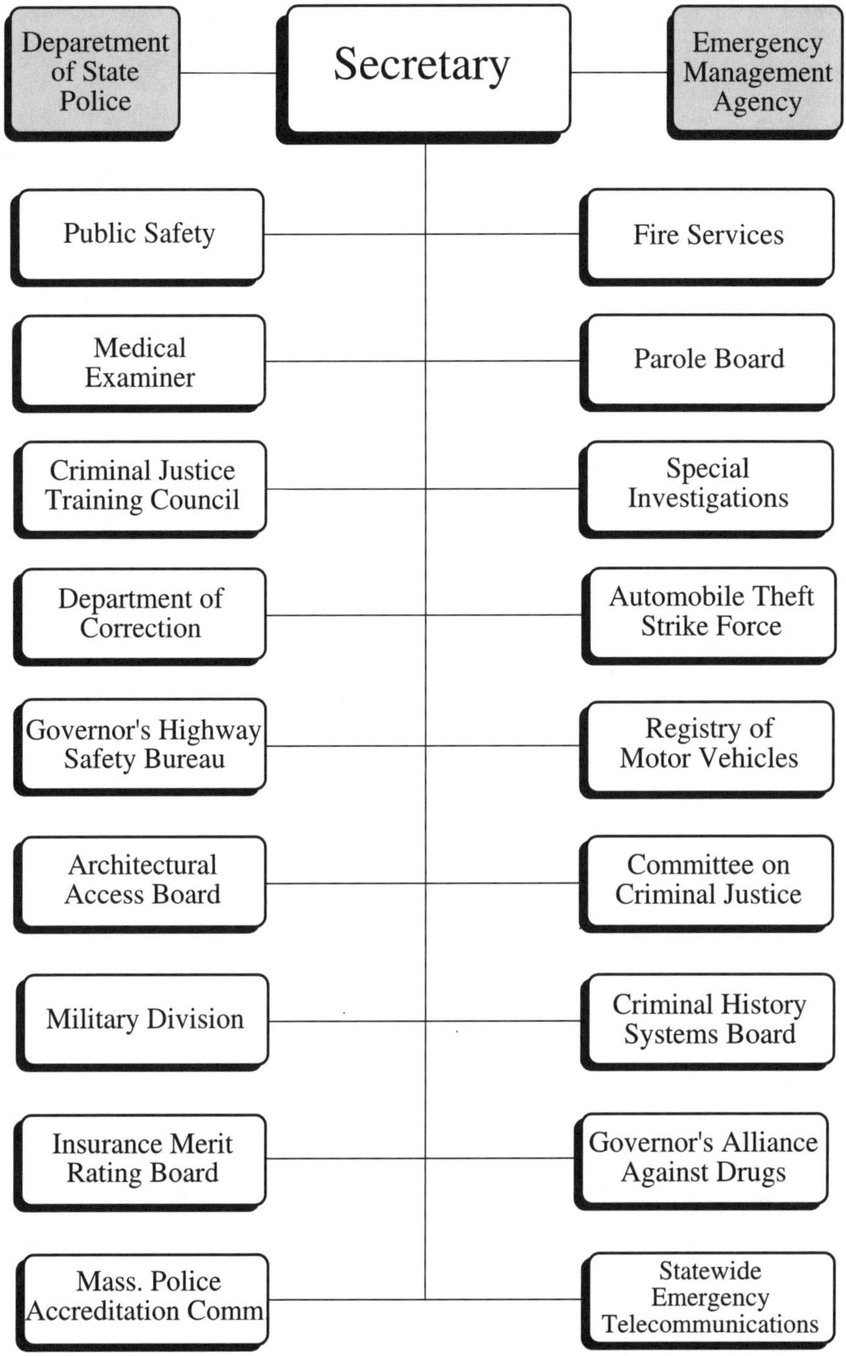
Deparetment of State Police
Secretary
Emergency Management Agency
Public Safety
Fire Services
Medical Examiner
Parole Board
Criminal Justice Training Council
Special Investigations
Department of Correction
Automobile Theft Strike Force
Governor's Highway Safety Bureau
Registry of Motor Vehicles
Architectural Access Board
Committee on Criminal Justice
Military Division
Criminal History Systems Board
Insurance Merit Rating Board
Governor's Alliance Against Drugs
Mass. Police Accreditation Comm
Statewide Emergency Telecommunications

Secretary	**Jane Perlov**	(617) 727-7775
Undersecretary	**Richard Grelotti**	727-7775
Undersecretary	**Robert E. Hayden, Jr.**	727-7775
Chief of Staff	**Kimberly Mahoney**	727-7775
General Counsel	**Susan Prosnitz**	727-7775
Director of Communications	**Charles E. McDonald**	727-7775

ARCHITECTURAL ACCESS BOARD

Executive Director	**Deborah Ryan**	727-0660

BUREAU OF SPECIAL INVESTIGATIONS

Director	**vacant**	727-6950

OFFICE OF THE CHIEF MEDICAL EXAMINER

Chief Medical Examiner	**Richard Evans, M.D.**	267-6767

COMMITTEE ON CRIMINAL JUSTICE

Executive Director	**Michael J. O'Toole**	727-6300

CRIMINAL HISTORY SYSTEMS BOARD

Executive Director	**Maureen Chew**	660-4600

DEPARTMENT OF CORRECTION

Commissioner	**Michael T. Maloney**	727-3300
Deputy Commissioner	**Kathleen M. Dennehy**	727-3300
Chief of Staff	**Ernest Vandergriff**	727-8612
General Counsel	**Nancy Ankers White**	727-3300

Assistant Deputy Commissioners:

Bridgewater Complex Administration	**Ronald Duval**	727-0417
Community Correction	**Timothy F. App**	727-9409
Secure Facilities	**James R. Bender**	727-7524
Asso. Comm./Administration	**vacant**	727-3300

DEPARTMENT OF PUBLIC SAFETY

Commissioner	**vacant**	727-3200
Deputy Commissioner	**Joseph S. Lalli**	727-3200
Chief of Inspections	**Thomas Rogers**	727-3200

DEPARTMENT OF STATE POLICE

Superintendent	**Col. Reed V. Hillman**	(508) 820-2350
Deputy Superintendent	**Lt. Col. Glenn B. Anderson**	(508) 820-2638
Assistant Superintendent, Standards and Training	**Lt. Col. Ronald J. Guillmette**	(508) 820-2333
Division Commanders:		
Field Services	**Lt. Col. John DiFava**	(508) 820-2344
Investigative Services	**Lt. Col. Paul J. Regan**	(508) 820-2312
Administrative Services	**Michael J. Byrne**	(508) 820-2355

EMERGENCY MANAGEMENT AGENCY

Director	**Peter F. LaPorte**	(508) 820-2010
Chief of Operations	**Jerome F. Meister**	(508) 820-2016
Chief of Staff	**Katy Bellemare**	(508) 820-2014
Deputy Director	**Quirino M. Iannazzo**	(508) 820-2011
Pyblic Information Officer	**Douglas Cope**	(508) 820-2010

STATEWIDE EMERGENCY TELECOMMUNICATIONS BOARD

Acting Director	**Robert H. Watkinson**	(781)944-9113

GOVERNOR'S ALLIANCE AGAINST DRUGS

Executive Director	**Michael Mather**	727-0786

GOVERNOR'S HIGHWAY SAFETY BUREAU

Executive Director	**Nancy J. Luther**	727-5073

CRIMINAL JUSTICE TRAINING COUNCIL

Executive Director	**Kevin Harrington**	727-7827

DEPARTMENT OF FIRE SERVICES

Fire Marshal	**Stephen D. Coan**	(978)567-3100
Deputy Fire Marshal	**Thomas P. Leonard**	(978)567-3100

MERIT RATING BOARD

Director	**Mary Ann Mulhall**	(617)267-3636

MILITARY DIVISION

Adjutant General	**Major Gen. Raymond A. Vezina**	(508)233-6552

PAROLE BOARD

Chair	**Sheila A. Hubbard**	(617)727-3271
Executive Director	**Natalie R. Hardy**	727-3271
Chief Legal Counsel	**M. Yvonne Gonzalez**	727-3271
Directors:		
Field Service	**Timothy A. Zadai**	727-3271
Institutional Services	**David McGrath**	727-3271
Human Resources and Staff Development	**Kathleen G. Skerry**	727-3271
Hearings and Revocations	**M. Noreen Murphy**	727-3271
Special Operations	**Donald E. LaFratta**	727-3271

POLICE ACCREDITATION COMMISSION

Executive Director	**Donna Taylor Mooers**	(781)942-4801

REGISTRY OF MOTOR VEHICLES

Registrar	**Richard D. Lyons**	(617)351-9916
Chief of Staff	**Gary M. Coon**	351-9916
Chief Financial Officer	**Mary Ellen Kelley**	351-9903
Chief Deputy Registrar	**Robert P. McDonnell**	351-9981
Deputy Registrar/Information Services	**Larry R. McConnell**	351-9983
Deputy Registrar/Vehicle Services	**Linda F. Kelly**	351-2700
Chief Legal Counsel	**Robert Horack**	351-9951
Deputy Registrar/Customer Service	**Ralph Rooney**	351-2700
Director of Human Resources	**Donna Bonaparte**	351-9919
Director of Public Relations	**Donna Rheaume**	351-9924
Director of Governmental Affairs	**Thomas Bonarrigo**	351-9956

Jane Perlov

Secretary

Executive Office of Public Safety
Address: One Ashburton Place, Rm 2133, Boston, MA 02108
Telephone: (617) 727-7775 **Fax:** (617) 727-0535
E-mail: Jane.Perlov@EPS.state.ma.us
Staff: Kimberly Mahoney, Chief of Staff; Ronnie Drimer, Administrative Assistant
Reports to: Governor A. Paul Cellucci

PERSONAL INFORMATION:
Marital Status: married (Bob)
Education: John Jay College, New York University, Columbia University
Previous Employment: New York Police Department, Deputy Chief Commanding officer, Detective Borough Queens
Years in Current Position: new **Years in State Service:** new

JOB DESCRIPTION:
Policy management and fiscal oversight of 22 agencies, boards and commissions. Agencies range from the Department of Correction to the Registry of Motor Vehicles and State Police agencies.

ORGANIZATIONS:
President, National Emergency Management Association, Rotary, Massachusetts Highway Association

Robert E. Hayden, Jr.

Undersecretary

Executive Office of Public Safety
Address: One Ashburton Place, Rm 2133, Boston, MA 02108
Telephone: (617) 727-7775 **Fax:** (617) 727-0535
E-mail: Robert.Hayden@state.ma.us
Reports to: Secretary Jane Perlov

PERSONAL INFORMATION:
Born: April 8, 1942 **Place of Birth:** Boston
Marital Status: married (Katy) **Children:** 4
Education: Suffolk University (B.S. '64)
Previous Employment: Chief of Police, Lawrence Police Dept., Deputy Superintendent of Boston Police Department.
Years in Current Position: 1 **Years in State Service:** 1

JOB DESCRIPTION:
Oversee Dept. of Correction, State Police, Parole Board, Architectural Access Board, County Corrections, Criminal Justice Training Council, E-911, Police Accreditation Commission.

Charles E. McDonald

Director of Communications

Executive Office of Public Safety
Address: One Ashburton Place, Suite 2133, Boston, MA 02108
Telephone: (617) 727-7775 ext. 507 **Fax:** (617) 727-4764
E-mail: cemcdonald@state.ma.us
Reports to: Secretary Jane Perlov

PERSONAL INFORMATION:
Born: May 27, 1949 **Place of Birth:** Winthrop
Marital Status: married (Kathleen Donovan) **Children:** 1
Education: Boston University, College of Communications (B.S., Journalism, '71)
Previous Employment: *Daily Evening Item*, State House Reporter ('83-'91)
Years in Current Position: 7 **Years in State Service:** 7

JOB DESCRIPTION:
Develop, supervise and coordinate all public information, including media relations for all agencies within the Secretariat of Public Safety, including the Department of Correction, State Police, Parole Board, Registry of Motor Vehicles, National Guard, Massachusetts Emergency Management Agency and Department of Public Safety

Deborah Ryan

Executive Director

Architectural Access Board
Address: One Ashburton Place, Room 1310, Boston, MA 02108
Telephone: (617) 727-0660 **Fax:** (617) 727-0665
Staff: Nancy Harrington, Secretary
Reports to: Secretary Jane Perlov

PERSONAL INFORMATION:
Years in Current Position: 9 **Years in State Service:** 23

JOB DESCRIPTION:
To direct the Access Board, which makes, alters, amends and repeals rules and regulations designed to make public buildings accessible to, functional for, and safe for use by physically handicapped persons. The board disseminates information on the rules and regulations to persons requesting this information, including, but not limited to, design and building professionals, architects, engineers, contractors, local and state building inspectors, building commissioners, public works officials and chief executives of cities and towns, and handicapped individuals.

Michael J. O'Toole

Executive Director

Committee on Criminal Justice
Address: 100 Cambridge St, Rm 2100, Boston, MA 02202
Telephone: (617) 727-6300 **Fax:** (617) 727-5356
E-mail: Michael.OToole-EPS@state.ma.us
Staff: Marjorie Browne, Administrative Assistant
Reports to: Secretary Jane Perlov

PERSONAL INFORMATION:

Born: Sept. 2, 1962 **Place of Birth:** Norwood
Marital Status: married (Linda Marie)
Education: Northeastern, (B.S. '85); Suffolk (M.A. '90) Suffolk Law School (anticipated '98)
Previous Employment: State Street Bank, U.S. Dept. of State, Motorola/ Codex, Massachusetts State Budget Bureau Office of the Comptroller; Executive Office of Public Safety
Years in Current Position: 1 **Years in State Service:** 7

JOB DESCRIPTION:

Oversee and direct the administration of state and federal criminal justice grants.

1999 PRIORITIES:

Assist in the development and implementation of the Secretary's strategic vision for 1999.

Department of Correction

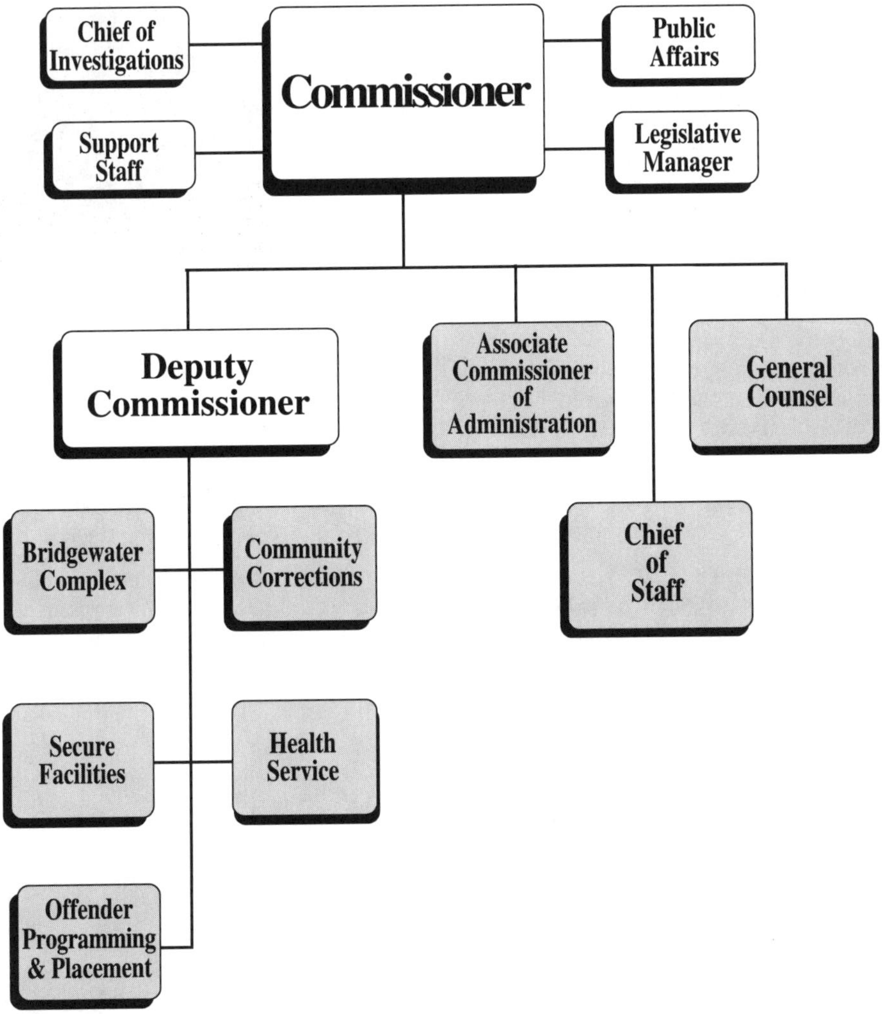

Michael T. Maloney

Commissioner

Department of Correction
Address: 100 Cambridge Street, 22nd Floor, Boston, MA 02202
Telephone: (617) 727-3300 ext. 101 **Fax:** (617) 727-3048
Staff: Deborah J. Mendoza, Executive Assistant
Reports to: Secretary Jane Perlov

PERSONAL INFORMATION:
Education: University of Massachusetts (B.A., Psychology, '73); Anna Maria College (M.A., Criminal Justice, '78)
Previous Employment: Depart of Correction (Deputy Commissioner, '89-'97); Massachusetts Correctional Institute (Cedar Junction, Superintendent, '85-'89; Norfolk, Deputy Superintendent, '80-'85; Director of Classification, '77-'80)
Years in Current Position: 1.5 **Years in State Service:** 25

JOB DESCRIPTION:
First in command of an agency employing approximately 4,833 individuals with an annual budget of more than $350 million and an inmate population census of 11,000. Responsibilities include the establishment of internal policies and procedures and management of external relations.

1999 PRIORITIES:
To continue to manage overcrowding and establish initiatives which focus on partnerships, teamwork, emergency technology, reparation to the community and responsiveness.

ORGANIZATIONS:
American Correctional Association, Correctional Association of Massachusetts, Northeastern Association of Correctional Administrators, International Community Corrections Association.

Ernest Vandergriff

Chief of Staff

Department of Correction
Address: 999 Barretts Mill Road, West Concord, MA 01742
Telephone: (617) 727-8612 **Fax:** (978) 727-8625
Reports to: Commissioner Michael T. Maloney

PERSONAL INFORMATION:
Education: Westfield State College (B.S., '76)
Previous Employment: U.S. Army
Years in Current Position: 1 **Years in State Service:** 22

Kathleen M. Dennehy

Deputy Commissioner

Department of Correction
Address: 100 Cambridge St. 22nd Floor, Boston, MA 02202
Telephone: (617) 727-3300 x162 **Fax:** (508) 792-4333
E-mail: kathyd@doc.state.ma.us
Staff: Stephanie Connolly, Executive Assistant
Reports to: Commissioner Michael T. Maloney

PERSONAL INFORMATION:
Born: May 4, 1954 **Place of Birth:** Boston
Marital Status: married (John Fay)
Education: Wheaton College (B.A. '76); Suffolk University School of Management (M.P.A. '84)
Previous Employment: Associate Commissioner, Classification, Programs and Health Services, '91-94; Dir. of Staff Development & Training '89-91; Old Colony Correctional Center, MCI Concord, MCI-CJ.
Years in Current Position: new **Years in State Service:** 21

JOB DESCRIPTION:
Second in command of agency employing 4833 individuals, with an annual budget of more than $350 million and an inmate population census of 11,000. Responsibilities include the management of all daily operations, prioritization of goals and objectives, management of inmate population, classification, education, programs, transportation and health services.

1999 JOB PRIORITIES:
Management of overcrowding.

Timothy F. App

Assistant Deputy Commissioner, Community Correction

Department of Correction
Address: 180 Morton Street, Jamaica Plain, MA 02130
Telephone: (617) 727-9409 **Fax:** (617) 727-2886
Reports to: Commissioner Michael T. Maloney

PERSONAL INFORMATION:
Education: Northeastern University (B.S., Correctional Practices, '81)
Previous Employment: U.S. Army (Sergeant, Military Police, '73-'76)
Years in Current Position: 7 **Years in State Service:** 21

JOB DESCRIPTION:
Responsible for development of policy and daily operations of the Department of Correction, Community Correction Division, nine correctional institutions, and the Community Residential Services Division.

ORGANIZATIONS:
International Community Correction Association; American Correctional Association; Association for the Treatment of Sexual Abusers (President of Massachusetts Chapter); Northeastern University, Criminal Justice Department (Part-time Faculty); Sex Offender Registry Board (Chair Designee)

James R. Bender

Assistant Deputy Commissioner for Secure Facilities

Department of Correction
Address: PO Box 9125, Concord, MA 01742
Telephone: (617) 727-7524 **Fax:** (978) 792-7628
Reports to: Deputy Commissioner Kathleen Dennehy

PERSONAL INFORMATION:

Marital Status: married (Barbara) **Children:** 2
Education: State University College (B.S.,'73); Northeastern University (M.S., Criminal Justice, '77)
Previous Employment: Massachusetts Department of Correction (Superintendent of North Central Correctional Institution; '85-'91; Superintendent of MCI Plymouth, '84-'85; Deputy Superintendent of Operations at MCI Concord, '83-'84; Deputy Superintendent of Treatment and Programs at MCI Concord, '81-'83; Director of Treatment at MCI Walpole, '80-'81)
Years in Current Position: 8 **Years in State Service:** 21

JOB DESCRIPTION:

Senior level management for the Department of Correction with direct supervision of seven Secure Facilities in the Department; responsibility for oversight of all fiscal and personnel transactions for these sites as well as ensuring policy compliance, disorder management, and the implementation of security procedures in State correctional facilities.

Nancy Ankers White

General Counsel

Department of Correction
Address: 100 Cambridge Street, 22nd Fl, Boston, MA 02202
Telephone: (617) 727-3300 ext. 124 **Fax:** (617) 727-7403
Reports to: Commissioner Michael T. Maloney

PERSONAL INFORMATION:

Education: University of Michigan (B.A., '76); Boston College Law School (J.D., '79)
Previous Employment: Willcox, Pirozzolo & McCarthy (Associate)
Years in Current Position: 11 **Years in State Service:** 16

JOB DESCRIPTION:

Defend prison officials in litigation brought by inmates in the state and federal courts; also provide legal opinions to the Department's 5000 employees.

Department of Public Safety

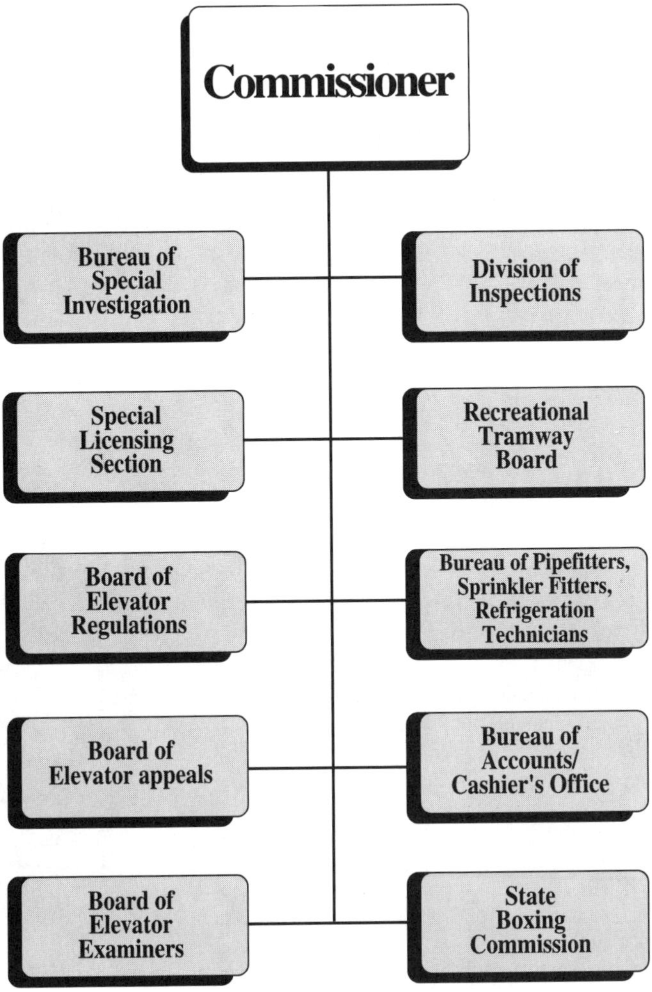

Joseph S. Lalli
Acting Commissioner

Department of Public Safety
Address: One Ashburton Place, Room 1301, Boston, MA 02108
Telephone: (617) 727-3200 **Fax:** (617) 727-5732
Staff: Jean McCarthy, Executive Assistant
Reports to: Secretary Jane Perlow

PERSONAL INFORMATION:
Education: Bacherlor of Arts - Criminal Justice ('82); New England School of Law (J.D. '88)
Marital Status: married (Sharon) **Children:** 1
Years in Current Position: new **Years in State Service:** 17

JOB DESCRIPTION:
Serve as chief administrator for the Department of Public Safety.

Col. Reed V. Hillman
Superintendent

Massachusetts State Police
Address: State Police General Headquarters, 470 Worcester Road, Framingham, MA 01702
Telephone: (508) 820-2350 **Fax:** (617) 727-6874
E-mail: reed.hillman@pol.state.ma.us
Staff: Lt. William Murphy, Chief of Staff; Roberta Hayes, Executive Assistant; Sharon Gallerani, Administrative Assistant
Reports to: Secretary Jane Perlov

PERSONAL INFORMATION:
Born: November 30, 1948 **Place of Birth:** Waltham
Marital Status: married (Therese) **Children:** 2
Education: Babson College (B.S., Business Administration); Suffolk University Law School (J.D.)
Previous Employment: Massachusetts State Police (Trooper, Corporal, Sergeant, Staff Sergeant, Lieutenant, Captain, Colonel and Superintendent, '74-'97); Attorney formerly in private practice
Years in Current Position: 2.5 **Years in State Service:** 24

JOB DESCRIPTION:
Command and supervision of Massachusetts State Police, comprising 2,700 sworn officers and civilians; management of $211 million budget.

Lt. Col. Glenn B. Anderson
Deputy Superintendent

Department of State Police
Address: State Police General Headquarters, 470 Worcester Road, Framingham, MA 01701
Telephone: (508) 820-2638 **Fax:** (617) 727-6874
E-mail: Glenn.Anderson@pol.state.ma.us
Staff: Lieutenant Donald S. Johnson; Christine Swanson, Executive Assistant
Reports to: Colonel Reed V. Hillman, Superintendent

PERSONAL INFORMATION:
Born: January 4, 1943 **Place of Birth:** Worcester
Marital Status: married (Susan) **Children:** 2
Education: Worcester State College; American International College
Years in Current Position: 3 **Years in State Service:** 33

JOB DESCRIPTION:
Oversee all departmental functions, principally the budget and day-to-day operations.

1999 PRIORITIES:
Continued expansion of the departments modern communications system; modernization of the department's forensic capabilities; continued fatal accident reduction effort.

ORGANIZATIONS:
International Association of Chiefs of Police; Massachusetts Chiefs Association; Worcester City Chiefs Association

Lt. Col. John DiFava
Commander, Division of Field Services

Department of State Police
Address: 470 Worcester Road, Framingham, MA 01701
Telephone: (508) 820-2344 **Fax:** (508) 820-2668
Staff: John F. Caulfield, Captain; Charles D. Heaton, Lieutenant; John H. McGillvray, Sergeant
Reports to: Lieutenant Colonel Glenn B. Anderson, Dep. Superintendent

PERSONAL INFORMATION:
Born: Jan. 19. 1952 **Place of Birth:** Boston
Marital Status: married (Marie) **Children:** 1
Education: Long Island University (B.A. '73); Boston University (M.Ed. '83)
Years in Current Position: 1 **Years in State Service:** 24

JOB DESCRIPTION:
Commanding the Division of Field Services, the largest divisional entity of the Massachusetts State Police. Comprised of more than 1500 officers, Field Services is responsible for the patrol functions and special units of the Department.

1999 PRIORITIES:
To increase the degree of partnerships and cooperative efforts with local and federal law enforcement agencies and to include the state police in greater detail with the community.

ORGANIZATIONS:
International Association of Chiefs of Police; Mass Chiefs Association, Sons of Italy in America

Lt. Col. Paul J. Regan

Assistant Superintendent, Division of Investigative Services

Department of State Police
Address: 470 Worcester Road, Framingham, MA 01702
Telephone: (508) 820-2312 **Fax:** (508) 820-2289
E-mail: Paul.Regan@pol.state.ma.us
Staff: Major John A. Burns, Det. Captains William M. Brown, Pehr B. Homes, David Ranteri, Captain John J. Kelly, and Leath Taylor.
Reports to: Colonel Reed V. Hillman, Superintendent

PERSONAL INFORMATION:
Born: November 28, 1948 **Place of Birth:** Chelsea
Marital Status: married (Lynda) **Children:** 2
Education: Northeastern University (B.S., Magna Cum Laude, Criminal Justice, '79); Anna Maria (M.S., Criminal Justice); North Shore Community College (A.S., Honors, Law Enforcement, '76)
Years in Current Position: 2.5 **Years in State Service:** 24

JOB DESCRIPTION:
In command of all investigative units within Department of State Police (e.g., attorneys general, district attorneys, organized crime).

1999 PRIORITIES:
To work with the district attorneys and attorney general to pass new legislation that will effectively combat crime.

ORGANIZATIONS:
New England Narcotic Officers Association; Disabled American Veterans (Life Member); Essex County Chiefs Association; Veterans of Foreign Wars, Post 1033

Michael J. Byrne

Chief Administrative Officer,
Division of Administrative Services

Department of State Police
Address: 470 Worcester Road, Framingham, MA 01701
Telephone: (508) 820-2355 **Fax:** (508) 820-2359
E-mail: mbyrne@pol.state.ma.us
Staff: Sgt. Thomas Ryan, Sue K. Viall, Assistant
Reports to: Colonel Reed V. Hillman, Superintendent

PERSONAL INFORMATION:
Born: April 25, 1954 **Place of Birth:** Fitchburg
Marital Status: married (Marie) **Children:** 1
Education: Tufts University (B.A.); Suffolk University (M.P.A.)
Previous Employment: Massachusetts Department of Revenue (Deputy Commissioner); Metropolitan District Commission (Deputy Commissioner)
Years in Current Position: 2 **Years in State Service:** 17

JOB DESCRIPTION:
Oversee personnel, finance, fleet management, research and development, facilities, supply, MIS, and records management.

1999 PRIORITIES:
Oversees personnel, finance, fleet management, research and development, facilities, supply, MIS and records management.

ORGANIZATIONS:
G.F.O.A.

Lt. Col. Ronald J. Guillmette

Assistant Superintendent
Office of Standards and Training

Department of State Police
Address: 470 Worcester Road, Framingham, MA 01702
Telephone: (508) 820-2333
E-mail: LTCRJG@AOL.COM
Staff: Major Bradley Hibbard, (Training) Major Thomas McLaughlin, (Standards), Lisa Richards, Administrative Assistant
Reports to: Colonel Reed V. Hillman, Superintendent

PERSONAL INFORMATION:
Born: Sept. 18, 1946 **Place of Birth:** Lawrence
Marital Status: married (Ann Marie) **Children:** 4
Education: University of Massachusetts ('88); Anna Maria ('92)
Years in Current Position: new **Years in State Service:** 30

JOB DESCRIPTION:
Responsible for all internal investigations, department inspections and training as pertains to state police personnel

ORGANIZATIONS:
Salisbury Beach Betterment Association; International Association of Chiefs of Police; International Association of Airport and Seaport Police

Peter F. LaPorte
Executive Director

Massachusetts Emergency Management Agency
Address: 400 Worcester Road, P.O. Box 1496, Framingham, MA 01701
Telephone: (508) 820-2010 **Fax:** (508) 820-2030
E-mail: Peter.LaPorte@state.ma.us
Staff: Quirino Iannazzo, Deputy Director; Katy Bellenare, Administrative Assistant; Douglas Cope, Public Information Officer.
Reports to: Secretaryj Jane Perlov

PERSONAL INFORMATION:
Born: April 19, 1963 **Place of Birth:** Attleboro
Education: Northeastern University (B.S. '86); New England School of Law (J.D. '94)
Previous Employment: New York City Police, Deputy Police Commissioner for Administration/Chief of Staff to Commissioner of NYC Police.

Jerome F. Meister
Chief of Operations

Massachusetts Emergency Management Agency
Address: 400 Worcester Road, P.O. Box 1496, Framingham, MA 01701
Telephone: (508) 820-2016 **Fax:** (508) 820-2030
Reports to: Director Peter LaPorte

PERSONAL INFORMATION:
Education: University of Connecticut (B.S., Business Administration, '57)
Years in Current Position: 13 **Years in State Service:** 16

JOB DESCRIPTION:
Train and coordinate State Emergency Management Team; prioritize and allocate state resources during times of emergency in order to preserve lives and property of citizens.

ORGANIZATIONS:
DAV; Retired Officers Association; JWV; Masons; Shriners; Lions

Quirino M. Iannazzo
Deputy Director

Massachusetts Emergency Management Agency
Address: 400 Worcester Road, Framingham, MA 01701
Telephone: (508) 820-2011 **Fax:** (508) 820-2030
E-mail: Bud.Iannazzo@state.ma.us
Reports to: Director Peter LaPorte

PERSONAL INFORMATION:
Born: June 1938 **Place of Birth:** Malden
Marital Status: married (Barbara) **Children:** 2
Education: Northeastern (B.S., Business, '69); Lesley College (M.S., Management, '85)
Previous Employment: Greater Boston Builders Association, Executive Director
Years in Current Position: 3 **Years in State Service:** 7

JOB DESCRIPTION:
Support the state director in providing leadership, programmatic and management control over agency operations, facilities and personnel.

Nancy J. Luther
Executive Director

Governor's Highway Safety Bureau
Address: 10 Park Plaza, Suite 5220, Boston, MA 02116
Telephone: (617) 973-8900 **Fax:** (617) 973-8917
E-mail: nancy.luther@hsb.state.ma.us
Staff: Andrea Worrall, Administrative Assistant
Reports to: Secretary Jane Perlov

PERSONAL INFORMATION:
Education: Westminster College (B.A., '67); Pennsylvania State University Graduate School ('67-'69)
Previous Employment: Salem House Publishers (Operations Manager); North American Phillips Lighting Corporation (Operations Supervisor)
Years in Current Position: 8 **Years in State Service:** 8

JOB DESCRIPTION:
Oversee highway safety initiatives and counter measures for the Commonwealth; establish goals and priorities in programs dealing with driver behavior. Supervisory responsibility for 13 staff members responsible for a budget of $3 million, which includes both federal and state money.

1999 PRIORITIES:
To keep Massachusetts roads among the safest in the nation.

ORGANIZATIONS:
Massachusetts Chiefs of Police Association; National Association of Governor's Highway Safety Representatives (NAGHSR); Beverly Hospital (Corporator); AASHTO Standing Committee on Highway Traffic Safety; Women's Transportation Seminar; American Association of University Women

Michael Mather

Executive Director

Governor's Alliance Against Drugs
Address: One Ashburton Place, Rm 611, Boston, MA 02108
Telephone: (617) 727-0786 **Fax:** (617) 727-6137
Staff: Brian Spencer, Programs Coordinator; Beth Doyle, Grants Program Manager; Timothy Turcotte, Fiscal Specialist; Melissa Hurley, Communications Coordinator, Alanna Fuoco, Executive Assistant.
Reports to: Secretary Jane Perlov

PERSONAL INFORMATION:

Born: March 12, 1951 **Place of Birth:** Brockton
Marital Status: married (Paula) **Children:** 2
Education: Anna Maria College ('99)
Previous Employment: Brockton Police Department, Park Division, Narcotics Division, and D.A.R.E. officer.
Years in Current Position: 1 **Years in State Service:** 1

JOB DESCRIPTION:

The administration and monitoring of a $1.9 million federal budget, $1.2 million being directly distributed to cities and towns in the Commonwealth in the form of mini-grants to youth anti-drug and violence initiatives ,and ultimately promoting a "drug-free" message to youth and adults in the Bay State.

1999 PRIORITIES:

To provide additional grant funds to youth and community groups through the creation of private/public partnerships and to reach as many people as possible through public service announcements, community coalitions and educational resources.

ORGANIZATIONS:

Massachusetts Police Association, Brockton Police Association

Kevin Harrington

Executive Director

Massachusetts Criminal Justice Training Council
Address: 411 Waverly Oaks Road, Suite 325, Waltham, MA 02452
Telephone: (617) 727-7827 **Fax:** (617) 727-6898
E-mail: Kevin.Harrington@state.ma.us
Reports to: SecretaryJane Perlov

PERSONAL INFORMATION:

Born: October 8, 1954 **Place of Birth:** Boston
Marital Status: married (Kathryn) **Children:** 3
Education: Northeastern University, Master's in Public Administration
Previous Employment: Deputy Commissioner, Mass Department of Public Safety
Years in Current Position: 1 **Years in State Service:** 21

Robert H. Watkinson

Acting Director

Statewide Emergency Telecommunications Board
Address: PO Box 156, Reading, MA 01867
Telephone: (781) 944-9113 **Fax:** (781)944-4721
E-mail: Robert.Watkinson@state.ma.us
Reports to: Undersecretary Robert Hayden

PERSONAL INFORMATION:
Born: July 28, 1940 **Place of Birth:** Mt. Vernon, NY
Marital Status: married (Helen) **Children:** 2
Education: Notre Dame (B.S. '63); UMASS-Amherst (M.B.A. '64)
Previous Employment: New England Telephone, Managing Director
Years in Current Position: 3 **Years in State Service:** 3

JOB DESCRIPTION:
Serve as Chief Administrator of the SETB. Implement and administer the state Enhanced 911 system.

1999 PRIORITIES:
Now that enchanced 9-1-1 is implemented statewide, the emphasis will be on upgrading the system and extending its benefits to cellular phones.

ORGANIZATIONS:
National Association of State 911 Administrators (NASNA); National Emergency Number Association (NENA) Regulatory Committee; Association of Public Safety Communications Officials (APCO).

Stephen D. Coan

State Fire Marshal

Department of Fire Services
Address: P.O. Box 1025, Stow, MA 01775
Telephone: (978) 567-3100 **Fax:** (978) 567-3121
Staff: Thomas P. Leonard, Deputy State Fire Marshal; William M. Hollick, Director of Fire Training; Barbara Steele, Administrative Assistant
Reports to: Secretary Jane Perlov

PERSONAL INFORMATION:
Born: January 12, 1951 **Place of Birth:** Boston
Years in Current Position: 16 **Years in State Service:** 23

JOB DESCRIPTION:
Direct the investigation of fires; administer the state fire code; direct statewide fire training.

1999 PRIORITIES:
Oversee the modernization of the State Fire Marshal's office.

ORGANIZATIONS:
International Association of Fire Chiefs; Fire Chiefs' Association of Massachusetts; National Fire Protection Association

Thomas P. Leonard

Deputy State Fire Marshal

Department of Fire Services
Address: P.O. Box 1025, Stow, MA 01775
Telephone: (978) 567-3100 **Fax:** (978) 567-3121
Staff: Leslie E. Hoffman, Director, Administrative Services; William M. Hollick, Acting Director, Massachusetts Firefighting Academy; William Alpine, Director, UST Program; James D. Weed, Director, Hazardous Materials Response; Barbara H. Steelc, Administrative Assistant
Reports to: Director Stephen D. Coan

PERSONAL INFORMATION:
Born: April 6, 1948 **Place of Birth:** Attleboro
Marital Status: married (Ellen) **Children:** 5 children, 2 stepchildren
Education: University of Massachusetts at Amherst (B.A.,'70); Bristol Community College (Associate's, Fire Science Technology, '74)
Previous Employment: Town of Mansfield (Fire Chief, '78-'83)
Years in Current Position: 2 **Years in State Service:** 15

JOB DESCRIPTION:
Responsible for all day-to-day operations of the agency, including oversight of all divisions of Department of Fire Services.

1999 PRIORITIES:
Strengthen fire services in the Commonwealth.

ORGANIZATIONS:
Fire Chiefs' Association of Massachusetts (Life Member); New England Association of Fire Chiefs; New York State Fire Chiefs; International Association of Fire Chiefs; Fire Department Safety Officers Association

Mary Ann Mulhall

Director

Merit Rating Board
Address: P.O. Box 199100, Roxbury, MA 02119
Telephone: (617) 267-3636 ext. 9601 **Fax:** (617) 351-9660
E-mail: MMulhall@MRB.state.ma.us
Staff: Robert Liberatore, Assistant Director; Diane Faverman, Administration Manager
Reports to: Secretary Jane Perlov
Years in Current Position: 12 **Years in State Service:** 20

JOB DESCRIPTION:
To serve as Director of the Motor Vehicle Insurance Merit Rating Board, which is responsible for the administration of the Safe Driver Insurance Plan. The Board maintains a database consisting of motor vehicle traffic violations, at-fault accident claim records and comprehensive claim records on individual operators. This information is used to adjust automobile insurance premiums based on the driving records of insured operators. The Board disseminates this information to Massachusetts automobile insurance carriers who apply "Safe Driver Insurance Plan Steps" to the vehicles listed on the policy. The Merit Rating Board is the sole repository for all motor vehicle violations issued in the Commonwealth. The Board receives approximately 1.2 million citations per year for entry into the database. This information is also used in the suspension or revocation of a driver's license by the Registry of Motor Vehicles.

Maj. Gen. Raymond A. Vezina

The Adjutant General

Military Division
Address: 50 Maple St. Milford, MA 01757
Telephone: (508) 233-6552 **Fax:** (508) 233-6554
E-mail: tag@shore.net
Staff: Helen M. Grant, Head Administrative Assistant; Major Michael Pacheco, Public Affiars Officer
Reports to: Gov. A. Paul Cellucci

PERSONAL INFORMATION:

Born: June 1, 1939 **Place of Birth:** Worcester
Marital Status: married (Elaine)
Education: Anna Maria (M.B.A., '88)
Previous Employment: Massachusetts Army National Guard
Years in Current Position: 5 **Years in State Service:** 4

JOB DESCRIPTION:

To serve as executive and administrative head of the Military Division of the Executive Branch of the Commonwealth; to act as military chief of staff to the Governor and Commander-in-Chief and Chief military aide-de-camp to the Governor; to plan and direct the administration, logistics, training and operations of the military forces of the Commonwealth; by state law, the adjutant general is the Commissioner of War Records, Chairman of the Military Reservation Commission and Armory Commission, Medal of Valor, Military Medal and Medal of Merit commissions; to provide guidance and supervision for the assistant adjutants general, inspector general, state judge advocate, state area command and all subordinate commanders; responsible for ensuring the Massachusetts National Guard units achieve and maintain operational readiness.

1999 PRIORITIES:

Keep National Guard soldiers and airmen on the top of the list of areas of readiness, mobilization, strength and education. Continue to provide the Commonwealth with prepared men and women to defend country and Commonwealth. Support the Massachusetts Summit: the Promise to our Youth in the areas of mentoring and protecting. Continue to launch Distance Learning Program and build partnerships with other agencies. Construct a state-of-the-art Emergency Operation Center in Milford and work closely with MEMA to share resources. Continue program of joint use in armories and facilities in the Commonwealth.

ORGANIZATIONS:

National Guard Association of Massachusetts (Executive Board); National Guard Association of the United States (Area I [Northeastern] Representative); Adjutants General Association of the United States; Worcester County Sheriff's Association; Sons of Italy; Harmony Club; Knights of Columbus; Armed Forces of Worcester, Inc.; Central Massachusetts Shelter for Homeless Veterans; American Legion

Sheila A. Hubbard

Chair

Massachusetts Parole Board
Address: 27-43 Wormwood Street, Suite 300, Boston, MA 02210
Telephone: (617) 727-3271 **Fax:** (617) 727-5047
Staff: Natalie R. Hardy, Executive Director; Ellen Starck, Administrative Secretary; M. Yvonne Gonzales, General Counsel
Reports to: SecretaryJane Perlov

PERSONAL INFORMATION:
Born: May 20, 1960 **Place of Birth:** Houston, TX
Marital Status: married **Children:** 1
Education: Yale University (B.A., Sociology/Political Science, '82); Harvard Law School (J.D., '85)
Previous Employment: Office of the Governor's Chief Legal Counsel (Deputy Legal Counsel to the Governor); Minority and Women Business Enterprise Office, Boston (Director); Mayor's Policy Office, Boston (Attorney/Policy Analyst)
Years in Current Position: 5 **Years in State Service:** 7

JOB DESCRIPTION:
The Chair serves as the executive and administrative head of the agency with the ultimate authority for all actions of the agency, which include directing assignments of the Board members, determining policy and direction of the agency, managing the supervision of parolees in the community, and being responsive to victims and the public on parole and related matters. The Chair also participates in votes of the Board on parole release and revocation decisions, as well as recommendations made to the Governor on matters of executive clemency.

Natalie R. Hardy

Executive Director

Massachusetts Parole Board
Address: 27-43 Wormwood Street, Suite 300, Boston, MA 02210
Telephone: (617) 727-3271 **Fax:** (617) 727-5047
Staff: Ellen M. Starck, Executive Assistant
Reports to: Chair Sheila A. Hubbard

PERSONAL INFORMATION:
Born: September, 15, 1961 **Place of Birth:** Brooklyn, NY
Education: City College of New York (B.A. '83); Northeastern University School of Law (J.D. '86)
Previous Employment: Office of the Attorney General, (Assistant Attorney General)
Years in Current Position: 5 **Years in State Service:** 10

JOB DESCRIPTION:
Management of the daily operations of the 250 person Parole Board including effective and timely coordination of parole hearings; effective subversion of parolees in the community.

M. Yvonne Gonzalez

Chief Legal Counsel

Massachusetts Parole Board
Address: 27-43 Wormwood Street, Suite 300, Boston, MA 02210
Telephone: (617) 727-3271 **Fax:** (617) 727-5047
Staff: Stanley Adelman, Senior Litigation Counsel; Lisa Prescott, Assistant Counsel; Julie Ching, Paralegal
Reports to: Chair Sheila A. Hubbard

PERSONAL INFORMATION:

Born: April 30, 1959 **Place of Birth:** Boston
Marital Status: married
Education: University of Massachusetts at Amherst (B.S., Finance, '81); University of Virginia, School of Law (J.D., '89)
Previous Employment: Federal Deposit Insurance Corporation (Litigation Attorney); Middlesex County District Attorney's Office (Assistant District Attorney)
Years in Current Position: new **Years in State Service:** 6

JOB DESCRIPTION:

The General Counsel and Legal Staff provide legal advice to the Chair and other agency staff. General Counsel and staff also represent the agency in litigation court cases filed by inmates, parolees, and others.

ORGANIZATIONS:

Massachusetts Bar Association

Timothy A. Zadai

Chief of Field Services

Massachusetts Parole Board
Address: 27-43 Wormwood Street, Boston, MA 02210
Telephone: (617) 727-3271 ext. 112 **Fax:** (617) 727-2753
Staff: Duane Lindblom, Deputy Chief; Jane Hayes, Word Processor Operator
Reports to: Executive Director Natalie Hardy

PERSONAL INFORMATION:

Born: March 5, 1946 **Place of Birth:** Spangler, PA
Marital Status: single
Education: St. Vincent College (B.A. '68); Clark University (M.A., Criminal Justice, '79); Old Dominion University (Teacher Certification)
Previous Employment: Parole Board (Deputy Chief Parole Supervisor, Parole Officer, Jr. Parole Officer); Department of Correction (Social Worker); U.S. Army (Administration Specialist)
Years in Current Position: 12 **Years in State Service:** 27

JOB DESCRIPTION:

Overall management of the Field Services unit, which is responsible for the supervision of all parolees.

1999 PRIORITIES:

Rewrite Policies and Procedures Manual for Field Services; implement intensive supervision in two field offices.

ORGANIZATIONS:
Massachusetts Police Association; New England Council on Crime and Delinquency; Massachusetts Chiefs of Police Association; Correctional Association of Massachusetts; American Probation and Parole Association

Kathleen G. Skerry

Director of Human Resources and Staff Development

Massachusetts Parole Board
Address: 27-43 Wormwood Street, Boston, MA 02210
Telephone: (617) 727-3271 **Fax:** (617) 727-2753
Staff: Joan Corcoran, Personnel Officer
Reports to: Executive Director Natalie Hardy

PERSONAL INFORMATION:
Years in Current Position: 13 **Years in State Service:** 26

JOB DESCRIPTION:
Responsible for policy development and implementation to provide leadership to the Agency in the areas of personnel, payroll, employee relations, training, and affirmative action.

Donald E. LaFratta

Chief of Special Operations

Massachusetts Parole Board
Address: 27-43 Wormwood Street, Boston, MA 02210
Telephone: (617) 727-3271 **Fax:** (617) 727-2753
Reports to: Executive Director Natalie Hardy

PERSONAL INFORMATION:
Born: October 1, 1952 **Place of Birth:** Attleboro
Marital Status: married (Catherine) **Children:** 3
Education: Assumption College (B.A., '74); Anna Maria College (M.A., Criminal Justice, '81) **Previous Employment:** St. Vincent's Home (Intake Coordinator, '74-'76)
Years in Current Position: 10 **Years in State Service:** 23

JOB DESCRIPTION:
Fugitive investigation and apprehension; interstate compact (parole); employment and background investigations; warrant processing.

1999 PRIORITIES:
Development of resources and innovations to assist unit to perform its tasks.

Donna Taylor Mooers

Executive Director

Police Accreditation Commission
Address: P.O. Box 568, Reading, MA 01867
Telephone: (781) 942-4801 **Fax:** (781) 942-4806
Staff: Gary H. Warson, Field Operation Director; Jennifer J. Doto, Program Specialist.
Reports to: Chief of Staff, Kim Mahoney

PERSONAL INFORMATION:

Born: Aug. 24, 1956 **Place of Birth:** Lynn
Marital Status: married (Don)
Education: Northeastern University, (B.S. '79)
Previous Employment: MBTA Police Department (Accreditation Manager/Staff Coordinator); Boston-Fenway Program/Boston Police Department (Coordinator, Public Safety Program)
Years in Current Position: 1 **Years in State Service:** 1

JOB DESCRIPTION:

Manage accreditation program for law enforcement agencies.

1999 PRIORITIES:

To develop and manage the accreditation process; provide accreditation manager training; recruit and certify assessors; and encourage statewide participation among police agencies.

Registry of Motor Vehicles

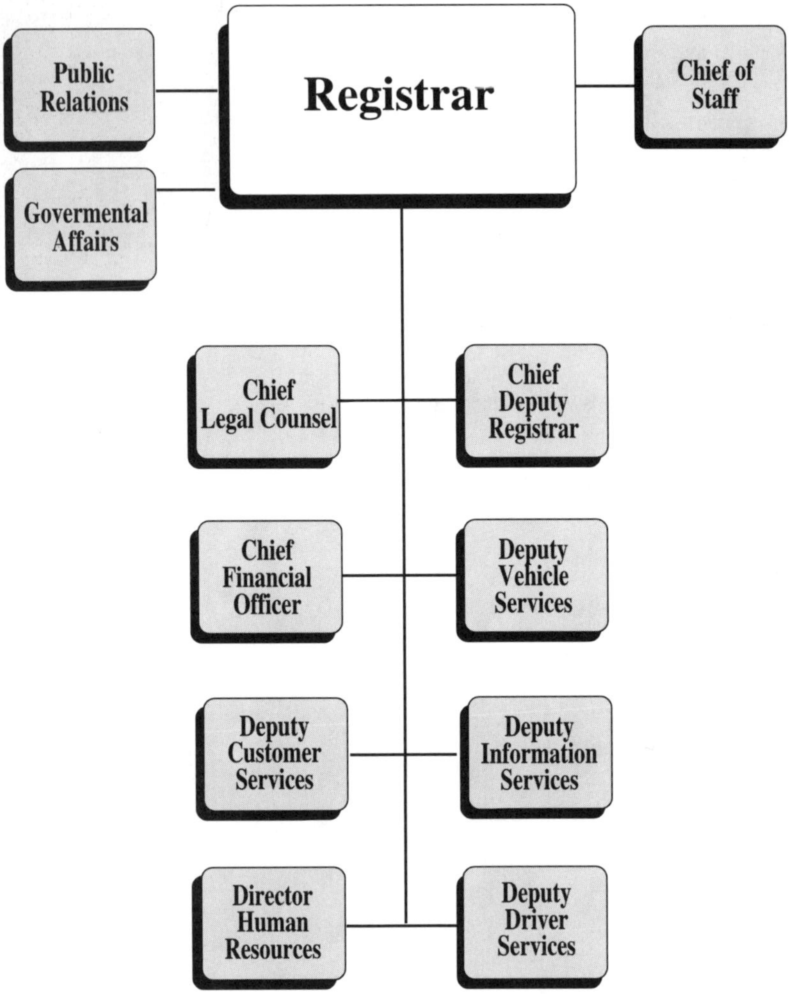

Richard D. Lyons

Registrar

Registry of Motor Vehicles
Address: P.O. Box 199100, Roxbury, MA 02119-9100
Telephone: (617) 351-9916 **Fax:** (617) 351-9971
E-mail: rlyons@rmv.state.ma.us
Staff: Chris Hollingsworth, Executive Assistant to Registrar
Reports to: Governor A. Paul Cellucci

PERSONAL INFORMATION:
Born: Oct. 24, 1941 **Place of Birth:** Lynn
Marital Status: married (Myra)
Education: Michigan State University, (B.A.)
Previous Employment: Mayor of Melrose
Years in Current Position: 1.5
Years in State Service: 8

JOB DESCRIPTION:
Oversee and enforce the laws pertaining to driver licensing, vehicle title and registration, special motor vehicle law enforcement and the adjudication for 4 million drivers annually. Also responsible for developing comprehensive Massachusetts and national safety programs that meet federal requirements ensuring that Massachusetts drivers obtain the very best in total customer service.

Gary M. Coon

Chief of Staff

Registry of Motor Vehicles
Address: P.O. Box 199100, Roxbury, MA 02119-9100
Telephone: (617) 351-9916 **Fax:** (617) 351-9971
E-mail: gcoon@rmv.state.ma.us
Staff: Chris Hollingsworth, Executive Assistant.
Reports to: Registrar Richard D. Lyons

PERSONAL INFORMATION:
Born: March 25, 1964 **Place of Birth:** Sacramento, CA
Education: Babson College (B.S. '87)
Previous Employment: State Representative, 17th Essex District (Andover & Lawrence) 1991-96.
Years in Current Position: 2 **Years in State Service:** 8

JOB DESCRIPTION:
Assist the Registrar in all policy development, strategic planning, and project leadership. Responsible for operations of all "Retail" field services locations across the state.

1999 PRIORITIES:
Support and facilitate all initiatives that will ensure achievement of the Agency's vision which is: "The Massachusetts Registry of Motor Vehicles will lead the drive for consumer convenience and quality service in government."

Robert P. McDonnell

Chief Deputy Registrar

Registry of Motor Vehicles
Address: P.O. Box 199100, Roxbury, MA 02119-9100
Telephone: (617) 351-9918 **Fax:** (617) 351-9923
Reports to: Registrar Richard D. Lyons

PERSONAL INFORMATION:

Born: August 23, 1938 **Place of Birth:** Brookline
Marital Status: married (Doreen) **Children:** 3
Education: University of Massachusetts (B.S., '89)
Years in Current Position: 2.5 **Years in State Service:** 36

JOB DESCRIPTION:

Responsible forfacilities management statewide.

Transportation & Construction

The Executive Office of Transportation and Construction coordinates and facilitates all modes of transportation. It oversees the design, construction, and maintenance of public transportation services and facilities. The secretariat reinforces the state's transportation systems, and thereby its economy. Its primary responsibilities include maintenance of state highways and bridge infrastructure, preservation of rail service, monitoring of air travel, and stimulation of economic growth related to transportation services.

Agencies and authorities within the executive office are:

- *Massachusetts Aeronautics Commission*
- *Massachusetts Port Authority*
- *Massachusetts Bay Transportation Authority*
- *Massachusetts Highway Department*
- *14 Regional Transit Authorities*

The Massachusetts Port Authority, Massachusetts Bay Transportation Authority, and 14 Regional Transit Authorities are independent agencies operating under the aegis of the Executive Office of Transportation and Construction but are not subject to its direct control.

Massachusetts Aeronautics Commission

The Massachusetts Aeronautics Commission is responsible for management and development of the state's airport systems plan. It has jurisdiction over the state's 47 public use airports, 38 seaplane ports, one balloon port, and numerous private use landing areas. Its agenda includes construction and improvement of airports, promotion of aviation safety, installation and maintenance of air navigation equipment, and reduction of airport-generated noise through operational procedures and land use controls. The Commission also regulates airplane registration, licenses and certifies airports and their managers, and administers the state's share of airport planning grants.

Massachusetts Port Authority

The Massachusetts Port Authority, through its maritime and aviation divisions, is responsible for the operation and maintenance of the Port of Boston, Logan International Airport, Hanscom Field, and the Tobin Bridge. It oversees passenger and freight transportation functions of its constituent units. Its current key projects include the economic redevelopment of Boston Harbor and renovation and modernization of Logan Airport.

Massachusetts Bay Transportation Authority

The Massachusetts Bay Transportation Authority is separate and distinct from EOTC and manages the nation's fifth largest public transit system. It operates and maintains bus, subway, trolley, and commuter rail services in the 78 cities and towns that make up the Metropolitan District. It also subsidizes water shuttle commuter ferries between the South Shore and Boston. The Authority promotes ridership, tourist and commuter pass incentives, senior citizen and disabled passenger access initiatives.

Massachusetts Highway Department

The Massachusetts Highway Department oversees the state's infrastructure system. It is responsible for planning, design, construction, and maintenance of roads and bridges. The Department administers federal highway funding and disburses state funds to municipalities under the various highway programs. The Massachusetts Highway Department currently oversees the Central Artery/Tunnel Project.

Regional Transit Authorities

The 14 Regional Transit Authorities provide commuter bus and van service for the transportation districts throughout the state.

Massachusetts Turnpike Authority

The Massachusetts Turnpike Authority operates and maintains the Massachusetts Turnpike, Boston Extension, and the Callahan, Sumner, and Ted Williams Tunnels. The Authority is also responsible for design and construction of the Central Artery Project. Facilities are financed by sale of revenue bonds to public investors and collection of motorist tolls. Revenues are used for operating expenses, maintenance, repairs, and debt liquidation. The Authority enforces heavy trucking regulations, traffic safety programs, and public information services.

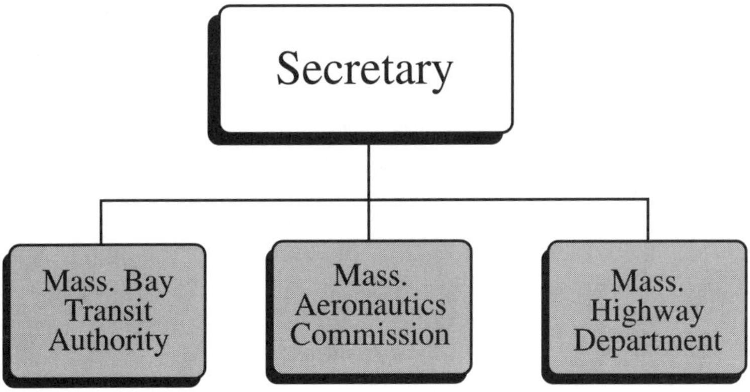
Secretary
Mass. Bay Transit Authority
Mass. Aeronautics Commission
Mass. Highway Department

Secretary and MBTA Chairman	**Kevin J. Sullivan**	(617) 973-8080
Undersecretary	**Abner A. Mason**	973-8090
Chief of Staff	**Charles E. Kostro, Jr.**	973-7000
Deputy Secretaries:		
Dep. Secretary for Transit Programs & Policy	**Toye L. Brown**	973-7019
Dep. Secretary for Multimodel Transportation	**Astrid Glynn**	973-7011
General Counsel/Dep. Secretary Environmental Policy	**Lauren Liss**	973-7000
Budget Director	**Adam Landry**	973-7035
Capital and Transportation Planning	**Julian M. Regan**	973-7040
Civil Rights Program Development	**Mary Fernandes**	973-7000
Communications	**Robin E. Bavaro**	973-8093

MASSACHUSETTS TURNPIKE AUTHORITY

Chairman	**James J. Kerasiotes**	(617)248-2800
CFO/Secretary Treasurer	**James Rooney**	248-2800
General Counsel	**James F. McGrail**	248-2800
Chief Real Estate Dev. & Env. Policy	**Robert M. Ruzzo**	248-2840
Dep. Chief of Operations	**James Kane**	248-2800
Central Artery/Tunnel Director	**Patrick J. Moynihan**	951-6071
Directors:		
Administration	**Jodi D'Urso Matthews**	973-7509
Civil Rights	**Lorenzo Parra**	248-2800
Communications	**Robert Bliss**	248-2800

MASSACHUSETTS HIGHWAY DEPARTMENT

Commissioner	**Mathew J. Amorello**	973-7800
Assistant Commissioner	**Joseph Donovan**	973-7800

Deputy Commissioner & Chief Counsel	**Edward J. Corcoran II**	973-7033
Chief Engineer	**Thomas F. Broderick**	973-7830
Assistant Chief Engineer	**Ron West**	973-7569
Deputy Chief Engineer	**Gordon Broz**	973-7740
Deputy Chief Engineer, Environment	**Gregory Prendergast**	973-7487
Deputy Chief Engineer, Construction	**David Anderson**	973-7490
Deputy Chief Engineer, Highway Eng.	**John Blundo**	973-7520

Directors:

Administrative Services	**Charles Smith**	973-7403
CEPO	**Mary Beth Begley**	973-7860
Civil Rights	**Patricia O'Brien**	973-7822
Audit Operations	**Elizabeth Pelligrini**	973-7875
Public Affairs	**Jon Carlisle**	973-7889
Deputy Secretary	**Maryellen Lyons**	973-7450
Information Technology	**Russ Grant**	973-7692
Right of Way	**Gerald Solomon**	973-7900
BTP&D	**Luisa Paiewonsky**	973-7313

MASSACHUSETTS AERONAUTICS COMMISSION

Chairman	**Sherman W. Saltmarsh, Jr.**	973-8881
Executive Director	**Stephen R. Muench**	973-8881
Airport Engineering Manager	**Robert J. Mallard**	973-8881
Chief Legal Counsel	**Wayne C. Kerchner**	973-8881

MASSACHUSETTS BAY TRANSPORTATION AUTHORITY (MBTA)

Board Chairman	**Kevin J. Sullivan**	973-7000
General Manager	**Robert H. Prince, Jr.**	222-5176
Deputy General Manager	**Philip Puccia III**	222-3106
Chief of Staff	**C. Mikel Oglesby**	222-3106

Chief Operating Officer	**Michael H. Mulhern**	222-3150
Chief Financial Officer	**Jonathan R. Davis**	222-4246
Chief of Design and Construction	**Howard M. Haywood**	222-3118
Chief of Employee Relations & Admin.	**Joan Martin**	222-4492
Chief of Labor Relations	**Patricia A. Day**	222-3283
General Counsel	**William A. Mitchell**	222-3160
Chief of Police	**Thomas J. O'Loughlin**	222-1100
Chief of Safety	**James T. Brown**	222-5135
Press Secretary	**Brian Pedro**	222-3310

MASSACHUSETTS PORT AUTHORITY (MASSPORT)

Chairman of the Board	**Mark E. Robinson**	568-1000
Executive Director and CEO	**Peter I. Blute**	568-1000
Deputy Executive Director	**Matthew J. Trant**	568-1020
Chief Legal Counsel	**Scott Kafker**	568-3131
Director of Personnel	**Kathleen Conlin**	568-3919
Director of Communications	**Josephine Cuzzi**	568-3107
Director of Administration and Finance, CFO	**Joseph Luca**	568-1036
Government and Community Affairs	**Thomas J. Butler**	568-3711
Director of Business Development	**David Forsberg**	568-1016
Director of Aviation Planning and Development	**Betty Desrosiers**	568-3500

Directors:

Aviation	**Thomas J. Kinton, Jr.**	561-1600
Maritime	**Michael Leone**	946-4413
Tobin Bridge	**Mary Jane O'Meara**	242-7979
Hanscom Field	**Barbara Patzner**	274-7200

Kevin J. Sullivan

Secretary of Transportation; MBTA Chairman

Executive Office of Transportation and Construction
Address: 10 Park Plaza, Room 3570, Boston, MA 02116-3974
Telephone: (617) 973-8080 **Fax:** (617) 973-8445
E-mail: Kevin.Sullivan@state.ma.us
Staff: Deborah Giordano, Administrative Assistant
Reports to: Governor A. Paul Celluci

PERSONAL INFORMATION:
Born: February 13, 1959 **Place of Birth:** Lawrence
Marital Status: married (Maryellen) **Children:** 2
Education: University of Lowell (B.S., Business Management, '80); Northeastern University Insurance Institute
Previous Employment: Massachusetts Highway Department (Dep. Commissioner, Assoc. Commissioner); City of Lawrence (Mayor, Alderman, Director of Health and Charities); T.A. Sullivan Insurance and Real Estate Agency
Years in Current Position: 3 **Years in State Service:** 6

JOB DESCRIPTION:
Supervise the Massachusetts Highway Department which maintains the state's road and bridge network; the Massachusetts Aeronautics Commission, which manages all regional airports throughout the state; and the Regional Transit Authorities which make up the Commonwealth's network of regional bus companies. Serve as chairman of the Massachusetts Bay Transportation Authority which provides multi-modal transit services to Eastern Massachusetts. Implement state policies regarding private railroads, transportation accessibility, and water transportation.

ORGANIZATIONS:
Greater Lawrence Big Brothers/Big Sisters; Lawrence Lions Club; Lawrence Knights of Columbus

Abner A. Mason

Undersecretary

Executive Office of Transportation and Construction
Address: 10 Park Plaza, Room 3170, Boston, MA 02116
Telephone: (617) 973-8090 **Fax:** (617) 973-8031
E-mail: Abner.Mason@state.ma.us
Staff: Alvin Rivera, Administrative Assistant
Reports to: Secretary Kevin J. Sullivan

PERSONAL INFORMATION:
Born: June 4, 1962
Place of Birth: Durham, NC
Marital Status: Domestic partner, Joseph J. White
Education: Harvard College (A.B. '85)
Previous Employment: Massachusetts Bay Transportation Authority, (Assistant Director of Construction)
Years in Current Position: 1
Years in State Service: 7

JOB DESCRIPTION:
Assist the Secretary of Transportation in daily oversight of the transportation agencies.

ORGANIZATIONS:
Boston Finance Commission (Appointed 1997); National Transit Institute Fellow (Appointed 1997); Log Cabin Education Fund (Board Member)

Charles E. Kostro, Jr.

Chief of Staff

Executive Office of Transportation and Construction
Address: 10 Park Plaza, Boston, MA 02116
Telephone: (617) 973-7000 **Fax:** (617) 973-8040
Staff: Susan M. Ruggiero, Executive Assistant
Reports to: Secretary Kevin J. Sullivan

PERSONAL INFORMATION:
Born: March 20, 1962 **Marital Status:** single
Education: University of Massachusetts (B.A. '85; M.A., '94)
Previous Employment: Executive Office of Transportation and Construction (Assistant Secretary); Massachusetts State House; Selectman, Town of Acton
Years in Current Position: 2 **Years in State Service:** 8

JOB DESCRIPTION:
Responsible for day-to-day operations of the Highway Department.

ORGANIZATIONS:
Acton Lions Club

Toye L. Brown

Deputy Secretary of Transportation; Intermodal Unit

Executive Office of Transportation and Construction
Address: 10 Park Plaza, Room 3170, Boston, MA 02116
Telephone: (617) 973-7019 **Fax:** (617) 523-6454
E-mail: TBrown@state.ma.us
Staff: Lorrain Young, Administrative Assistant
Reports to: Secretary Kevin J. Sullivan

PERSONAL INFORMATION:
Born: April 12 **Place of Birth:** Columbus, Ohio
Education: Ohio State University (B.Sc. '64); Columbia University (M.S.W. '67); Brandeis University (Ph.D. '75)
Previous Employment: Director, MBTA; President, Freedom House, Boston.
Years in Current Position: 6 **Years in State Service:** 6

JOB DESCRIPTION:
Manage and oversee state and federal capital and operating grants to regional transit authorities; administer transportation through MBTA and KTAs under Welfare Reform.

1999 PRIORITIES:
Improve transit services statewide within budget constraints; expand options; increase access to public transit for working poor.

ORGANIZATION:
Women's Transportation Seminar; United Way of Mass Bay; COMTO/Coalition of Minority Transportation Officials; Trustee, Roxbury Community College; Chair, Governor's African-American Advisory Commission.

Julian M. Regan

Deputy Secretary for Capital and Transportation Planning

Executive Office of Transportation and Construction
Address: 10 Park Plaza, Suite 3170, Boston, MA 02116
Telephone: (617) 973-7040 **Fax:** (617) 973-7808
Staff: Sally Picard, Administrative Assistant

PERSONAL INFORMATIO
Marital Status: married (Roseann)
Education: Suffolk University (B.S.B.A. ;86); Suffolk University (M.B.A. '92)
Previous Employment: Mass Bay Transportation Authority - Budget director; The Boston Company, Inc. Assistant Vice President.
Years in Current Position: 2 **Years in State Service:** 2

JOB DESCRIPTION:
Manage capital plan and develope State Transportation plans. Develop and implement operating budgets.

Robin E. Bavaro

Director of Communications

Executive Office of Transportation and Construction
Address: 10 Park Plaza, Suite 3170, Boston, MA 02116
Telephone: (617) 973-8093 **Fax:** (617) 523-6454
Reports to: Secretary Kevin J. Sullivan

PERSONAL INFORMATION:
Education: Simmons College (B.A. '86)

JOB DESCRIPTION:
Create and implement communications strategy for Executive Office of Transportation and associated agencies including MBTA, MHD and MAC.

James J. Kerasiotes

Massachusetts Turnpike Authority Chairman

Executive Office of Transportation and Construction
Address: 10 Park Plaza, Room 5170, Boston, MA 02116
Telephone: (617) 248-2800 **Fax:** (617) 248-2916
Staff: Helen Adamson, Assistant
Reports to: Governor A. Paul Cellucci

PERSONAL INFORMATION:
Born: December 5, 1953 **Place of Birth:** Peekskill, NY
Marital Status: married (Barbara) **Children:** 3
Education: State University of New York, New Paltz (B.A., '75); Northeastern University (M.A., '79)
Previous Employment: Massachusetts Highways (Commissioner); Deputy Commissioner of Commerce; Undersecretary of Transportation; Newswest (Publisher); Adion, Inc. (Chairman)
Years in Current Position: 3 **Years in State Service:** 12

JOB DESCRIPTION:
Oversee the operation and maintenance of the state's 135-mile toll highway and three harbor crossings: Sumner, Callahan and Ted Williams Tunnels. Responsibilities also include oversight and management of the largest public works project in North America - the Central Artery/Ted Williams Tunnel Project.

ORGANIZATIONS:
Board of Overseers, Northeastern University; Board of Directors, International Bridge, Tunnel and Turnpike Association.

Robert M. Ruzzo

Chief of Real Estate Development & Environmental Policy

Massachusetts Turnpike Authority
Address: 10 Park Plaza, Suite 5170, Boston, MA 02116
Telephone: (617) 248-2840 **Fax:** (617) 523-0729
Staff: Joan DeBeasi, Administrative Assistant
Reports to: Chairman James J. Kerasiotes

PERSONAL INFORMATION:
Born: January 24, 1960 **Place of Birth:** Dorchester
Marital Status: single
Education: Colby College (B.A., '81); Georgetown Law School (J.D., '84)
Previous Employment: Executive Office of Transportation and Construction (General Counsel and Deputy Secretary); Central Artery Project (Senior Counsel); Sherburne, Powers & Needham, P.C. (Partner)
Years in Current Position: 3 **Years in State Service:** 5

JOB DESCRIPTION:
To serve as legal advisor for all aspects of Massachusetts Turnpike Authority operations.

1999 PRIORITIES:
Continue to manage development of turnpike surplus land and air rights; represent the Authority in Air Rights Master Plan process; establish competitive process to select provider of services at turnpike areas; continue Turnpike's aggressive environmental program, including the construction of park n' ride spaces.

ORGANIZATIONS:
American, Massachusetts, and Boston Bar Associations; Environmental League of Massachusetts; WTS; Boston College High School Magis Guild

James F. McGrail
General Counsel

Massachusetts Turnpike Authority
Address: 10 Park Plaza, Room 5170, Boston, MA 02116
Telephone: (617) 248-2820 **Fax:** (617) 248-2916
Staff: Carolyn J. Kain, Deputy General Counsel
Reports to: Chairman James J. Kerasiotes

PERSONAL INFORMATION:
Born: November 15, 1965 **Place of Birth:** Cambridge
Marital Status: married (Christine) **Children:** 1
Education: Georgetown University (B.A. '87); Suffolk University Law School (J.D. '94)
Previous Employment: Executive Office of Transportation - Undersecretary/General Counsel; Massachusetts Bay Transportation Authority - Chief of Staff.
Years in Current Position: new **Years in State Service:** 10

ORGANIZATIONS:
Massachusetts Bar Association, Boston Bar Association

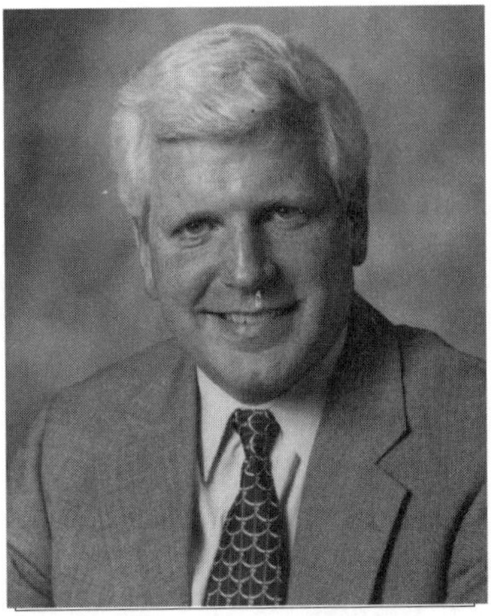

Patrick J. Moynihan
Central Artery/Tunnel Director

Massachusetts Turnpike Authority
Address: One South Station, Boston, MA 02110
Telephone: (617) 951-6071 **Fax:** (617) 261-1466
Staff: William Flynn, Chief of Staff/Deputy Project Director; Sarah Jenik, Administrative Assistant
Reports to: Chairman James J. Kerasiotes

PERSONAL INFORMATION:
Born: Aug. 13, 1954 **Place of Birth:** Springfield
Marital Status: married (Katherine F.) **Children:** 4
Education: Northeastern University (B.S. '77); New England School of Law (J.D. '88)
Previous Employment: Massachusetts Bay Transportation Authority (General Manager, 1995-97); Executive Office of Transportation and Construction (Undersecretary and General Counsel ,1992-95); Massachusetts Highway Department (Deputy Commissioner and Chief Counsel, 1991-92); Assistant Attorney General (1987-91); State Auditor's Office (Division

Director, 1983-87): Massachusetts Department of Public Works (Associate Commissioner, 1982-83); Town of Northbridge (Town Administrator, 1978-81)
Years in Current Position: new **Years in State Service:** 18

JOB DESCRIPTION:
Direct oversight of the largest interstate highway project in the United States with expenditures of over $10 billion in federal and state funds.

Jodi D'Urso Matthews

Director of Administration

Massachusetts Turnpike Authority
Address: 10 Park Plaza, Room 5170, Boston, MA 02116
Telephone: (617) 973-7509 **Fax:** (617) 248-2916
Reports to: James J. Kerasiotes, Chairman

PERSONAL INFORMATION:
Born: June 3, 1964 **Place of Birth:** Haverhill
Marital Status: Married (Dennis Matthews)
Education: Emerson College (B.S. '86)
Previous Experience: Executive Office of Transportation and Construction - Director of Public Affairs.
Years in Current Position:2 **Years in State Service:** 10

JOB DESCRIPTION:
Design, develop and manage a coordinated and integrated plan for policy development and public affairs strategies for the MTA; Manage communication departments at both the MTA and the Central Artery-Ted Williams Tunnel Project.

Massachusetts Highway Department

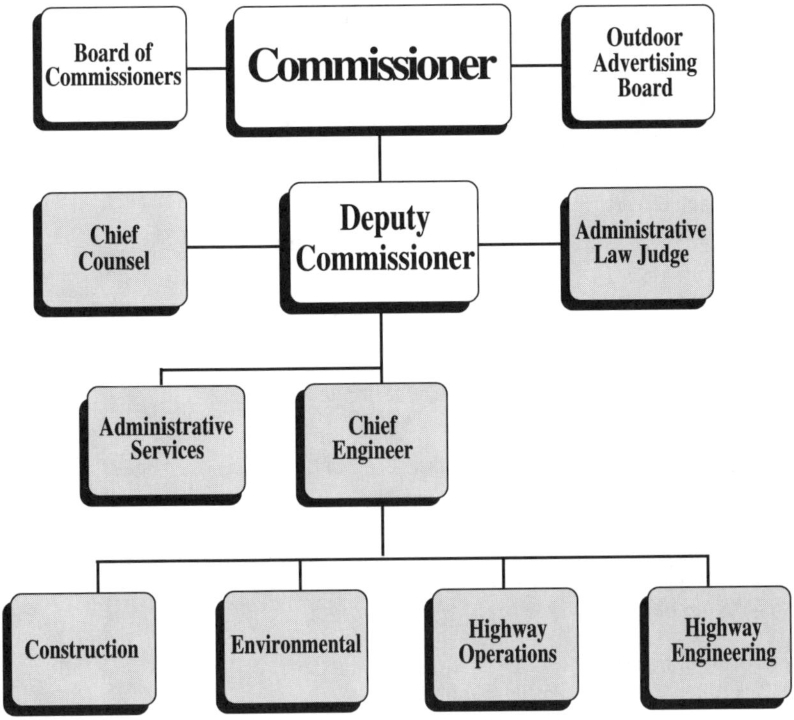

Edward J. Corcoran II

Deputy Commissioner & Chief Counsel

Massachusetts Highway Department
Address: 10 Park Plaza, Room 3170, Boston, MA 02116
Telephone: (617) 973-7033 **Fax:** (617) 973-8040
Reports to: CommissionerMathew J. Amorello

PERSONAL INFORMATION:
Born: May 9, 1957 **Place of Birth:** Newport, RI
Marital Status: married (Alison) **Children:** 3
Education: Brown University (A.B., '79); Suffolk University School of Law (J.D., '83)
Previous Employment: Corcoran, Peckham & Hayes, P.C. (Associate Attorney)
Years in Current Position: 1 **Years in State Service:** 7

JOB DESCRIPTION:
General agency administration, policy development and legal advice

1999 PRIORITIES:
Develop innovative approaches to procurement of major transportation projects.

ORGANIZATIONS:
Boys' Clubs & Girls' Clubs of Newport, RI (Vice President, Board of Directors)

Gregory Prendergast

Deputy Chief Engineer, Environmental Division

Massachusetts Highway Department
Address: 10 Park Plaza, Room 4260, Boston, MA 02116
Telephone: (617) 973-7484
E-mail: G_PRENDERGAST@ENVIRON@DPW_BOS **Fax:** (617) 973-8879
Staff: John N. Mattuchio, Assistant to the Deputy Chief
Reports to: Chief Engineer Thomas F. Broderick, P.E.

PERSONAL INFORMATION:
Born: February 27, 1944 **Place of Birth:** Boston
Marital Status: married (Christine) **Children:** 4
Education: Lowell University (B.S., Civil Engineering, '73)
Years in Current Position: 6 **Years in State Service:** 34

JOB DESCRIPTION:
Direct the preparation and review of the preliminary design and federal and state environment documents for major highway projects with an aggregate value of $900 million; oversee the processing of federal, state, and local environmental clearances for the Massachusetts Highway Department's $400 million construction and maintenance program. Oversee Mass highway's Environmental Management System for maintaining environmental compliance at statewide highway maintenance facilities; coordinate and recommend environmental policy issues.

ORGANIZATIONS:
American Public Works Association; American Association of the State Highway and Transportation Officials; Society of American Military Engineers; American Society of Environmental Professionals

Sherman W. Saltmarsh, Jr.
Chairman

Massachusetts Aeronautics Commission
Address: 10 Park Plaza, Room 6620, Boston, MA 02116
Telephone: (617) 973-8881 **Fax:** (617) 973-8889
Reports to: Secretary Kevin Sullivan

JOB DESCRIPTION:
The Massachusetts Aeronautics Commission is charged with the safety and effectiveness of the facilities for air transportation within, to, and from the Commonwealth. The Commission oversees 102 private and public airports, 38 seaplane ports, 147 heliports, and one balloon port. The focus of the Commission's program includes construction and improvement of airports, the installation and maintenance of air navigational equipment, and the reduction of the impact of airport-generated noise through operational procedures and land use controls.

Stephen R. Muench
Executive Director

Massachusetts Aeronautics Commission
Address: 10 Park Plaza, Room 6620, Boston, MA 02116
Telephone: (617) 973-8881 **Fax:** (617) 973-8889
E-mail: steve.muench@state.ma.us
Staff: Lorraine A. Bohanan, Executive Secretary
Reports to: Sherman Saltmarsh, Jr., Chairman

PERSONAL INFORMATION:
Born: June 25, 1948 **Place of Birth:** Covington, KY
Marital Status: married (Louise Hughes Muench) **Children:** 3
Education: Christian Brothers College, (B.S. - Civil Engineering)
Previous Employment: Aviation Services Holdings (Senior V.P. ,C.D.D.); Van Dusen Airport Services (Senior V.P.) Texaco, Inc.) Manager Operations International Aviation Sales)
Years in Current Position: 5 **Years in State Service:** 7

JOB DESCRIPTION:
General supervision and control over aeronautics throughout Commonwealth; certify public use airports; oversee 42 public use airports; administer federal and state funding programs; enforce state laws and regulations pertaining to aeronautics.

1999 PRIORITIES:
Promote aviation while establishing a safe, efficient airport system that meets the current and future air transportation and economic needs of the Commonwealth.

ORGANIZATIONS:
Aero Club of New England; Massachusetts Airport management Association; National Association of State Aviation Officials.

Robert H. Prince, Jr.

General Manager

Massachusetts Bay Transportation Authority
Address: 10 Park Plaza, Room 3910, Boston, MA 02116
Telephone: (617) 222-5176 **Fax:** (617)222-6180
Staff: Maryanne Walsh, Special Assistant
Reports to: Secretary Kevin Sullivan

PERSONAL INFORMATION:
Born: July 15, 1949 **Place of Birth:** Boston
Marital Status: married (Judy) **Children: 2**
Education: Attended Tuskegee University
Previous Employment: MBTA: Chief Operating Officer, Assistant General Manager for Subway Operations, Assistant General Manager for Human Resources, Special Assistant to the General Manager, Deputy Superintendent of Rail Lines, Night/Weekend Supervisor of Rail Lines, Night System-wide Superintendent of Rail Lines, Night System-wide Superintendent, Spare Chief Dispatcher, Spare Information Officer, Dispatcher, Train Starter, Chief Inspector, yard motor person, motor person, guard, collector, and bus operator.
Years in Current Position: 1.5 **Years in State Service:** 22

JOB DESCRIPTION:
Responsible for providing the daily operations and administrative leadership for the Authority. Responsible under the direction of the Secretary of Transportation and MBTA Board of Directors, for the management policies and practices and setting standards of excellence to which all operations compliance and administrative functions perform. Direct responsibility for the oversight of 6,700 employees and 725,000 commuters daily.

1999 PRIORITIES:
Reinvestment in the Authority's infrastructure and employees,.

ORGANIZATIONS:
COMTO, Board Member of the Arnold Arboretum Association, WTS, World Unity Inc.

Philip Puccia III

Deputy General Manager

Massachusetts Bay Transportation Authority
Address: 10 Park Plaza, Room 3910, Boston, MA 02116
Telephone: (617) 222-3106 **Fax:** (617)222-6180
E-mail: ppuccia@mbta.com
Staff: Maureen Greenwood, Administrative Assistant
Reports to: General Manage Robert H. Prince, Jr.

PERSONAL INFORMATION:
Born: March 5, 1965 **Place of Birth:** Malden
Marital Status: married (Dorothy) **Number of Children:** 3
Education: Fordham University (B.A. '87); University of Massachusetts (M.B.A. '87)
Previous Employment: Massachusetts Bay Transportation Authority, Chief of Staff; Special Assistant to the Secretary of Transportation and Construction, Massachusetts Highway Department, Assistant to the Commissioner.

Years in Current Position: new **Years in State Service:** 7

JOB DESCRIPTION:
Assist the General Manager in managing day-to-day operations. Particular emphasis is placed on strategic planning for administrative operations and development of the MBTA's five year $1.5 billion capital plan.

1999 PRIORITIES:
Continue to improve customer service while minimizing costs on a per passenger basis and use all recommended innovative financing tools to enhance capital investments.

ORGANIZATIONS:
Alternate member of the MBTA Pension Board and a member of the leadership American Public Transportation Association; Finance committee leadership APTA, and board member for Massachusetts Alliance for Small Contractors.

C. Mikel Oglesby

Chief of Staff

Massachusetts Bay Transportation Authority
Address: 10 Park Plaza, Room 3910, Boston, MA 02116
Telephone: (617) 222-3106 **Fax:** (617) 222-6180
Staff: Pamela Stafford, Administrative Assistant
Reports to: General Manager Robert H. Prince, Jr.

PERSONAL INFORMATION:
Born: Jan. 2, 1965 **Place of Birth:** Boston
Marital Status: single
Education: University of Massachusetts (B.B.A. '87); Massachusetts Institute of Technology, Post Graduate Seminar series.
Previous Employment: Massachusetts Bay Transportation Authority, Operation Section Chief - Administration and Finance, Project Manager of Human Resources Information System, Special Assistant to the General Manager.
Years in Current Position: 1 **Years in State Service:** 9

JOB DESCRIPTION:
Oversee the General Manager's senior management team in the administration and development of major policy initiative, large scale project management, and budgetary oversight

1999 PRIORITIES:
To carry out major rehabilitation in the Authority's infrastructure and reinvest in employees.

ORGANIZATIONS:
Member of "Leadership Aptg" Second Class, Treasurer of City-wide Educational Coalition, Vice President of Conference of Minority Transportation Officials, Member of WTS

Thomas J. O'Loughlin

Chief of Police

Massachusetts Bay Transportation Authority
Address: 240 Southampton Street Boston, MA 02118
Telephone: (617) 222-1100 **Fax:** (617) 2221035
E-mail: (tpolice@mbta.com
Staff: Maureen M. Lee, Executive assistant; Janet L. Rivera-Jones, Executive Coordinator
Reports to: General Manager Robert H. Prince, Jr.

PERSONAL INFORMATION:
Place of Birth: Boston
Marital Status: married
Education: Boston State College (B.S. '81); New England School of Law (J.D. '90)
Previous Employment: Wellesley Police Department (Chief 1992-97); Wayland Police Department), Chief (1986-92); Boston Housing Authority Police Superintendent (1978-86)
Years in Current Position: 2 **Years in State Service:** 21

JOB DESCRIPTION:
Providing police services for the customers and employees of the MBTA

ORGANIZATIONS:
Massachusetts SIDS Center; Governor's Neighborhood Crime Watch Commission; Massachusetts State Emergency Telecommunications Board (E-911)

Massachusetts Port Authority

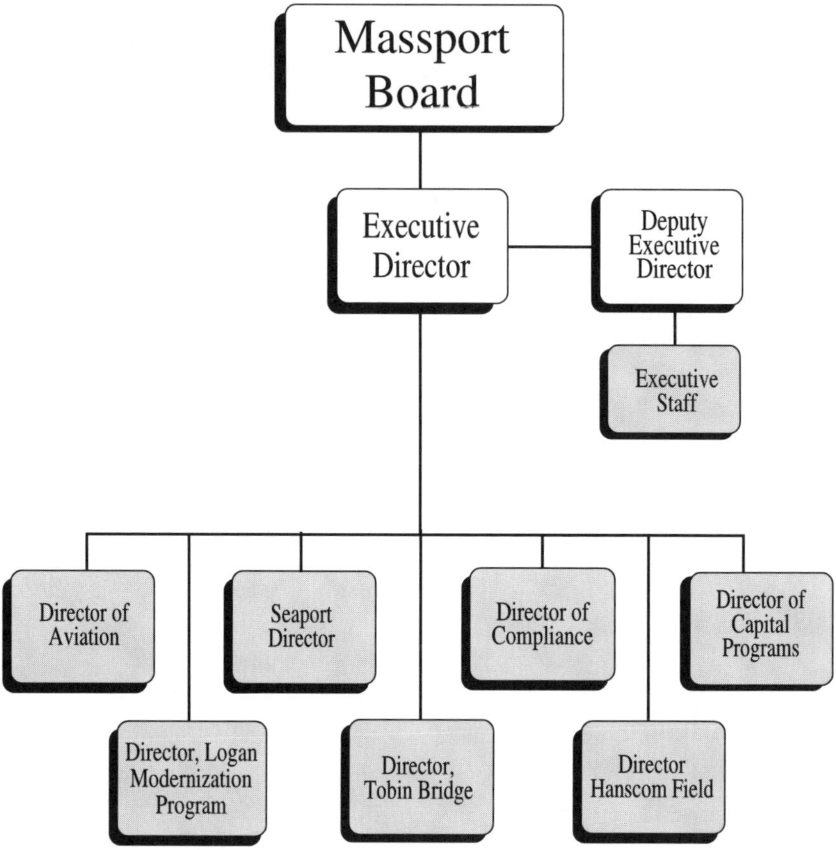

Peter I. Blute

Executive Director and CEO

Massachusetts Port Authority
Address: One Harborside Drive, Suite 200S, East Boston, MA 02128-2909
Telephone: (617) 568-1000 **Fax:** (617) 568-1022
Staff: Matthew J. Trant, Deputy Executive Director; Lisa Donati, Executive Assistant
Reports to: Governor A. Paul Cellucci

PERSONAL INFORMATION:
Marital Status: married (Robi) **Children:** 2
Education: Boston College (B.A.,'78)
Previous Employment: U.S. Congressman; Massachusetts State Representative
Years in Current Position: 2

JOB DESCRIPTION:
To serve as Chief Executive Officer of New England's principal public Port Authority with responsibility for Logan International Airport, Hanscom Field, the Port of Boston, and the Tobin Memorial Bridge.

Matthew J. Trant

Deputy Executive Director

Massachusetts Port Authority
Address: One Harborside Drive, Suite 200S, East Boston, MA 02128
Telephone: (617) 568-1020 **Fax:** (617) 568-1022
Staff: Christine Hastie, Executive Assistant, Leslie Kirwan, Assistant Director, Charlotte Amorello, Special Assistant
Reports to: Executive Director & CEO Peter Blute

PERSONAL INFORMATION:
Born: July 30, 1965 **Place of Birth:** Westfield
Marital Status: married (Gina) **Children:** 1
Education: University of Maryland (B.A.. Economics)
Previous Employment: U.S. Congressman Peter Blute (Chief of Staff); U.S. Dept. of Transportation
Years in Current Position: 2

JOB DESCRIPTION:
Serve as the chief advisor to the Executive Director on Massport Authority policy. Provide broad management and overall direction to Massport's operating departments, which include Logan International Airport, Port of Boston, Foreign Trade Development Unit, Office of Tourism, Hanscom Airfield, and the Tobin Memorial Bridge.

Mark E. Robinson
Chairman

Massachusetts Port Authority
Address: One Harborside Drive, Suite 2005, East Boston, MA 02126
Telephone: (617) 568-1000 **Fax:** (617) 568-1022
E-mail: Robinsme@Bingham.com
Staff: Charlotte J. Amorello
Reports to: Massport Board

PERSONAL INFORMATION:

Born: April 30, 1954
Place of Birth: Nashville, TN
Marital Status: married (Sarah) **Children:** 3
Education: Duke University ('76); Boston University Law School ('79)
Previous Employment: Bingham, Dana LLP (presently of Counsel); Massachusetts Executive Office for Administration and Finance (Secretary, '93-'94); Office of the Governor (Chief of Staff, '91-'93); Hale and Dorr (Litigation Partner)
Years in Current Position: 3 **Years in State Service:** 8

JOB DESCRIPTION:

Chairman of New England's principal public Port Authority with responsibility for Logan International Airport, Hanscom Field, The Maritime Port of Boston and the Tobin Memorial Bridge.

ORGANIZATIONS:

Massachusetts Bar Association; District of Columbia Bar Association

SECTION III

State Departments

Consumer Affairs & Business Regulation

The Office of Consumer Affairs is the state's advocate for consumer rights, and functions primarily to protect and assist consumers. The Office of Consumer Affairs upholds Chapter 93A (The Massachusetts Consumer Protection Law, which is one of the strongest in the nation) and advises consumers of their rights within the law.

This office coordinates policy analysis and planning for the following eight regulatory agencies under its supervision:

- *Alcoholic Beverages Control Commission*
- *Board of Registration in Medicine*
- *Department of Telecommuni cations and Energy*
- *Division of Banks*
- *Division of Insurance*
- *Division of Registration*
- *Division of Standards*
- *State Racing Commission*

The Office of Consumer Affairs publishes brochures on consumer rights and offers an information hotline that serves as a resource to consumers across the Commonwealth. The hotline's staff advises consumers of their rights and remedies and assists in the resolution of disputes.

The Consumer Affairs Office also oversees the New and Used Vehicle Warranty Arbitration Program. This state-mandated service provides general information about the lemon law and used vehicle warranty law and assists consumers in determining whether their vehicle qualifies for refund or replacement under the applicable statute.

Alcoholic Beverages Control Commission

The Alcoholic Beverages Control Commission (ABCC) administers all activities of the alcoholic beverages industry in Massachusetts. It oversees the manufacturing, importing, storage, transportation, and sales of all alcoholic beverages in the Commonwealth. The ABCC directly licenses the statewide activities of liquor manufacturers, transporters, wholesalers, and brokers. It also regulates interstate and international alcoholic beverage businesses by issuing certificates of compliance. While individual municipalities within the Commonwealth grant licenses to retailers of alcoholic beverages within their jurisdictions, the ABCC gives final approval of all such licenses. The Commission investigates applications for licenses, prosecutes violations of pertinent statutes and regulations, and adjudicates disputes among members of the industry. It also serves as an appeals board regarding local licensing actions.

Board of Registration in Medicine

The Board of Registration in Medicine is responsible for overseeing the qualifications of physicians and surgeons practicing in Massachusetts. It ensures that doctors who are licensed in the Commonwealth are properly qualified and that doctors who violate the law are disciplined. In the late fall of 1996, the Board of Medicine opened a telephone hotline (the first of its kind in the nation) for consumers to access comprehensive information on all of the licensed physicians in Massachusetts. The Board also approves schools for training medical laboratory technologists and X-ray technicians. In addition, the Board appoints a committee responsible for the registration and licensing of acupuncturists.

Department of Telecommunications & Energy (DTE)

The Department of Telecommunications & Energy (DTE) regulates the rates and quality of service of public utilities and common carriers operating in the Commonwealth. These companies conduct more than $8 billion of business in the state and provide electricity, gas, telecommunications, cable television, water, railway, trucking and bus services. The DTE sets utility rates, enforces safety regulations, oversees service quality, licenses and certifies service providers, sites energy facilities, and adjudicates consumer complaints.

Within the Department of Public Utilities is the ***Energy Facilities Siting Board***, a body composed of representatives of the Executive Offices of Consumer Affairs, Economic Affairs, Environmental Affairs, state utilities, and labor interests. It is staffed by a group of attorneys, economists, engineers, planners, and environmental scientists who are responsible for approving proposals for the energy facilities of gas and electric utilities and third-party developers in the Commonwealth. The Board reviews the long-range forecast of utility supply and demand as the basis for approval of new energy facilities, including power plants, transmission lines, substations, pipelines, storage, and liquification facilities. It acts as the lead agency for the development of hydroelectric power. The Board represents the Commonwealth before federal agencies reviewing energy projects, issues certificates of environmental need and public necessity for facilities, certifies oil refineries, and issues eminent domain orders for pipelines.

Division of Energy Resources

The Division of Energy Resources (DOER) formulates and oversees the implementation of the state's energy policy and operates the majority of the state energy programs. DOER works with all forms of energy resources, including renewables, fossil fuels, nuclear, and conservation. It offers programs to inform residential, commercial, and governmental consumers of the benefits of conservation and renewable energy usage. DOER also offers information on grants, loans, and tax credits available to developers and users of renewable energy sources.

Division of Banks

The Division of Banks regulates, supervises, and audits trust companies, savings banks, cooperative banks, credit unions, finance companies, mortgage brokers, and collection agencies doing business in the Commonwealth. The Division of Banks also grants charters and approves branches, acquisitions, and mergers of the financial institutions it supervises. It promotes the public interest by fostering the safety and soundness of financial institutions, by encouraging fair competition and reinvestment in the community, and by supervising small loan interest rate, credit, and savings transaction compliance.

Division of Insurance

The Division of Insurance regulates all aspects of the insurance industry in the Commonwealth. It licenses more than 800 insurance companies and health maintenance organizations (HMOs) and more than 100,000 insurance personnel. The Division of Insurance conducts financial examinations of domestic and foreign insurance companies, audits licensees, reviews rates and policy forms, and participates in rate setting.

Division of Registration

The Division of Registration oversees the 32 Boards of Registration which were created to protect the health and safety of consumers in Massachusetts. The individual boards of registration and examination license professions and trades based upon criteria and regulations set forth in statute. Each board establishes standards of professional conduct, holds disciplinary hearings, and can revoke or suspend licenses after investigation of serious complaints. A centralized Investigative Unit exists to handle consumer complaints.

Division of Standards

The Division of Standards is responsible for enforcing the standards and testing the accuracy of all types of weighing and measuring devices used in the sale of food, fuels, and other products. It regulates the retail sale of gasoline and sets standards for lubricating oils and antifreeze, including the inspection of all fuel-dispensing pumps. It determines the standards for accuracy and safety of all thermometers. It tests and approves coin-operated machinery, licenses transient vendors and auctioneers, and registers motor vehicle damage repair shops. The Division also enforces unit pricing and item pricing regulations.

State Racing Commission

The State Racing Commission regulates all paramutual activities in the Commonwealth. The Commission oversees thoroughbred, harness, and greyhound racing. It licenses all tracks, including owners, trainers, veterinarians, blacksmiths, and other agents and employees of the tracks.

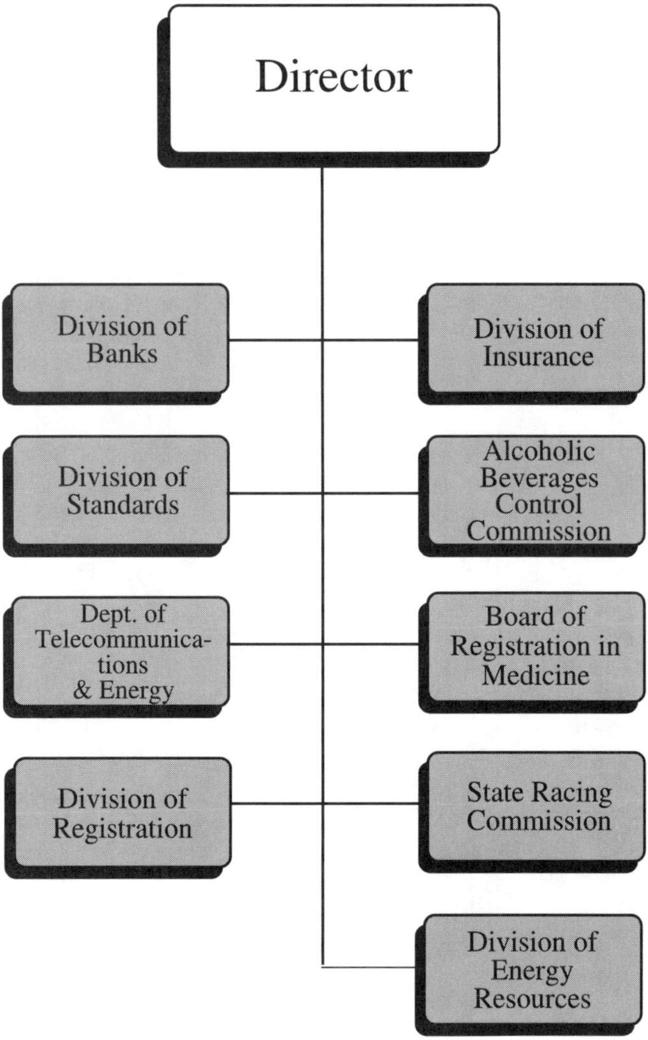
Director
Division of Banks
Division of Insurance
Division of Standards
Alcoholic Beverages Control Commission
Dept. of Telecommunications & Energy
Board of Registration in Medicine
Division of Registration
State Racing Commission
Division of Energy Resources

Director	**Daniel A. Grabauskas**	*(617) 727-7755*
Deputy Director & Chief of Staff	**Kate McCormack**	*727-7755*
General Counsel	**David Veator**	*573-7755*
Chief Financial Officer	**Graham Holmes**	*573-7309*
Dep. Director & Dir. of Communications	**Kimberly Hinden McDonald**	*573-7308*
Director of Consumer Education	**Kerry Smith**	*573-7320*
Exec. Asst. to the Director	**Ellen M. Cassidy**	*573-7303*

ALCOHOLIC BEVERAGES CONTROL COMMISSION

Chairman	**Walter J. Sullivan. Jr.**	*727-3040*
Commissioner	**Suzanne Iannella**	*727-3040*
Commissioner	**Frederick W. Riley**	*727-3040*

BOARD OF REGISTRATION IN MEDICINE

Chairman	**Nishan Kechjian, M.D.**	*589-5100*
Vice-Chair	**Carl M. Sapers**	*589-0770*
Secretary	**Mary Anna Sullivan M.D.**	*(508) 583-0110*
Executive Director	**Alexander F. Fleming**	*727-1788*
Deputy Director/General Counsel	**Penelope Wells**	*727-1788*

DEPARTMENT OF TELECOMMUNICATIONS AND ENERGY

Chairman	**Janet Gail Besser**	*305-3520*
Commissioner	**Eugene Sullivan**	*305-3519*
Commissioner	**James Connelly**	*305-3517*
Commissioner	**W. Robert Keating**	*305-3522*
Commissioner	**Paul B. Vasington**	*305-3521*

Directors:

Executive Director	**Timothy J. Shevlin, Jr.**	*305-3691*

Deputy Director for Administration	**Gail J. Soares**	305-3692
Deputy Director for Legislative Affairs	**Martha Leavitt**	305-3610
Cable Division	**Alicia Matthews**	727-4615
Consumer Division	**Claudine Langlois**	305-3631
Electric Power Division	**Thomas Bessette**	305-3610
Energy Facilities Siting Division	**Diedre Matthews**	305-3525
Pipeline Engineering and Safety	**Robert Smallcomb**	305-3721
Natural Gas Division	**George Yiankos**	305-3545
Legal Division	**vacant**	305-3610
Rates and Revenue Requirements	**Kevin Brannelly**	305-3663
Telecommunications	**Michael Isenberg**	305-3540
Transportation Division	**Brian Cristy**	305-3559

DIVISION OF BANKS

Commissioner	**Thomas J. Curry**	727-3145
Senior Deputy Commissioner	**Steven L. Antonakes**	727-3145
First Deputy Commissioner	**Edward J. Geary**	727-3145
Deputy Commissioner and General Counsel	**Joseph A. Leonard. Jr.**	727-3145
Consumer Assistance	**Michael Gavin**	727-3145

DIVISION OF INSURANCE

Commissioner	**Linda Louise Ruthardt**	521-7794
Asst. Commissioner Market Conduct	**Craig Spratt**	521-7338
Acting General Counsel	**Daniel Judson**	521-7308
First Deputy Commissioner	**Julie M. Bowler**	521-7301
Acting Director, State Rating Bureau	**Robert MacNicholl**	521-7794
Chief Hearing Officer	**Susan G. Anderson**	521-7794
Consumer Services	**Solmaria Marquez**	521-7794

Ex. Asst. to the Commissioner	**Albert Gill**	*521-7301*

DIVISION OF ENERGY RESOURCES

Commissioner	**David L. O'Connor**	*727-4732*
Deputy Commissioner/Operations and Resources	**Paul A. Melkonian**	*727-4732*
Deputy Commissioner/Programs	**Patricia Deese Stanton**	*727-4732*
Directors:		
Renewable and Institutional/ Residential and Commercial	**Jack Bevelaqua**	*727-4732*
General Counsel	**Robert Sydney**	*727-4732*
Policy	**Laura L. Canter**	*727-4732*
Public Information	**Joyce McMahon**	*727-4732*

DIVISION OF REGISTRATION

Director	**William G. Wood**	*727-3074*
Deputy Director for Enforcement and General Counsel	**Anne L. Collins**	*727-3074*
Deputy Director for Administration	**Craig R. Chamberlain**	*727-0100*
Deputy Director for Licensure	**Ellen J. Kolemainen**	*727-1945*

DIVISION OF STANDARDS

Director	**Donald B. Falvey**	*727-3480*
Assistant Director	**Charles H. Carroll**	*727-3480*

STATE RACING COMMISSION

Chairman	**Robert M. Hutchinson, Jr.**	*727-2581*
Associate Commissioner	**Christopher Decas**	*727-2581*
Associate Commissioner	**Arthur Khoury**	*727-2581*

Daniel A. Grabauskas

Director

Office of Consumer Affairs and Business Regulation
Address: One Ashburton Place, Room 1411, Boston, MA 02108
Telephone: (617) 727-7755 **Fax:** (617) 727-1399
Staff: Jeremy McDiarmid, Special Assistant; Ellen Cassidy, Executive Assistant
Reports to: Governor A. Paul Cellucci

PERSONAL INFORMATION:
Education: College of the Holy Cross (B.A. Political Science)
Previous Employment: Chief of Staff, Department of Economic Development; Deputy Secretary, Exec. Office of Communities and Development; Chief of Staff, Exec. Office of Health and Human Services.
Years in Current Position: 1 **Years in State Service:** 10

JOB DESCRIPTION:
Oversee nine state agencies that regulate business and professions. The purpose of the Office of Consumer Affairs and Business Regulation is to coordinate policy and planning for the agencies under its supervision and to protect the public from unfair and deceptive trade practices while encouraging business development and growth.

Kate McCormack

Deputy Director and Chief of Staff

Office of Consumer Affairs and Business Regulation
Address: One Ashburton Place, Room 1411, Boston, MA 02108
Telephone: (617) 727-7755 **Fax:** (617) 727-6094
Reports to: Director Daniel A. Grabauskas

PERSONAL INFORMATION:
Born: May 24, 1965 **Place of Birth :** Winchester
Marital Status: married (James G. Renicek)
Education: Union College, (B.A./B.S.) New England School of Law ('93)
Previous Employment: Department of Revenue/Legislative Counsel; Executive Office of Health and Human Services/Director of Special Projects; Department of Public Health/Director of Media Relations; North Shore Chamber of Commerce/Director of Public Affairs and Registered Lobbyist.
Years in Current Position: 1 **Years in State Service:** 9

JOB DESCRIPTION:
Advise the Director of policy initiatives and long-term planning. Direct, manage and review agency decisions and actions involving future policy objectives, intra-agency coordination, program for streamlining and move. Oversee the Division of Insurance, the Board of Registration in Medicine and the Division of Energy Resources.

Graham Holmes

Chief Financial Officer

Office of Consumer Affairs and Business Regulation
Address: One Ashburton Place, Room 1411, Boston, MA 02108
Telephone: (617) 573-7309 **Fax:** (617) 227-6094
E-mail: Gray.Holmes@state.ma.us
Staff: Sarah Johnson, Director of Accounting; Theresa Kelly, Personnel Director; Carol Poltz, Budget Director.
Reports to: Director Daniel Grabauskas

PERSONAL INFORMATION:
Born: March 23, 1953 **Place of Birth:** Waltham
Marital Status: married (Jody Newton) **Children:** 2
Education: Harvard College (B.A., '75; Ed.M., '82); Boston University (M.B.A., '85)
Previous Employment: Office of Consumer Affairs (Budget Director); Massachusetts Board of Medicine (Director of Operations); Harvard University (Director of Fellowships); Nichols School (teacher)
Years in Current Position: 1 **Years in State Service:** 10

JOB DESCRIPTION:
Oversee budget planning and reporting, accounts payable and receivable, human resources.

Kimberly Hinden McDonald

Director of Communications

Office of Consumer Affairs and Business Regulation
Address: One Ashburton Place, Room 1411, Boston, MA 02108
Telephone: (617)573-7308 **Fax:** (617) 227-6094
Reports to: Director Daniel Grabauskas

PERSONAL INFORMATION:
Born: August 15, 1965 **Place of Birth:** Newton
Marital Status: single
Education: Mt. Ida College (B.A., '86)
Previous Employment: Boston Housing Authority (Director of Communications, '94-'95); Massachusetts Attorney General's Office (Deputy Press Secretary, '91-'95); WCVB-TV (Assignment Editor, '86-'91)
Years in Current Position: 1 **Years in State Service:** 7

JOB DESCRIPTION:
Handle media relations for the Office of Consumer Affairs and Business Regulation and the nine agencies overseen by this office.

Walter J. Sullivan, Jr.
Chairman

Alcoholic Beverages Control Commission
Address: 100 Cambridge Street, Room 2204, Boston, MA 02202
Telephone: (617) 727-3040 ext. 312 **Fax:** (617) 727-1258
Staff: Peter J. Connelly, Executive Secretary; William Kelley, Jr., Legal Counsel; Maurice DelVendo, Chief Investigator
Reports to: Director Daniel Grabauskas

PERSONAL INFORMATION:
Born: August 26, 1959 **Place of Birth:** Brighton
Marital Status: married (Susan) **Children:** 2
Education: Boston College (B.A., '82); Boston College Law School (J.D., '88)
Previous Employment: Office of the Attorney General (Assistant Attorney General, General, Chief, Asset Forfeiture Unit); Middlesex County District Attorney's Office (Associate District Attorney, Director, Asset Forfeiture Unit)
Years in Current Position: 2 **Years in State Service:** 16

JOB DESCRIPTION:
Oversee the agency and its responsibility of controlling and regulating alcoholic beverages and the alcoholic beverages industry.

1999 PRIORITIES:
Develop partnerships with other law enforcement agencies to work on under-age drinking and community policing programs; expand educational programs to include private-public partnerships in order to increase educational programs to licensees and to children under 21 years of age, from middle school through college; expand partnership with Department of Revenue for programs that will protect revenue stream to Commonwealth.

ORGANIZATIONS:
Hingham Democratic Town Committee; Hingham Housing Partnership; Massachusetts Development Disabilities Council; Cambridge Discovery (Director); Boston College Law School Alumni Council.

Suzanne Iannella
Associate Commissioner

Alcoholic Beverages Control Commission
Address: 100 Cambridge Street, Boston, MA 02202
Telephone: (617) 727-3040 ext. 302 **Fax:** (617) 727-1258

PERSONAL INFORMATION:
Born: August 5, 1951 **Place of Birth:** Boston
Marital Status: single
Education: Boston College (B.A.)
Previous Employment: Daniel A. Mullin Associates (real estate broker)
Years in Current Position: 1

JOB DESCRIPTION:
Attend hearings, write decisions, approve licenses and transfers.

1999 PRIORITIES:
Reduce under-age drinking by educating minors as to the serious penalties; ensure that licensed premises comply with the Department of Revenue.

ORGANIZATIONS:
Republican State Committee; Neighborhood Association of Back Bay; Middlesex Club

Frederick W. Riley
Commissioner

Alcoholic Beverages Control Commission
Address: 100 Cambridge Street, Boston, MA 02202
Telephone: (617) 727-3040 **Fax:** (617) 727-1258

PERSONAL INFORMATION:
Born: November 23, 1939 **Place of Birth:** Revere
Education: Suffolk University (B.S., '67); Boston College (M.A., '69); Suffolk University Law School (J.D., '72)
Previous Employment: Department of the Attorney General
Years in Current Position: 4 **Years in State Service:** 12

JOB DESCRIPTION:
Supervise liquor industry, hold administrative hearings, set policy, approve licenses.

ORGANIZATIONS:
Massachusetts Bar Association; Phi Sigma Tau, National Honor Society for Philosophy (Charter Member)

Carl M. Sapers
Vice Chairman

Board of Registration in Medicine
Address: Hill & Barlow, One International Place,
Telephone: (617) 428-3000 **Fax:** (617) 428-3500
E-mail: csapers@hillbarlow.com
Staff: Mahtowin Munro, Assistant

PERSONAL INFORMATION:
Born: July 16, 1932 **Place of Birth:** Boston
Marital Status: married (Judith) **Children:** 3
Education: Harvard (B.A. '53); Harvard Law (L.L.B. '58)
Years in Current Position: 3 **Years in State Service:** 3

Alexander F. Fleming

Executive Director

Board of Registration in Medicine
Address: 10 West Street, 3rd Floor, Boston, MA 02111
Telephone: (617) 727-1788 ext. 321 **Fax:** (617) 451-9568
Staff: Barbara Rose, Executive Assistant
Reports to: Director Daniel Grabauskas

PERSONAL INFORMATION:

Born: March 25, 1949 **Place of Birth:** New Haven, CT
Marital Status: married (Karla) **Children:** 1
Education: University of Michigan (B.A., Political Science/Education, '71); Suffolk University Law School (J.D., '80)
Previous Employment: Disabled Persons Protection Commission (Executive Director); Department of Social Services (Deputy General Counsel)
Years in Current Position: 8 **Years in State Service:** 18

JOB DESCRIPTION:

Chief Executive Officer of State Medical Licensing and Disciplinary Board.

1999 PRIORITIES:

Maintain and improve physician profiles, expand information available on web site, continue work on physician retraining.

Penelope Wells

Deputy Director, General Counsel

Board of Registration in Medicine
Address: 10 West Street, 3rd Floor, Boston, MA 02111
Telephone: (617) 727-1788 ext. 316 **Fax:** (617) 451-9568
E-mail: PWells@state.ma.us
Staff: Debra Stoller, Deputy General Counsel; Caroline Fiore, Assistant General Counsel; Carol Meany, Assistant General Counsel; Virginia Cunningham, Paralegal
Reports to: Executive Director Alexander F. Fleming

PERSONAL INFORMATION:

Education: Wellesley College (B.A., '73); Boston University School of Law (J.D., '77)
Previous Employment: Executive Office of Consumer Affairs and Business Regulation (Assistant Secretary); Massachusetts Cable Commission (Executive Director); Massachusetts Cable Commission (General Counsel); Kalba Bowen Associates (Project Manager); Federal Communications Commission (General Attorney)
Years in Current Position: 7 **Years in State Service:** 13

Department of Telecommunications and Energy

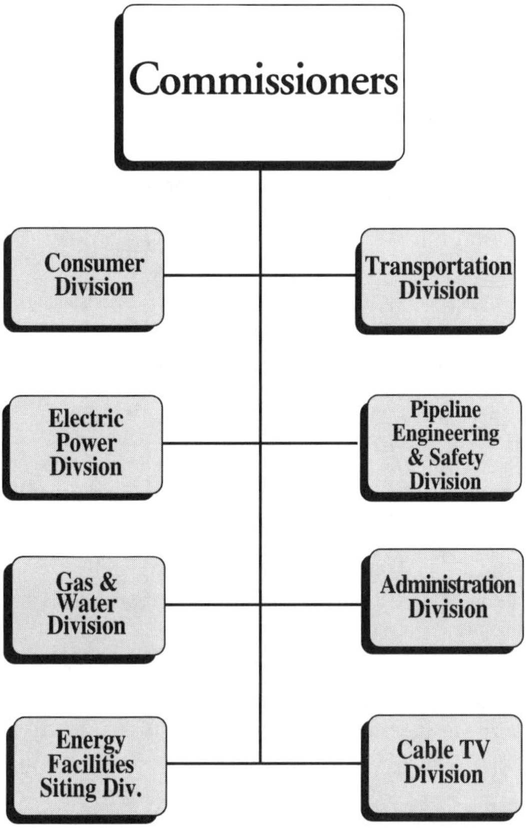

Janet Gail Besser
Chair

Department of Telecommunications and Energy
Address: 100 Cambridge Street, 12th Floor, Boston, MA 02202
Telephone: (617) 305-3520 **Fax:** (617) 723-8812
E-mail: Janet.Gail.Besser@state.ma.us
Staff: Maxine Tassinari-Teixeira, Administrative Assistant
Reports to: Director Daniel Grabauskas

PERSONAL INFORMATION:
Born: May 2, 1957 **Place of Birth:** Philadelphia
Marital Status: married (Daniel Seibert) **Children:** 2
Education: Williams College (B.A., '79); JFK School of Government, Harvard University (M.A., '85)
Previous Employment: Commissioner, Massachusetts Department of Telecommunications and Energy; National Independent Energy Producers (Policy Director); Massachusetts Department of Public Utilities (Director of Electric Power Division); New Hampshire Public Utilities Commission (Manager of Energy Planning)
Years in Current Position: 1 **Years in State Service:** 9

JOB DESCRIPTION:
To decide cases that determine the rates and affect the operation of privately owned electric, gas, and water companies as well as common carriers such as telephones, railway, truck, and bus companies in Massachusetts and to ensure the safety of related facilities and equipment.

1999 PRIORITIES:
To continue implement electric industry restructuring which will bring lower electric rates to Massachusetts consumers; to integrate competition in telecommunications and gas.

ORGANIZATIONS:
Past President, New England Conference of Public Utilities Commissioners; National Association of Regulatory Utility Commissioners; Electric Power Research Institute (Advisory Council); Energy Foundation Utility Futures Group; Commonwealth Children's Center (Board of Directors)

Eugene Sullivan
Commissioner

Department of Telecommunications and Energy
Address: 100 Cambridge St. 12th Fl, Boston, MA 02202
Telephone: (617) 305-3519 **Fax:** (617) 723-8812
E-mail: eugene.sullivan@state.ma.us
Staff: Jennifer O'Brien, assistant
Reports to: Director Daniel Grabauskas

PERSONAL INFORMATION:
Born: December 25, 1953 **Place of Birth:** Wakefield
Marital Status: married (Mary) **Children:** 1
Education: Boston College (B.A. '81); Harvard (MPA, '82)
Previous Employment: President Boston Transit Group
Years in Current Position: 1 **Years in State Service:** 1

JOB DESCRIPTION:
Oversight of public utilities and cable television industry.

1999 PRIORITIES:
Continue progress towards true industry deregulation and competition while protecting consumer interests.

James Connelly
Commissioner

Department of Telecommunications and Energy
Address: 100 Cambridge St., 12th Fl, Boston, MA 02202
Telephone: (617) 305-3517 **Fax:** (617) 723-8812
E-mail: jconnelly @state.ma.us
Reports to: DirectorDaniel Grabauskas

PERSONAL INFORMATION:
Education: University of Massachusetts at Amherst (B.A.; M.A.); Suffolk University Law School (J.D.)
Previous Employment: Office of Consumer Affairs and Business Regulation (General Counsel); Department of Public Utilities (General Counsel); Boston Gas Company; The MITRE Corp.
Years in Current Position: 1 **Years in State Service:** 4

ORGANIZATIONS:
Massachusetts, Maine, and District of Columbia Bar Associations

W. Robert Keating
Commissioner

Department of Telecommunications and Energy
Address: 100 Cambridge St., 12th Fl, Boston, MA 02202
Telephone: (617) 305-3522 **Fax:** (617) 723-8812
E-mail:robert.keating@state.ma.us
Staff: Rita McQueeney, Administrative Assistant
Reports to: Director Daniel Grabauskas

PERSONAL INFORMATION:
Education: University of Massachusetts at Amherst (B.A.); University of Maine, Orono (M.S.)
Marital Status: married **Children:** 3
Years in Current Position:1 **Years in State Service:**1

JOB DESCRIPTION:
To decide cases that determine rates and affect the operations of monopoly utility companies (electric; natural gas, telecommunications; water) and to implement rules and regulations to move these industries to a competitive environment, consistent with the legislative intent.

1999 PRIORITIES:
To help establish a workable competitive environment for the electric, gas and telecommunications industries.

Paul B. Vasington
Commissioner

Department of Telecommunications and Energy
Address: 100 Cambridge St., 12th Fl, Boston, MA 02202
Telephone: (617) 305-3521 **Fax:** (617) 723-8812
E-mail: paul.vasington@state.ma.us
Staff: Jennifer O'Brien, assistant
Reports to: Director Daniel Grabauskas

PERSONAL INFORMATION:
Born: Nov. 17, 1966 **Place of Birth:** Nyack, NY
Marital Status: married (Erin) **Children:** 2
Education: Boston College (B.A. '89); Harvard (M.P.P. '91)
Previous Employment: National Economic Research Associates, Inc. Senior Analyst.; Department of Public Utilities, Director of Telecommunications.
Years in Current Position: 1 **Years in State Service:** 7

JOB DESCRIPTION:
Oversight of public utilities.

1999 PRIORITIES:
Promotion of competition and deregulation of utility industries.

Thomas J. Curry
Commissioner of Banks

Division of Banks
Address: 100 Cambridge Street, Room 2004, Boston, MA 02202
Telephone: (617) 727-3145 ext. 361 **Fax:** (617) 727-7631
Staff: Jean H. Powers, Administrative Assistant
Reports to: Director Daniel Grabauskas

PERSONAL INFORMATION:
Education: Manhattan College (B.A., '78); New England School of Law (J.D., '81)
Previous Employment: Secretary of State's Public Records Division (Legal Counsel)
Years in Current Position: 4 **Years in State Service:** 15

JOB DESCRIPTION:
Maintain a safe and sound competitive banking and financial services environment throughout the Commonwealth and ensure compliance with community reinvestment and consumer protection laws by chartering, licensing, and supervising state regulated financial institutions in a professional and innovative manner.

Edward J. Geary
First Deputy Commissioner of Banks

Division of Banks
Address: 100 Cambridge Street, Room 2004, Boston, MA 02202
Telephone: (617) 727-3145 ext. 329 **Fax:** (617) 727-7631
Staff: Diane Straccia, Administrative Assistant
Reports to: Commissioner Thomas J. Curry

PERSONAL INFORMATION:
Born: March 8, 1947 **Place of Birth:** Boston
Marital Status: married (Deborah) **Children:** 2
Education: Boston College (B.A.) Graduate School of Savings Banking at Brown University ('77)
Previous Employment: Massachusetts Division of Banks (Senior Deputy Commissioner)
Years in Current Position: 22 **Years in State Service:** 30

Joseph A. Leonard, Jr.
Deputy Commissioner of Banks and General Counsel

Division of Banks
Address: 100 Cambridge Street, Room 2004, Boston, MA 02202
Telephone: (617) 727-3145 ext. 317 **Fax:** (617) 727-7631
Staff: Gary M. Backaler, Deputy General Counsel; Cynthia A. Begin, Assistant General Counsel
Reports to: Commissioner Thomas J. Curry

PERSONAL INFORMATION:
Born: June 14, 1950 **Place of Birth:** Boston
Education: Boston Latin School; Boston College ('72); Suffolk University Law School ('85)
Previous Employment: Massachusetts Division of Banks and Loan Agencies (First Deputy Commissioner of Banks); Joint Committee on Banks and Banking, Massachusetts Legislature (Research Director)
Years in Current Position: 11 **Years in State Service:** 22

Linda Louise Ruthardt
Commissioner of Insurance

Division of Insurance
Address: 470 Atlantic Avenue, Boston, MA 02210
Telephone: (617) 521-7794 **Fax:** (617)521-7758
Reports to: Director Daniel Grabauskas

PERSONAL INFORMATION:
Born: January 10, 1945 **Place of Birth:** Reading, PA
Marital Status: married (Guy)
Education: New England Conservatory of Music (B.A., Music/Voice, '67); Insurance Institute of America (A.R.M ., '75)
Previous Employment: G.S. of the U.S.A. (Director, Risk and Insurance); Raytheon (Manager, Employee Disability Programs); Barry Wright Corporation (Director, Risk Management)

Years in Current Position: 5 **Years in State Service:** 5

JOB DESCRIPTION:

Oversee insurance regulation that provides consumers with products of the insurance industry as they need or want by law.

ORGANIZATIONS:

American Camping Association; American Red Cross; Camp Fire Boys & Girls, Inc.

Julie M. Bowler

First Deputy Commissioner

Division of Insurance
Address: 470 Atlantic Avenue, Boston, MA 02210
Telephone: (617) 521-7301 **Fax:** (617) 521-7758
E-mail: Julie.M.Bowler@state.ma.us
Reports to: Commissioner Linda Ruthardt

PERSONAL INFORMATION:

Born: April 7, 1963 **Place of Birth:** Springfield
Education: Assumption College (B.A. '85); University of Dallas (M.A. '87); Georgetown University Doctoral Candidate; UMASS (M.B.A. est. 2000)
Marital Status: single
Previous Employment: Division of Medical Assistance (Insurance Program Consultant); Blue Cross Blue Shield (Government Relations); Minority Leaders Office) Director of Research and Budget)
Years in Current Position: new **Years in State Service:** 5

JOB DESCRIPTION:

Manage operations of the Division of Insurance, coordinate legislative activities and oversee special projects.

Susan G. Anderson

Chief Hearing Officer

Division of Insurance
Address: 470 Atlantic Avenue, Boston, MA 02210
Telephone: (617) 521-7794 **Fax:** (617) 521-7770
Staff: Shelagh Ellman-Pearl, Chief Health Insurance Hearing Officer; Jean Farrington, Sharon Kamowitz, Hearing Officers
Reports to: Commissioner Linda Ruthardt

PERSONAL INFORMATION:

Education: Mount Holyoke College (A.B. '73); Boston University School of Law (J.D., '76)
Previous Employment: Division of Insurance (Hearing Officer)
Years in Current Position: 8 **Years in State Service:** 10

JOB DESCRIPTION:

Preside over adjudicatory and regulatory hearings, coordinate work of hearing officers.

ORGANIZATIONS:

Women's Bar Association; Massachusetts Bar Association

Solmaria Marquez

Director of Consumer Service

Division of Insurance
Address: 470 Atlantic Avenue, Boston, MA 02210
Telephone: (617) 521-7794 **Fax:** (617) 521-7772
Reports to: Assistant Commissioner Craig Spratt

PERSONAL INFORMATION:
Born: January 13, 1962 **Place of Birth:** Framingham
Marital Status: married (Cesar)
Education: Salem State College (B.S., Business Administration, '96)
Years in Current Position: 2 **Years in State Service:** 11

JOB DESCRIPTION:
Oversee the daily activities of the Consumer Service Section while making sure consumer insurance inquiries are handled and resolved; report patterns of noncompliance by insurance companies.

David L. O'Connor

Commissioner

Division of Energy Resources
Address: 100 Cambridge Street, Room 1500, Boston, MA 02202
Telephone: (617) 727-4732 **Fax:** (617) 727-0030
Staff: Dorothy Cloherty, Assistant to the Commissioner
Reports to: Director Daniel Grabauskas

PERSONAL INFORMATION:
Born: November 26, 1952
Place of Birth: Bridgeport, CT
Marital Status: married (Daria Lyons O'Connor) **Children:** 2
Education: Middlebury College (B.A., '74); Harvard University (M.P.A., '94)
Previous Employment: Massachusetts Executive Office for Administration and Finance (Chief of Staff); Massachusetts Office of Dispute Resolution (Executive Director)
Years in Current Position: 4 **Years in State Service:** 13

JOB DESCRIPTION:
Direct agency which develops and implements state energy policies and programs.

1999 PRIORITIES:
Reduce energy prices and increase customer choice by restructuring electric and gas utilities.

ORGANIZATIONS:
Cambridge Dispute Settlement Center (President); Paulist Center, R.C. Community

Paul A. Melkonian

Deputy Commissioner for Operations & Resources

Division of Energy Resources
Address: 100 Cambridge Street, Room 1500, Boston, MA 02202
Telephone: (617) 727-4732 **Fax:** (617) 727-0030
E-mail: paul.melkonian@state.ma.us
Reports to: Commissioner David O'Connor

PERSONAL INFORMATION:

Born: July 9, 1962 **Place of Birth:** Melrose
Marital Status: married (Donna) **Children:** 2
Education: Cambridge College (M.M. candidate, '00)
Previous Employment: Chief of Staff, Senator Richard Tisei ('94-'97); Department of Employment & Training (Personnel officer, '91-94')
Years in Current Position: 1 **Years in State Service:** 8

JOB DESCRIPTION:

As the Division's chief administrative officer, I manage all budget, spending, contracting, and other fiscal activities. Acquire and manage the resources necessary for the division's operations, including facilities information technology, supplies, equipment, and human resources.

ORGANIZATIONS:

Stoneham School Committee (1993- present)

Patricia Deese Stanton

Deputy Commissioner for Programs

Division of Energy Resources
Address: 100 Cambridge Street, Room 1500, Boston, MA 02202
Telephone: (617) 727-4732 **Fax:** (617) 727-0030
Staff: Edna Dankens, Secretary
Reports to: Commissioner David O'Connor

PERSONAL INFORMATION:

Education: Tufts ('70); MIT ('76) ;Harvard ('96)
Previous Employment: Assistant Commissioner Department of Environmental protection
Years in Current Position: 2 **Years in State Service:** 12

Laura L. Canter

Director of Policy

Division of Energy Resources
Address: 100 Cambridge Street, Room 1500, Boston, MA 02202
Telephone: (617) 727-4732 **Fax:** (617) 727-0030
E-mail: Laura.Canter@state.ma.us
Staff: Lillian Larci, Administrative Assistant
Reports to: Commissioner David O'Connor

PERSONAL INFORMATION:

Born: February 28, 1965 **Place of Birth:** Detroit
Education: Emerson College (B.A. '86); Bentley College (M.B.A. '91)
Previous Employment: Massachusetts Development Finance Agency, Manager, Strategic Initiatives; State Street Bank and Trust Company, Assistant Vice President
Years in Current Position: new **Years in State Service:** 3

JOB DESCRIPTION:

Developing agency policy and managing policy unit staff.

Joyce A. McMahon

Director of Public Information

Division of Energy Resources
Address: 100 Cambridge Street, Room 1500, Boston, MA 02202
Telephone: (617) 727-4732 **Fax:** (617) 727-0093
E-mail: joyce.mcmahon@state.ma.us
Staff: Jerome Shea, Wayne Mastin, Karin Pisiewski, Consumer Editors
Reports to: Paul Melkonian, Deputy Commissioner

PERSONAL INFORMATION:

Born: August 29, 1964 **Place of Birth:** Beverly
Education: Emerson College, (B.S. '86)
Previous Employment: Peabody Downtown Partnership, Executive Director (1990-94); Caravan for Commuters, Marketing Specialist (1989-90); New Medico Assoc., Conference Manager (1988-89); S.D. Warren Co. Public Relations Assistant (1986)
Years in Current Position: new **Years in State Service:** 3

JOB DESCRIPTION:

Plan and direct all media and communication activities for the agency. Oversee development of all publications and manage public education campaigns.

1999 PRIORITIES:

Educating Massachusetts's electricity consumers about the changes in the industry and their options in the new market.

ORGANIZATIONS:

City Councillor, City of Beverly, (1994-present); Spar & Spindle Girl Scout Council, Board of Directors; League of Women Voters - member.

William G. Wood

Director

Division of Registration
Address: 100 Cambridge Street, Room 1520, Boston, MA 02202
Telephone: (617) 727-3074 ext. 6 **Fax:** (617) 727-2197
Staff: Craig Chamberlain, Deputy Director, Administration; Anne Collins, Deputy Director, Enforcement; Ellen Kolemainen, Deputy Director, Professional Licensure
Reports to: Director Daniel Grabauskas

PERSONAL INFORMATION:
Born: September 25, 1953 **Place of Birth:** Pennsylvania
Marital Status: married (Elisa Miale Wood) **Children:** 1
Education: Boston College (B.A. '86)
Previous Employment: Chief Legislative and Administrative Aide for State Senator Paul V. Doane; Wood & Associates (Partner, Public Relations)
Years in Current Position: 8 **Years in State Service:** 11

JOB DESCRIPTION:
Oversee 32 occupational licensure boards; responsible for providing legal, investigative and administrative services to the boards.

1999 PRIORITIES:
Provide 24 hours per day, seven days per week consumer access to public information in licensee database.

Anne L. Collins

Deputy Director for Enforcement/General Counsel

Division of Registration
Address: 100 Cambridge Street, Room 1520, Boston, MA 02202
Telephone: (617) 727-3074 **Fax:** (617) 727-2197
E-mail: acollins@state.ma.us; Anne L. Collins@Admin@Reg
Staff: Ray Pejeri
Reports to: Director William G. Wood

PERSONAL INFORMATION:
Born: April 28, 1961 **Place of Birth:** Newton
Marital Status: single
Education: Trinity College (B.A., '83); Northeastern University, School of Law (J.D., '88)
Years in Current Position: 7
Years in State Service: 9

Craig R. Chamberlain
Deputy Director for Administration

Division of Registration
Address: 100 Cambridge Street, Room 1520, Boston, MA 02202
Telephone: (617) 727-0100 **Fax:** (617) 727-2197
E-mail: Craig.Chamberlain@state.ma.us
Staff: Susan Dolabary, Manager, Accounting Services; Timothy Healy, Manager, Computer Services
Reports to: Director William G. Wood

PERSONAL INFORMATION:
Born: Dec. 5, 1943 **Place of Birth:** Springfield
Marital Status: married (Pamela Young Chamberlain)
Children: 2
Education: Babson College (B.S. '65)
Previous Employment: Mahoney, Chamberlain Insurance Inc. (president); Chamberlain & Sona Realty Co. (managing partner)
Years in Current Position: 6 **Years in State Service:** 7

JOB DESCRIPTION:
Oversee the accounting and computer service units of the Division of Registration. Responsible for the day to day operation of the physical support systems for the boards and service units.

1999 PRIORITIES:
Coordinate the Division move from the Saltonstall Building to a new location at 239 Causeway Street.

Donald B. Falvey
Director

Division of Standards
Address: One Ashburton Place, Boston, MA 02108
Telephone: (617) 727-3480 **Fax:** (617) 727-5705
Staff: Charles H. Carroll, Assistant Director
Reports to: Director Daniel Grabauskas

PERSONAL INFORMATION:
Years in Current Position: 37 **Years in State Service:** 47

JOB DESCRIPTION:
To direct statutory operations of the Division. Administration of Weights and Measures throughout the Commonwealth.

Charles H. Carroll

Assistant Director

Division of Standards
Address: One Ashburton Place, Boston, MA 02108
Telephone: (617) 727-3480 **Fax:** (617) 727-5705
Staff: Mary DeYoung, Business Management Specialist; Steven Berard, Inspector
Reports to: Director Donald B. Falvey

PERSONAL INFORMATION:
Born: October 23, 1940 **Place of Birth:** Chelsea
Marital Status: married (June) **Children:** 4
Years in Current Position: 14 **Years in State Service:** 40

JOB DESCRIPTION:
Assist the Director in managing the Division's operations as mandated by statute. The primary mission of the Division is the administration of weights and measures law enforcement.

Robert M. Hutchinson, Jr.

Chairman

Massachusetts State Racing Commission
Address: One Ashburton Place, Room 1313, Boston, MA 02108
Telephone: (617) 727-2581 **Fax:** (617) 227-6062
Staff: Elizabeth M. Barry, Executive Secretary; George Collins, Auditor; Michael J. Callahan, Special Assistant to the Commissioner

PERSONAL INFORMATION:
Born: October 8, 1942
Marital Status: married (Deborah) **Children:** 3
Education: University of Massachusetts at Amherst (B.A., '64); University of Bridgeport (M.A.'73); Kennedy School Executive Program; Sloan School Executive Training Program
Previous Employment: Johnson, Mee & May (Administrator); Commonwealth of Massachusetts (Registrar of Motor Vehicles); Town of Lexington (Town Manager); Town of Plainville, Connecticut (Assistant Town Manager); Town of Stratford, Connecticut (Assistant Town Manager); Executive Office for Administration and Finance (Assistant Secretary)
Years in Current Position: 6 **Years in State Service:** 21

JOB DESCRIPTION:
Supervise day-to-day operation of the Racing Commission, ensuring the integrity of operations. Regulatory responsibilities include but are not limited to licensing, law enforcement, auditing, accounting and systems for this $545 million per year activity.

1999 PRIORITIES:
Modernize and update automated financial systems, updating licensing, modernization of plans. Update regulatory structure regarding racing and gaming.

ORGANIZATIONS:
Better Business Bureau (Director); International City Management; American Society of Public Administration; American Association of Motor Vehicle Administrators

Economic Development

The Department of Economic Development is responsible for setting economic policy, promoting Massachusetts as a place to do business, increasing the job base, and generating economic activity in the Commonwealth.

The following agencies are within the Department of Economic Development:

- *Massachusetts Office of Business Development*
- *Massachusetts Office of International Trade and Investment*
- *Massachusetts Office of Travel and Tourism*
- *Office of Film and Video Development*
- *State Office of Minority and Women's Business Assistance*

The Department also provides general policy guidance for the following quasi-public agencies engaged in economic development initiatives, although it does not manage or control these agencies:

- *Corporation for Business, Work, and Learning*
- *Community Development Corporation*
- *Massachusetts Development Finance Agency*
- *Massachusetts Technology Development Corporation*
- *Massachusetts Technology Park Corporation*
- *Massachusetts Small Business Development Center*

Office of Business Development

The Office of Business Development (MOBD) serves communities across the Commonwealth. MOBD works to attract new businesses by facilitating their relocation to Massachusetts. Whether a company needs to train employees for a new manufacturing line, find financing for an innovation, or work through the licensing issues surrounding a new construction, the MOBD serves as their one contact.

With the creation of five One-Stop Business Centers, individuals in large companies or small businesses no longer need to know all of the services and regulations of the state. Now, one phone number provides access to the full spectrum of business development resources.

Massachusetts Trade Office

The Massachusetts Trade Office (formerly known ad the Office of International Trade and Investment (MOITI) seeks to stimulate export development and foreign investment in Massachusetts industries. MassTrade assists Massachusetts companies looking to export products or services by providing export counseling, coordinating participation in trade shows and Governor and Lieutenant Governor-led trade missions, arranging meetings with foreign buying missions, and hosting strategic industry and market seminars. MassTrade also works with foreign businesses interested in investment, joint ventures, or partnerships with Massachusetts companies. As the international division of Massachusetts state government, MassTrade has forged a number of agreements with foreign government and trade promotion organizations. These accords establish direct links to foreign trade officials and provide a framework for joint trade activities.

Office of Travel and Tourism

The Massachusetts Office of Travel and Tourism (MOTT) manages a year-round advertising and marketing program to increase travel to Massachusetts from domestic and foreign markets. MOTT also provides marketing support and technical assistance to Massachusetts travel businesses and tourism marketing organizations. The agency coordinates its activities with the state's regional tourist councils in describing cultural, historical, and recreational places and events. MOTT also works closely with other state and regional agencies on marketing, tourism services, and infrastructure issues.

Office of Film and Video Development

The Office of Film and Video Development seeks to promote economic growth by encouraging motion picture and television production in Massachusetts. The office works to attract out-of-state productions to the Commonwealth and to assist the local production industry. It functions as a liaison between the film industry and local and state governments. The office also offers a number of technical services to visiting and local production companies, including location scouting, on-location assistance, and theatrical staffing resources.

State Office of Minority and Women Business Assistance

The mission of the Office of Minority and Women Business Assistance (SOMWBA) is to foster and support the development and growth of minority and women's business enterprises and non-profit organizations. SOMWBA facilitates their participation in the mainstream of the state's economy through increased access to business and economic development opportunities. It promotes the fullest utilization of these socially and economically disadvantaged enterprises by federal, state, and local agencies, and the private sector. SOMWBA offers services in certification, enforcement, business assistance, and advocacy. Certification services provide constituents access to affirmative procurement programs. Enforcement efforts help to ensure that only bona fide enterprises are certified. Business assistance services provide a central resource and referral service to constituents. Advocacy efforts help to ensure that the needs and concerns of minority and women's businesses not only are heard, but are also promoted, in order to provide equal access and opportunity to all.

Corporation for Business, Work, and Learning

The Corporation for Business, Work, and Learning was created by the merger of the Bay State Skills Corporation and the Industrial Services Program, and provides services that promote business modernization, economic growth, and employment opportunities. The corporation educates, trains, and motivates individuals to maximize their productive potential in the workplace. It works in partnership with companies, entrepreneurs, and industry groups through finance and consulting services to improve competitiveness and to benefit the workforce. The corporation designs, tests, and disseminates new approaches to manufacturing, business operations, program delivery, teaching, and learning to inform and influence the practices of industry, education, and government.

Massachusetts Development Finance Agency

The Massachusetts Development Finance Agency (MassDevelopment) was created by the affiliation of the Massachusetts Industrial Finance Agency and the Massachusetts Government Land Bank, and is the state's largest source of financing for economic and community development projects. MassDevelopment provides predevelopment assistance funds, tax-exempt and taxable bonds, and a variety of loan and loan guarantee programs. The agency also provides concentrated financing and technical support to large-scale real estate development projects.

Massachusetts Technology Park Corporation

Massachusetts Technology Park Corporation is a public-private partnership consisting of two operating divisions -- the Massachusetts Technology Park and the Massachusetts Technology Collaborative (MTC). The mission of the corporation is to serve as the principal agent of the Commonwealth in creating a more attractive and responsive environment for the development, growth, and expansion of technology-intensive industries in Massachusetts by forging collaborative relationships among industry, universities, and government that result in increased innovation, commercial activity, and job creation. The purpose of MTC is to implement collaborative programmatic initiatives, one of which is the Federal Technology Funding Program (FEDTech). The overall goal of FEDTech is to spur the development of new technology in Massachusetts by assisting companies in securing funds from the federal government through the Technology Reinvestment Program under the Advanced Research Projects Agency, and the Advanced Technology Program at the National Institute of Science and Technology.

Massachusetts Technology Development Corporation

The Massachusetts Technology Development Corporation (MTDC) provides venture capital financing to new and expanding high technology companies that have the capacity to generate significant employment growth and other public benefits in Massachusetts. MTDC assistance provides a magnet to attract private risk or venture capital investments in the early stage of a firm's development. The purposes of MTDC's investments are to help create primary employment in technology-based industries in Massachusetts; attract and leverage private investment in Massachusetts companies; foster the application of technological innovations where Massachusetts companies are or can be leaders; and nurture entrepreneurship among Massachusetts citizens, planting the seeds for long-term economic development.

Massachusetts Small Business Development Center

The Massachusetts Small Business Development Center (MSBDC) at the University of Massachusetts at Amherst is a quasi-public agency dedicated to providing to small businesses a high-quality program of one-to-one management and technical assistance, counseling, and educational programs by effectively combining the resources of government, education, and the private sector. Through a network of regional and specialty centers, the MSBDC provides free counseling to prospective and existing small businesses on topics such as business plan development, finance, cash flow management, human resource issues, marketing, and international trade.

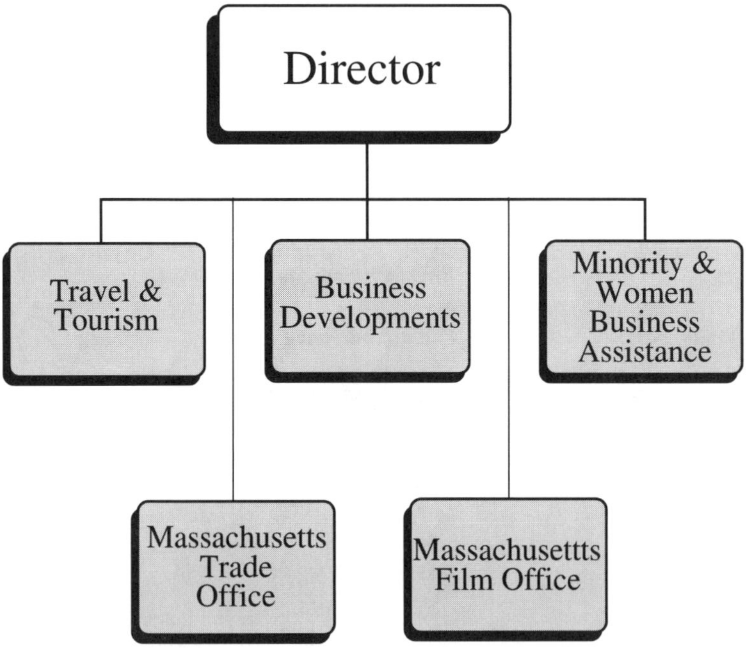
Director
Travel & Tourism
Business Developments
Minority & Women Business Assistance
Massachusetts Trade Office
Massachusettts Film Office

Department of Economic Development

Director	**Carolyn Boviard**	727-8380
Chief of Staff	**Gordon Carr**	727-8380
Chief Financial Officer	**Diana Salemy**	727-8380
Director of Communications	**Alex J. Sutton**	727-8380
General Counsel	**J. Todd Fernandez**	727-8380

MASSACHUSETTS FILM OFFICE

Director	**Robin E. Dawson**	973-8800

MASSACHUSETTS OFFICE OF BUSINESS DEVELOPMENT

Acting Director	**Bruce William Stebbins**	727-3206
Regional Director, Boston	**Richard Sweeney**	727-1515
Regional Director, Springfield	**Matthew M. Kerwood**	(413) 784-1580
Regional Director, Worcester	**Charles Miller**	(508) 757-2075
Regional Director, Dartmouth	**Larry Cameron**	(508) 997-1438
Regional Director, Lowell	**Orlando Salazar**	(508) 970-1193

MASSACHUSETTS TRADE OFFICE

Executive Director	**Kathleen S. Molony**	367-1830
Deputy Director	**Nam Van Pham**	367-1830

MASSACHUSETTS OFFICE OF TRAVEL AND TOURISM

Executive Director	**Mary Jane McKenna**	973-8500
Deputy Director	**Jonathan Hyde**	973-8500

STATE OFFICE OF MINORITY AND WOMEN BUSINESS ASSISTANCE

Executive Director	**vacant**	973-8692
Senior Director of Business and Advocacy	**David Villeneuve**	973-8692

Director of Business and Advocacy	**Davida K. Craig**	*973-8692*

MASSACHUSETTS SMALL BUSINESS DEVELOPMENT CENTER

State Director	**Georgiana Parkin** *(Interim)*	*(413) 545-6301*

MASSACHUSETTS TECHNOLOGY COLLABORATIVE

President	**Joseph D. Alviani**	*(508) 870-0312*
Deputy Director/General Counsel/ Secretary	**Philip F. Holahan**	*(508) 870-0312*

J. Todd Fernandez

General Counsel

Department of Economic Development
Address: One Ashburton Place, Room 2100, Boston, MA 02108
Telephone: (617) 727-8380 **Fax:** (617) 727-8797
E-mail: tfernandez@state.ma.us
Reports to: Director Carolyn Boviard

PERSONAL INFORMATION:
Born: November 30, 1964
Place of Birth: Tampa, FL
Education: Boston University (Cum Laude, 20th Century European History, '86); Boston University School of Law ('89)
Previous Employment: Executive Office of Consumer Affairs & Business Regulation (Assistant Secretary); Mahoney, Hawkes and Goldings (Litigation Attorney); Office of Business Development (Chief Legal Counsel)
Years in Current Position: 1 **Years in State Service:** 4

JOB DESCRIPTION:
Provide general corporate, environmental and administrative legal counsel; develop and implement economic development policy, programs and legislation; coordinate economic development policy with environmental policy; chair Municipal Permit Streamlining Committee.

ORGANIZATIONS:
Massachusetts Gay and Lesbian Equal Rights Lobby; Massachusetts Gay and Lesbian Anti-Violence Fund

Robin E. Dawson

Director

Massachusetts Film Office
Address: 10 Park Plaza, Suite 2310, Boston, MA 02116
Telephone: (617) 973-8800 **Fax:** (617) 973-8810

E-mail: film@state.ma.us
Staff: Tim Grafft, Deputy Director; John Alzapiedi, Production Coordinator; Ann Scanlon, Marketing & Events Coordinator; Susan Salerno, Office Manager; Bonnie Flood, Program Manager
Reports to: Director Carolyn Boviard

PERSONAL INFORMATION:
Place of Birth: Rockport **Marital Status:** single

Previous Employment: Office of the Governor (Special Assistant)
Years in Current Position: 4 **Years in State Service:** 8

JOB DESCRIPTION:
Generate revenue and jobs through film and television production in the Commonwealth.

1999 PRIORITIES:
Increase level of film and television production; work with local production community; create and develop additional filmmaking incentives.

ORGANIZATIONS:
Rockport Congregational Church

Bruce William Stebbins
Director

Massachusetts Office of Business Development
Address: One Ashburton Place, Boston, MA 02108
Telephone: (617) 727-3206 **Fax:** (617) 727-8797
E-mail: Bruce.Stebbins@state.ma.us
Staff: Camille Passatempo, Administrative Secretary
Reports to: Director Carolyn Boviard

PERSONAL INFORMATION:
Born: November 16, 1965 **Place of Birth:** Springfield
Marital Status: single
Education: George Washington University (B.A., Political Science, '87)
Previous Employment: Governor's Western Massachusetts Office (Director); White House Office of Political Affairs (Associate Director); Office of the Secretary, U.S. Department of Transportation (Staff Assistant)
Years in Current Position: 1 **Years in State Service:** 6

JOB DESCRIPTION:
Responsible for the opertion of the state's primary business retention and attraction effort. Oversee agency with five regional offices.

ORGANIZATIONS:
Make-a-Wish Foundation of Western Massachusetts; East Longmeadow Republican Town Committee; Court Appointed Special Advocates; The Children's Study Home; Springfield Rotary Club; Friends of Pine Knoll; East Longmeadow Schols Committee

Matthew M. Kerwood
Regional Director

Massachusetts Office of Business Development
Address: Springfield State Office Building, 436 Dwight St. Rm B-40, Springfield, MA 01103
Telephone: (413) 784-1580 **Fax:** (413) 739-9175
E-mail: matt.kerwood@state.ma.us
Staff: Arthur D. Levin, Project Manager; John P. Sweklo, Business Finance Specialist; Susan Torino, Administrative Assistant
Reports to: Director Bruce W. Stebbins

PERSONAL INFORMATION:
Born: November 12, 1968 **Place of Birth:** Pittsfield
Marital Status: married (Jennifer)
Education: Fairfield University (B.A. '90)
Previous Employment: State Senator Jane Swift, Legislative Aid
Years in Current Position: new **Years in State Service:** 7

JOB DESCRIPTION:
Planning, managing, coordinating and monitoring the state's overall regional economic development efforts. In consultation with the Director, but with a wide latitude for independent decision making, the Regional Director supervises 3-6 regional office staff who provide support to assist businesses to create, maintain and relocate jobs to Massachusetts. The Regional Director is also responsible for coordinating the efforts of a Regional Advisory Board for the formation of regional economic development plans and strategies.

ORGANIZATIONS:
Berkshire Regional Food and Land Council; Pittsfield Proud Committee; Berkshire County Republican Association

Larry Cameron

Southeastern Regional Director

Massachusetts Office of Business Development
Address: UMASS Dartmouth, 285 Old Westport Road, Dartmouth MA 02747-2300
Telephone: (508) 997-1438 **Fax: (508)** 997-3067
E-mail: LarryCameron@state.ma.us
Staff: Norma Sylvia, Administrative Assistant
Reports to: Bruce Stebbins, MOBD Executive Director

PERSONAL INFORMATION:
Born: May 19, 1946 **Place of Birth:** Quincy
Education: UMASS Dartmouth, (1975); Suffolk University, MPA
Previous Employment: Town of Rowley, administrative assistant; Town of Sherborn, town administrator; Town of Dartmouth, Executive Secretary.
Years in Current Position: 3 **Years in State Service:** 5

JOB DESCRIPTION:
Management and operation of MOBD "One Stop" regional business assistance center for Southeastern Massachusetts, (includes Bristol, Plymouth, Barnstable, Dukes, and Nantucket counties, and portions of Norfolk and Middlesex counties).

1999 PRIORITIES:
Assisting businesses in South Eastern Massachusetts to expand, grow and prosper; to attract new companies to the region.

ORGANIZATIONS:
Mass Alliance for Economic Development, Greater New Bedford Industrial Foundation

Kathleen S. Molony
Executive Director

Massachusetts Trade Office
Address: 10 Park Plaza, Suite 3720, Boston, MA 02116
Telephone: (617) 367-1830 **Fax:** (617) 227-3488
E-mail: Kmolony@state.ma.us
Reports to: Director Carolyn Boviard

PERSONAL INFORMATION:
Marital Status: Married (Richard Hollingsworth)
Children: 2
Education: Princeton (B.A. '71); University of Michigan (Ph.D. '80)
Previous Employment: Standard & Poor's DRI, Principal; Princeton University, lecturer and instructer
Years in Current Position: new **Years in State Service:** 4

JOB DESCRIPTION:
Assist small and medium-sized companies to enter export markets; attract foreign investment to Massachusetts; brief Governor's office on international policy and economic developments.

ORGANIZATIONS:
The Boston Club, Japan Society of Boston, Women in World Trade, World Affairs Council, Association for Asian Studies, Tanglewood Festival Chorus.

Nam Van Pham
Deputy Executive Director

Massachusetts Trade Office
Address: 10 Park Plaza, Suite 3720, Boston, MA 02116
Telephone: (617) 367-1830 **Fax:** (617) 227-3488
E-mail: Nam.Pham@state.ma.us
Reports to: Director Kathleen Malony

PERSONAL INFORMATION:
Education: University of Minnesota (B.S. '81); Harvard's Kennedy School of Government (MPA, '83)
Previous Employment: BankBoston, Asia Pacific Desk Manager; Mass. Office for Refugees and Immigrants, Executive director
Years in Current Position: new **Years in State Service:** 6

JOB DESCRIPTION:
Governor's Asian American Commission (Chairman)

Mary Jane McKenna

Executive Director

Massachusetts Office of Travel and Tourism
Address: 10 Park Plaza, Suite 4510, Boston, MA 02116
Telephone: (617) 973-8500 **Fax:** (617) 973-8525
Reports to: Director Carolyn Boviard

PERSONAL INFORMATION:
Previous Employment: Office of U.S. Representative Peter Blute (District Director, '93-'95); Massachusetts House of Representatives ('83-'93)
Years in Current Position: 3

JOB DESCRIPTION:
Market Massachusetts as a visitor destination

Joseph D. Alviani

President

Massachusetts Technology Collaborative
Address: 75 North Drive, Westborough, MA 01581-3340
Telephone: (508) 870-0312 ext. 200 **Fax:** (508) 898-2275
Staff: Nancy Falvey, Executive Assistant
E-mail: alviani@mtpc.org
Reports to: Board of Directors of Massacusetts Technology Park Corporation

PERSONAL INFORMATION:
Marital Status: married (Betsy Stengel) **Children:** 4
Education: Dartmouth College (B.A., '67); Harvard Law School (J.D., '70); JFK School of Government (Fellow, '92-'93)
Previous Employment: Partner in the law firm of Mintz, Levin, Cohn, Ferris, Glovsky and Popeo, P.C., serving as Chairman of the firm's Government and Public Affairs Department and as President of ML Strategies, Inc.; Secretary, Executive Office of Economic Affairs (1985-89)
Years in Current Position: 5 **Years in State Service:** 9

1999 PRIORITIES:
As the operating arm of the Massachusetts Technology Park Corporation, to continue to create and support the institutional framework necessary for the timely, sustained, and effective design, implementation and evaluation of public policies to advance technology-related economic growth in the Commonwealth.

ORGANIZATIONS:
Massachusetts Taxpayers Foundation; Massachusetts Networks Eductional Partnership, Chairperson; Judge Baker Children's Center; Students Against Destructive Decisions

Philip F. Holahan

Deputy Director, General Counsel, and Secretary

Massachusetts Technology Collaborative
Address: 75 North Drive, Westborough, MA 01581
Telephone: (508) 870-0312 ext. 260 **Fax:** (508) 898-2275
E-mail: holahan@mtpc.org
Staff: Veronica Rand Demakis, Executive Administrator
Reports to: President Joseph D. Alviani

PERSONAL INFORMATION:

Marital Status: married (JoAnne O'Connor) **Children:** 2
Education: College of the Holy Cross (A.B., '75); Boston University Law School (J.D., '78; LL.M., '83); Harvard University, JFK School of Government (M.P.A., '90)
Previous Employment: Executive Office of Economic Affairs (Assistant Secretary and General Counsel); Massachusetts Board of Higher Education (General Counsel)
Years in Current Position: 15 **Years in State Service:** 18

ORGANIZATIONS:

Massachusetts and Boston Bar Associations; Volunteer Lawyers Project

Housing & Community Development

The Department of Housing and Community Development (DHCD) is a state-level agency concerned with local issues and community development for the cities and towns of the Commonwealth. The DHCD acts as the leading advocate for local governments and community agencies. In this role, DHCD makes state and federal funds and technical assistance available to strengthen communities and help them plan new developments, encourage economic development, revitalize older areas, improve local government management, build and manage public housing, stimulate affordable housing through the private sector, and respond to the needs of low-income people. The Office administers the state's public housing programs, coordinates its anti-poverty efforts, allocates federal community development programs, and provides a variety of services to local government officials.

The Department is responsible for a diversity of programs and services that are administered through the following four divisions:

- *Division of Neighborhood Services*
- *Division of Community Services*
- *Division of Public Housing and Rental Assistance*
- *Division of Private Housing*

Director's Office

The Director, appointed by the Governor, administers and maintains executive authority over all phases of departmental activities and coordinates policy with the Governor and the rest of the state administration. The Director is a member of the Boards of Directors of the Massachusetts Housing Finance Agency, Massachusetts Housing Partnership, Massachusetts Government Land Bank, Community Economic Development Assistance Corporation, and the Local Government Advisory Committee.

The DHCD includes the offices of the Deputy Director, Assistant Director's Program Administration, Communications Office, Chief Counsel, Planning and Policy, and Administration and Finance.

Division of Neighborhood Services

This division is the conduit through which the DHCD serves Massachusetts' low-income population. It is responsible for planning, implementing, and monitoring the delivery of federal and state anti-poverty, neighborhood economic development, homelessness prevention, fuel assistance, and weatherization programs across the Commonwealth, working in cooperation with the federal government and other state agencies, local and regional non-profit organizations, and the private sector.

Division of Community Services

The Division of Community Services is concerned with the complex problems facing Massachusetts' communities and uses the agency's financial and human resources to help municipal governments holistically. This division is involved with infrastructure development and improvement, municipal government capacity building, land use planning, local economic development, housing rehabilitation, and social services. This division also provides a referral service to help communities access the services they need both inside and outside DHCD.

Division of Public Housing and Rental Assistance

This division is responsible for administrative oversight of all state-aided public and private housing programs that address the housing needs of low- and moderate-income families, the elderly, and persons with disabilities. It is comprised of five bureaus. The Bureau of Federal Rental Assistance covers rental subsidies, the upgrading of substandard rental housing, and a wide spectrum of support services tied to rental subsidy; and the Bureau of Massachusetts Rental Assistance provides subsidies in a flexible way that is more responsive to client choices. The Bureau of Housing Management oversees the operation and management of 254 local housing authorities and their 49,368 public housing units. The Bureau of Housing Finance has fiscal oversight of the financial records and capital expenditures of local housing authorities. The Bureau of Housing Development and Construction is responsible for the design, development, and construction of new public housing units and the modernization of existing ones.

Division of Private Housing

The Division of Private Housing provides affordable homeownership and rental opportunities in the private sector. Among the programs that are administered by the division are those that fund and encourage the development of mixed-income projects sponsored by community housing partnerships and developers, that make housing overstock and foreclosure properties available to first-time homebuyers, and that provide advantageous home financing terms for low- and moderate-income families.

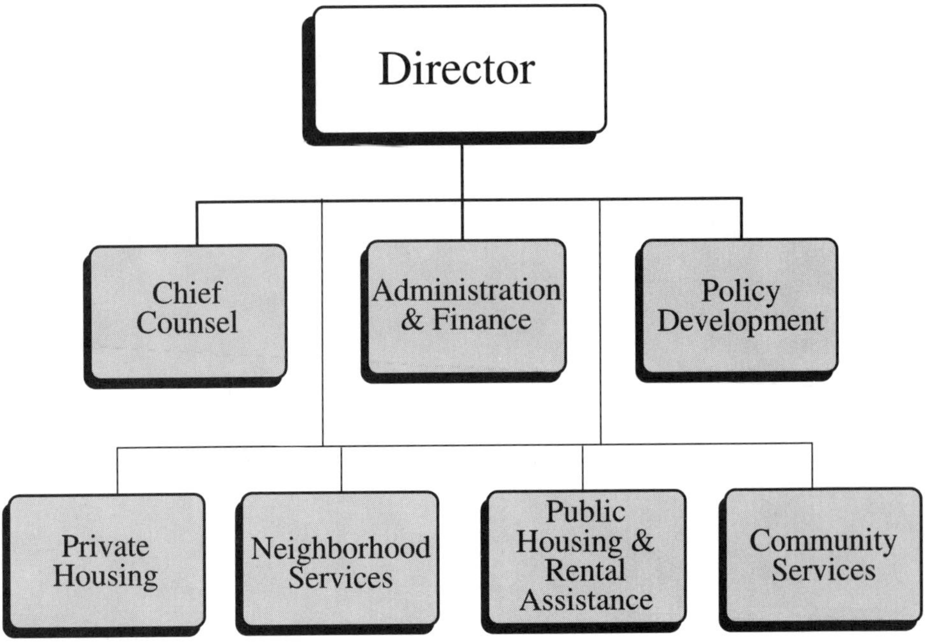
Director
Chief Counsel
Administration & Finance
Policy Development
Private Housing
Neighborhood Services
Public Housing & Rental Assistance
Community Services

Director	**Jane Wallis Gumble**	(617) 727-7765
Deputy Director	**Marc A. Slotnick**	727-7765
Chief Counsel	**Alexander Whiteside**	727-7078
Chief of Staff	**Tara G. Frier**	727-7765
Dep. Dir. for Finance & Administration	**Thomas Simard**	727-7147
Director of Communications	**Eric W. Gedstad**	727-7765

DIVISION OF COMMUNITY SERVICES

Associate Director	**Mary M. Greendale**	727-7001
Director, Municipal Programs	**Robert Ebersole**	727-7001
Director, Municipal Programs	**Mark Siegenthaler**	727-7001

DIVISION OF PUBLIC HOUSING AND RENTAL ASSISTANCE

Associate Director	**L. Paul Galante, Jr.**	727-7130

Bureau Directors:

Bureau of Asset Management	**Carole E. Collins**	727-7765
Federal Rental Assistance	**Mary-Anne Morrison**	727-7130
Massachusetts Rental Voucher Program	**Donna M. Goguen**	727-7130
Housing Finance	**Paul J. Johnson, Jr.**	727-7130

BUREAU OF NEIGHBORHOOD SERVICES AND ECONOMIC OPPORTUNITY

Associate Director	**Roger Provost**	727-7004

Bureau Directors:

Energy Programs	**James Hays**	727-7004
Economic Opportunity	**Kenneth Spicer**	727-7004
Policy and Planning	**Sandra L. Hawes**	727-7004

DIVISION OF PRIVATE HOUSING

Associate Director	**Catherine Racer**	727-7824

Jane Wallis Gumble

Director

Department of Housing and Community Development
Address: One Congress St., 10th Fl. Boston, MA 02114
Telephone: (6187) 727-7765 **Fax:** (617) 727-5060
Reports to: Govenor A. Paul Cellucci

PERSONAL INFORMATION:
Born: September 29, 1954
Place of Birth: Honesdale, PA
Marital Status: married
Education: Lehigh University (B.A.,, '76); Boston University (J.D., '81)
Previous Employment: Awdeh and Co. (Partner and Regional Counsel)
Years in Current Position: 2 **Years in State Service:** 7

JOB DESCRIPTION:
Work with and advocate on behalf of the Commonwealth's 351 cities and towns; support communities through innovative programs in economic development, municipal services, and affordable housing.

1999 PRIORITIES:
Create innovative community development programs that support job creation and retention, generate economic development, and build the capacity of cities and towns; work with community officials to restructure local government through regionalization, privatization, and consolidation of services to reduce costs and improve service delivery. Empower individuals and families through a series of programs that prevent homelessness and dependence in favor of nurturing economic independence and building self-sufficiency; work through public/private partnerships to rehabilitate foreclosed properties into decent, affordable housing; promote first-time home ownership and foster safe, stable neighborhoods in revitalized communities; streamline the excessive regulations and mandates that prevent the most effective use of public funds and most effective operation of local and state agencies.

Marc A. Slotnick

Deputy Director for Policy

Department of Housing and Community Development
Address: One Congress St., 10th Fl. Boston, MA 02114
Telephone: (617) 727-7765 **Fax:** (617) 727-5060
E-mail: mslotnick@state.ma.us
Staff: Carlo DeSantis, Policy Development Coordinator; Terri Bruce, Administrative Assistant
Reports to: Director Jane Gumble

PERSONAL INFORMATION:
Born: April 20, 1942 **Place of Birth:** Boston
Marital Status: married (Marsha) **Children:** 3
Education: Harvard College (A.B. '64); New York University School of Law (J.D., '68)
Previous Employment: New England Communities, Inc. (President, '72-'92); Newton Community Development Foundation (Executive Director, '69-'75)
Years in Current Position: 2.5 **Years in State Service:** 8

JOB DESCRIPTION:
Develop and coordinate implementation of policy and program initiatives for the Agency's administration of $500,000,000 annually in housing, community and economic development, planning, anti-poverty, and municipal grant and loan programs.

ORGANIZATIONS:
Harvard Alumni Association (Director); Harvard Class of '64 (Treasurer); Combined Jewish Philanthropies (Overseer); New England Chapter of the New York University Law Alumni Association (Director and past President); Mind/ Body Medical Institute of N.E. Deaconess Hospital at Harvard Medical School (Founding Trustee)

Thomas Simard

Deputy Director for Administration and Finance

Department of Housing and Community Development
Address: One Congress St. 10th Fl, Boston, 02114
Telephone: (617) 727-7147 **Fax:** (617) 727-5060
Staff: Kathy Murphy, Administrative Assistant
Reports to: Director Jane Gumble

PERSONAL INFORMATION:
Born: July 24, 1965
Marital Status: Married (Patricia)
Education: United States Military Academy (B.S. '87); New Hampshire College (M.B.A. '94)
Previous Employment: House Committee on Ways and Means, United States Army
Years in Current Position: 3 **Years in State Service:** 8

JOB DESCRIPTION:
Oversee management of human resources, finance, information services, procurement, and operational services.

Alexander Whiteside

Chief Counsel

Department of Housing and Community Development
Address: One Congress St., 10th Fl. Boston, MA 02114
Telephone: (617) 727-7078 **Fax:** (617) 727-7129
Staff: Corinne E. Lax, Werner Lohe, Christine McClave, Harriet Moss, Timothy Solomon, Counsel; Candace Tempesta, Contract Specialist; Maria Paine, Paralegal
Reports to: Director Jane Gumble

PERSONAL INFORMATION:
Born: August 29, 1944 **Place of Birth:** Boston
Marital Status: single **Children:** 2
Education: Harvard College (A.B., '66); Fordham Law School (J.D., '69); Boston University Law School (L.L.M., '75)
Previous Employment: Putnam, Bell & Russell

Years in Current Position: 6.5 **Years in State Service:** 6.5

ORGANIZATIONS:
Milton Planning Board; Milton Hospital (Corporator); Massachusetts Society for the Prevention of Cruelty to Children

Tara G. Frier

Chief of Staff

Department of Housing and Community Development
Address: One Congress St., 10th Fl. Boston, MA 02114
Telephone: (617) 727- 7765 **Fax:** (617) 727-5060
Reports to: Director Jane Gumble

PERSONAL INFORMATION:
Born: September 7, 1964 **Place of Birth:** Norwood
Marital Status: married (Ted) **Children:** 1
Education: Boston University (B.S., Journalism, '86)
Previous Employment: WBZ–TV 4 (Assistant to the News Director, writer/producer); Massachusetts Historical Commission (Grants Manager); State House Tours and Government Education (Assistant Director)
Years in Current Position: 5 **Years in State Service:** 9

JOB DESCRIPTION:
To effectively promote DHCD programs and policies to various media outlets.

Eric W. Gedstad

Communications Director

Executive Office of Housing and Community Development
Address: One Congress St., 10th Fl. Boston, MA 02114
Telephone: (617) 727-7765 **Fax:** 617-727-5060
Staff: Teresa Hilton, Communications Specialist
Reports to: Director Jane Gumble

PERSONAL INFORMATION:
Born: Sept, 4, 1967 **Place of Birth:** Peoria, IL
Marital Status: married (Abby)
Education: Boston University (B.S. '89)
Previous Employment: Mass. Office of Travel and Tourism (Communications Director), Office of the Governor (speech writer), Mass. Housing and Finance Agency (Government Relations Analyst), Massachusetts House of Representatives (Press Secretary, Research Analyst)
Years in Current Position: 7 **Years in State Service:** 9

JOB DESCRIPTION:
Oversee and coordinate all media and external communications for the Department.

Mary M. Greendale

Associate Director

Division of Community Services
Address: One Congress St., 10th Fl. Boston, MA 02114
Telephone: (617) 727-7001 **E-mail:** MGreendale@state.ma.us
Staff: Kathleen Collette, Administrative Assistant
Reports to: Director Jane Gumble

PERSONAL INFORMATION:
Previous Employment: MetroWest Red Cross (Executive Director)
Years in Current Position: 7 **Years in State Service:** 9

JOB DESCRIPTION:
Oversee CDBG and State grant programs directed at community development and municipal capacity building.

1999 PRIORITIES:
Broaden community development technical assistance to communities by using a regional team structure.

ORGANIZATIONS:
Selectman, Town of Holliston

Robert Ebersole

Director, Municipal Development Programs

Division of Community Services
Address: One Congress St., 10th Fl. Boston, MA 02114
Telephone: (617) 727-7001 ext. 450 **E-mail:** robert.ebersole@state.ma.us
Reports to: Associate Director Mary Greendale

PERSONAL INFORMATION:
Education: Northeastern University (B.S., Criminal Justice); Suffolk University School of Law (J.D., '82); Harvard University, JFK School of Government (M.P.A.., Public Administration, '88)
Previous Employment: City of Chelsea (Chief Financial Officer Receivership, '91-'92); Town of Lexington (Revenue Officer, Treasurer, '89-'91); Town of Lunenburg (Town Clerk, Tax Collector, Treasurer, '83-'89)
Years in Current Position: 4 **Years in State Service:** 7

JOB DESCRIPTION:
Oversee the application review and selection process for federal and state community and economic development grant programs providing over $82 million annually to municipalities.

Mark Siegenthaler
Director, Municipal Development Programs

Division of Community Services
Address: One Congress St., 10th Fl. Boston, MA 02114
Telephone: (617) 727-7001 ext. 409 **E-mail:** MSiegenthaler@state.ma.us
Reports to: Associate Director Mary Greendale

PERSONAL INFORMATION:
Education: University of Massachusetts at Amherst (B.A., Psychology); Tufts University (M.A., Urban & Environmental Policy)
Previous Employment: University of Massachusetts Medical Center; Metropolitan Area Planning Council
Years in Current Position: 4 **Years in State Service:** 14

JOB DESCRIPTION:
Management of assistance programs on planning and development issues, municipal management, and regionalization. Services include planning grants, land use technical assistance, and a regionalism resource center.

L. Paul Galante, Jr.
Associate Director

Division of Public Housing and Rental Assistance
Address: One Congress St., 10th Fl. Boston, MA 02114
Telephone: (617) 727-7130 **Fax:** (617) 727-0082
Reports to: Director Jane Wallace Gumble

JOB DESCRIPTION:
Responsible for administrative oversight of all state-aided public housing programs, which address the housing needs of low- and moderate-income families, the elderly, and people with special needs.

Carole E. Collins
Director

Bureau of Asset Management
Address: One Congress St., 10th Fl. Boston, MA 02114
Telephone: (617) 727-7765 ext. 665 **Fax:** (617) 727-7127
E-mail: Carole.Collins@state.ma.us
Staff: Paul McPartland - Asset Management Coordinator Laura Carreiro - Budget Specialist; Robert Nadeau KcKinney - Program Coordinator; Ita Mullarkey, Housing and Human Service Coordinator; Christine DeVore, Maura Hamilton, Program Management Coordinators
Reports to: Associate Director Paul Galante

PERSONAL INFORMATION:
Born: September 24, 1948 **Place of Birth:** Pittsfield
Marital Status: married (Roland Rouse) **Children:** 1
Education: University of Massachusetts at Amherst (B.A., '71; M.Ed., '74)
Previous Employment: EOCD (Deputy Director, Bureau of Housing Management); Amherst Housing Authority (Executive Director)

Years in Current Position: 1 **Years in State Service:** 27

JOB DESCRIPTION:
Approve operating budgets and oversee the management, maintenance and administration of 50,000 state assisted housing units at 250 local housing authorities in the Commonwealth.

1999 PRIORITIES:
Refocus the Bureau's mission to stress results-oriented management of individual developments and develop programs and systems that safeguard the Commonwealth's $5 billion investment in state public housing.

ORGANIZATIONS:
Friends of Boston's Long Island Shelter for the Homeless (Vice-Chair and Founding Member); Citizen's Housing and Planning Association; Newton Community Development Foundation

Mary-Anne Morrison

Director, Bureau of Federal Rental Assistance Programs

Division of Public Housing and Rental Assistance
Address: One Congress St., 10th Fl. Boston, MA 02114
Telephone: (617) 727-7130 ext. 655 **Fax:** (617) 727-7891
Staff: Jennie Rawski, Senior Housing Specialist; Matt Judge, Senior Housing Inspection Supervisor; Anne Philbrick, Section 8 Housing Specialist; Peggy O'Brien, Home TBRA Specialist ; Emily Miller, Supportive Housing Specialist; Larry Gome, Contract Monitor; Cynthia Casey, Program Support
Reports to: Associate Director Paul Galante

PERSONAL INFORMATION:
Born: January 30, 1949 **Place of Birth:** New Hampshire
Marital Status: married (John) **Children:** 2
Education: Boston University, (B.A. '72)
Previous Employment: Executive Office of Communities and Development (Program Manager, Division of Housing; Section 8 Director) Division of Leased Housing; Boston Housing Authority (Coordinator, Lead Paint Poisoning Elimination Program)
Years in Current Position: 14 **Years in State Service:** 27

JOB DESCRIPTION:
Direct the Commonwealth's $150 million Section 8 program, which provides rental assistance to over 16,000 very low-income households annually.

Donna M. Goguen

Director, Massachusetts Rental Voucher Program

Division of Public Housing and Rental Assistance
Address: One Congress St., 10th Fl. Boston, MA 02114
Telephone: (617) 727-7130 **Fax:** (617) 727-0082
Staff: Ann Cwartkowski, Charlie Vasiliades, Housing Specialists; Paul Nixon, Senior Housing Officer; Edward Power, Inspection Officer; Brenda Royer, Management Specialist
Reports to: Associate Director Paul Galante

PERSONAL INFORMATION:

Born: August 22, 1946
Place of Birth: Stoughton
Marital Status: married (Roger)
Children: 2
Education: Southeastern Massachusetts University (B.S.'79); University of Massachusetts at Boston (M.S., '88)

Previous Employment: State and Federal Rental Assistance Programs, South Shore Housing Development Corp. (Director)
Years in Current Position: 10
Years in State Service: 12

JOB DESCRIPTION:

Director of the Massachusetts Rental Voucher Program, which provides rental assistance to 15,000 households throughout the Commonwealth and is administered by 160 local housing agencies.

Paul J. Johnson, Jr.

Director of Housing Finance

Division of Public Housing and Rental Assistance
Address: One Congress St., 10th Fl. Boston, MA 02114
Telephone: (617) 727-130
Fax: (617) 727-0082
Staff: Wayde Porrovecchio, Deputy Director, Housing Finance; Helen Carpenter, Sheila Kupchaumis, Secretaries.
Reports to: Associate Director Paul Galante

PERSONAL INFORMATION:

Born: November 30, 1948
Place of Birth: Somerville
Education: Salem State (B.A. '74); Lesley College (M.A. '86)
Previous Employment: Cambridge Housing Authority (Assistant Director of Fiscal Affairs)
Years in Current Position: 7
Years in State Service: 13

JOB DESCRIPTION:

Direct development and implementation of fiscal policy and financial procedures related to the production and management of state-aided public housing.

Roger Provost

Associate Director

Bureau of Neighborhood Services and Economic Opportunity
Address: One Congress St., 10th Fl. Boston, MA 02114
Telephone: (617) 727-7004
Fax: (617) 727-4259
E-mail: RProvost@state.ma.us
Staff: Peter Donko-Hanson, Director of Finance; Debra Michaud, Administrative Assistant; George Dekeon, Special Projects Manager
Reports to: Director Jane Gumble

PERSONAL INFORMATION:

Born: October 7, 1951
Place of Birth: Massachusetts
Marital Status: married (Jackie Lewis)
Children: 2
Education: Bridgewater State College (B.S., '78); Assumption College (M.A., '80)
Previous Employment: Provost Real Estate (Principal/Broker); Massachusetts Senate (Legislative Aide); Bridgewater State College (Assistant to the Dean of Graduate and Continuing Education); Town of Bridgewater (Local Official, 12 years)

Years in Current Position: 7 **Years in State Service:** 13

JOB DESCRIPTION:
Manage federal and state programs and legislative issues, including LIHEAP (Fuel Assistance Program); WAP (Weatherization Assistance Program); CSBG (Community Services Block Grant Program); CEED (Community Enterprise Economic Development); HSP (Housing Services Program); HIP (Homelessness Intercept Program).

James Hays

Director, Bureau of Energy Programs

Bureau of Neighborhood Services and Economic Opportunity
Address: One Congress St., 10th Fl. Boston, MA 02114
Telephone: (617) 727-7004 **Fax:** (617) 727-4259 **E-Mail:** James.Hays@state.ma.us
Reports to: Associate Director Roger Provost

PERSONAL INFORMATION:
Education: American International College (B.S., '58); Western New England College (M.B.A., '67); C.P.A.
Previous Employment: Gem Industries, Inc. (Treasurer, Comptroller)
Years in Current Position: 7 **Years in State Service:** 7

JOB DESCRIPTION:
Director of state fuel assistance and weatherization programs for low-income sector.

ORGANIZATIONS:
IMA; Mass. Society of Certified Personal Accountants; National Association for State Community Action Programs

Kenneth Spicer

Director of Economic Opportunity

Bureau of Neighborhood Services and Economic Opportunity
Address: One Congress St., 10th Fl, Boston, MA 02114
Telephone: (617) 727-7004 **Fax:** (617) 727-4259 **E-mail:** KSpicer@state.ma.us
Staff: Sandra L. Hawes, Deputy Director for Policy and Planning
Reports to: Associate Director Roger Provost

PERSONAL INFORMATION:
Born: August 21,1949 **Place of Birth:** Jacksonville, FL
Marital Status: married (Patricia) **Children:** 3
Education: Bethune-Cookman College (B.S., '71); University of Massachusetts at Boston, McCormack Institute (M.S., Public Affairs, '90); Northeastern University (current Ph.D. program, Law, Policy and Society); Harvard University, JFK School of Government (Program for Senior Executives of the Commonwealth, '94)
Previous Employment: Executive Office of Communities and Development, Office of the Secretary (Director, Office of Affirmative Action)
Years in Current Position: 6 **Years in State Service:** 11

JOB DESCRIPTION:

Direct strategic planning, policy development and program implementation activities of state and federally-funded homelessness prevention, anti-poverty, community and neighborhood economic development; and special project initiatives of the Commonwealth.

ORGANIZATIONS:

National Forum for Black Public Administrators, Inc.; Alpha Phi Alpha Fraternity, Inc.

Sandra L. Hawes

Director of Neighborhood Services and Economic Opportunity

Department of Housing and Community Development
Address: One Congress St., 10th Fl. Boston, MA 02114
Telephone: (617) 727-7004 **Fax:** (617) 727-4259
E-mail: Sandra.Hawes@state.ma.us
Staff: Sandra L. Hawes, Deputy Director for Policy and Planning
Reports to: Director Kenneth Spicer

PERSONAL INFORMATION:

Born: Feb. 18, 1949 **Place of Birth:** Massachusetts
Marital Status: single **Children:** 1
Education: University of Massachusetts - Boston
Previous Employment: Rural Housing Improvement; Housing Assistance Corporation
Years in Current Position: 7 **Years in State Service:** 12

JOB DESCRIPTION:

Implementation of a reorganization of the Bureau to address the increase demands of program oversight. The reorganization of the Bureau will address the program staffing and management needs.

ORGANIZATIONS:

National Association for State and Community Service Program, Executive Board Member

Labor & Workforce Development

The Department of Labor and Workforce Development is responsible for the interests of all working men and women in the Commonwealth. The office is charged with promoting the health, safety, legal, and economic interests of the Commonwealth's workers and the preservation of productive and fair paying jobs. This department supervises programs ranging from the workers' compensation system to the regulation of prevailing wage matters and job training programs. In addition, the department has fiscal responsibility for all workforce development activities within the Commonwealth.

The department oversees the agencies described here.

Division of Apprentice Training (DAT)

DAT is responsible for promoting apprenticeship in the Commonwealth and developing work-based pre-apprentice programs in cooperation with local school officials. DAT also certifies apprentice programs and institutes administrative decertification proceedings against apprentice program sponsors who violate the division's standards.

Division of Occupational Safety (DOS)

DOS regulates the residential lead paint and asbestos abatement industries. It also performs occupational safety and health investigations and works with employers to eliminate any unsafe conditions in the workplace. This division also oversees the Massachusetts blood-lead registry and operates a chemical analysis laboratory. DOS also regulates employment agencies, nanny agencies, and model agencies and administers the Massachusetts prevailing wage laws.

Division of Employment and Training (DET)

DET (formerly under the Executive Office of Economic Affairs) is responsible for administering the Commonwealth's unemployment insurance program which provides payments to individuals who have become unemployed through no fault of their own. Through federal funding, DET also oversees an employment services program that provides information on available job openings and assists employers in hiring qualified workers who are seeking employment. DET is also responsible job training programs which assist economically disadvantaged workers in obtaining the necessary skills to enter the workforce. In addition, DET administers the state unemployment health insurance program which provides limited health coverage to unemployed individuals who are eligible for unemployment benefits.

Finally DET is responsible for collecting, processing, and maintaining labor market information, including region-specific data on emerging, mature, and critical industries throughout the Commonwealth.

Division of Industrial Accidents (DIA)

DIA is responsible for administering and enforcing the Massachusetts workers' compensation laws. DIA is comprised of two subdivisions; one for administration and one for dispute resolution. The administration subdivision receives and maintains reports on workers' injuries, provides vocational rehabilitation services to injured workers, licenses and oversees those employers who wish to be self-insured, and collects assessments, fines, and other payments owed to the Workers' Compensation Trust Fund. The administration subdivision also investigates allegations of employer violations of the mandatory workers' compensation coverage requirements and imposes sanctions, including stop work orders. The subdivision of dispute resolution employs 24 judges who, among other things, adjudicate disputes concerning employees' compensation claims.

MassJobs Council

The MassJobs Council is comprised of 32 state and local officials, business leaders, educators, and training providers who assist in the development of a workforce training system. The Council meetings are chaired by the Lieutenant Governor and a private sector business leader who is appointed by the Governor. The functions of the Council include developing a system that most efficiently uses the resources available for workforce development; assessing the effectiveness of the workforce development programs; and making the programs responsive to the needs of the business community and the trainees. According to legislation, the Council must file an annual report with the Governor and the

Legislature on the progress of the various workforce development programs.

Labor Relations Commission (LRC)

The LRC is responsible for administering the Commonwealth's public employee collective bargaining law. This law gives most public employees the right to form, join, or participate in unions, to bargain collectively over the terms of employment, and to engage in concerted activities for mutual aid and protection. The majority of the LRC's resources are devoted to deciding unfair labor practice cases. However, the LRC is also responsible for conducting representative elections and preventing labor strikes. This agency is headed by three commissioners who are appointed by the Governor.

Joint Labor-Management Committee (JLMC)

The JLMC exercises broad oversight responsibility for all collective bargaining negotiations between municipal police officers or firefighters and municipalities in the Commonwealth. Through mediation and other voluntary forms of dispute resolution, the JLMC assists labor and management in reaching negotiated settlements of disputes concerning the terms of collective bargaining agreements. The Committee is comprised of 14 members appointed by the Governor. Six members represent management, six represent labor, and two are neutral. The Committee is headed by a chairman and vice-chairman who serve as the two neutrals.

Board of Conciliation and Arbitration (BCA)

The BCA provides mediators to assist parties in both the public and private sectors in negotiating collective bargaining agreements. BCA also supplies arbitrators and mediators who adjudicate union grievances. Finally, BCA's staff develops and presents programs to educate the community in the resolution of disputes and maintenance of good labor/management relations. This agency is headed by a chairman who is appointed by the Governor.

Corporation for Business, Work, and Learning (CBWL)

As part of the 1996 reorganization, the Industrial Services Program merged with the Bay State Skills Corporation to form this single quasi-public agency. CBWL also provides re-employment assistance to dislocated workers and administers various federally funded job training programs. In addition, CBWL oversees the Economic Stabilization Trust Fund which provides high-risk financing for the corporate restructuring of viable but troubled companies that would face large employment loss if such restructuring does not occur.

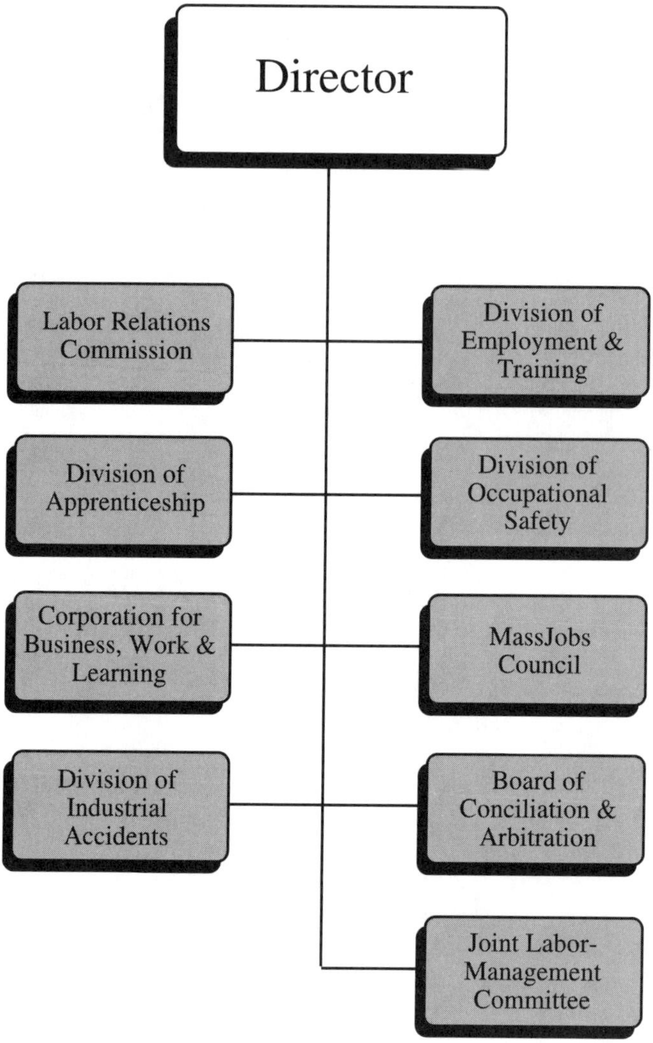
Director
Labor Relations Commission
Division of Employment & Training
Division of Apprenticeship
Division of Occupational Safety
Corporation for Business, Work & Learning
MassJobs Council
Division of Industrial Accidents
Board of Conciliation & Arbitration
Joint Labor-Management Committee

Director	**Angelo R. Buonopane**	*(617) 727-6573*
Chief of Staff	**Janice S. Tatarka**	*727-6573*
General Counsel	**vacant**	*727-6573*
Chief Financial Officer	**Joan F. Lenihan**	*727-6573*
Dep. Dir. of Workforce Development	**Jonathan Raymond**	*727-6573*
Career Center Program Director	**Kim McLaughlin**	*727-6573*
Federal Grants Manager	**vacant**	*727-6573*

BOARD OF CONCILIATION AND ARBITRATION

Chairman	**Elizabeth E. Laing**	*727-3466*
Vice-Chairman	**James F. Kelly, Jr.**	*727-3466*

DIVISION OF INDUSTRIAL ACCIDENTS

Commissioner	**James J. Campbell**	*727-4900*

Directors:

Deputy Commmisioner	**Thomas Griffin**	*727-4900*
Dir. of Administration Division	**William Sivert**	*727-4900*

JOINT LABOR-MANAGEMENT COMMITTEE

Chairman	**John T. Dunlop**	*727-9690*
Vice-Chairman	**Morris A. Horowitz**	*727-9690*
Senior Staff Representative/Labor	**James P. Costello**	*727-9690*
Senior Staff Representative/ Management	**Donald P. Hawkes**	*727-9690*

LABOR RELATIONS COMMISSION

Chairman	**Robert C. Dumont**	*727-3505*
Commissioner	**vacant**	*727-3505*
Commissioner	**Helen Moreschi**	*727-3505*

DIVISION OF EMPLOYMENT & TRAINING

Deputy Director	**John A. King**	626-6600
Chief Counsel	**Robert Ganong**	626-6813
Associate Director for Administration & Finance	**Henry O. Marcy, 4th**	626-6603
Associate Director of Unemployment and Field Operations	**Richard L. Dill**	626-6604
Associate Director of Revenue	**Richard T. Sullivan**	626-5054
Assoc. Dir., Job Training & Employment	**Joan I. Branton**	626-6600
Chief of Staff	**Susan McKelliget**	626-6600
Associate Director, Technology	**Jeffrey Ritter**	626-6688

DIVISION OF APPRENTICESHIP TRAINING

Deputy Director	**Gayann Wilkinson**	727-3486

DIVISION OF LABOR MARKET INFORMATION

Director	**Rena Kottcamp**	626-6556

DIVISION OF OCCUPATIONAL SAFETY

Deputy Director	**Robert J. Prezioso**	727-3452
Occupational Hygiene Program Manager	**Paul Aboody Jr.**	969-7177
General Counsel	**Linda M. Hamel**	727-3452
Lead and Asbestos Program Manager	**Ernest W. Kelley**	(413)448-8746
Prevailing Wage & Statistics Program Manager	**Stewart C. Field**	727-3492
Administrative Services	**Jill Nelson-Dowd**	727-3452

CORPORATION FOR BUSINESS, WORK AND LEARNING

President	**Suzanne Teegarden**	727-8158
Vice President	**Barbara Baran**	727-8158

Angelo R. Buonopane

Director

Department of Labor and Workforce Development
Address: One Ashburton Place, Room 1402, Boston, MA 02108
Telephone: (617) 727-6573 **Fax:** (617) 727-1090
E-mail: Angelo.Buonopane@state.ma.us
Staff: Janice Tatarka, Chief of Staff; Joan Lenihan, Chief Financial Officer; Jonathan Raymond, Deputy Director of Workforce Development
Reports to: Govenor A. Paul Cellucci

PERSONAL INFORMATION:

Born: December 15, 1947 **Place of Birth:** Boston
Marital Status: married (Marguerite) **Children:** 6
Education: Boston Trade School (Apprenticeship Mason)
Previous Employment: Massachusetts Highway Department, Central Artery Project (Director of Labor Relations)
Years in Current Position: 2 **Years in State Service:** 2.5

JOB DESCRIPTION:

Fiscal and managerial oversight of the Division of Employment and Training, Division of Industrial Accidents, Division of Occupational Safety, Division of Apprentice Training, Board of Conciliation and Arbitration, Labor Relations Commission, Joint Labor-Management Committee, and Division of Labor Market Information. Fiscal oversight of the Massachusetts Jobs Council, One-Stop Career Center office, and programs within the Corporation for Business, Work, and Learning.

1999 PRIORITIES:

Continue to rollout the Massachusetts One Stop Career Center project; prepare for the implementation of the new federal Workforce Investment Act; and create, continue and enhance programs which improve the skills of the Massachusetts workforce.

Janice S. Tatarka

Chief of Staff

Department of Labor and Workforce Development
Address: One Ashburton Place, Rm 1402, Boston, MA 02108
Telephone: (617) 727-6573 **Fax:** (617) 727-1090
E-mail: Janice.Tatarka@state.ma.us
Reports to: Director Angelo Buonopane

PERSONAL INFORMATION:

Born: July 10, 1955 **Place of Birth:** Homestead, PA
Education: Brown University (B.A. '77); Suffolk University Law School
Years in Current Position: 1.5 **Years in State Service:** 16

JOB DESCRIPTION:

Coordinating Labor and Workforce issues of the division within DLWD, the former Executive Office of Labor; overseeing the federal Welfare to Work Program; representing the director as needed and requested.

1999 PRIORITIES:
To continue the rollout of the Massachusetts One Stop Career Center: to prepare for the implementation of the new federal Workforce Investment Act; and to create, continue and enhance programs which improve the skills of the Massachusetts workforce.

ORGANIZATIONS:
Chelsea, MA Zoning Board of Appeals

Joan F. Lenihan

Chief Financial Officer

Department of Labor and Workforce Development
Address: One Ashburton Place, Rm 1402, Boston, MA 02108
Telephone: (617) 727-6573 x105 **Fax:** (617) 727-1090
Staff: Janice Fennell, Financial Manager; Paula Hubley, Program Coordinator
Reports to: Director Angelo Buonopane

PERSONAL INFORMATION:
Born: Oct. 28, 1957 **Place of Birth:** Boston
Marital Status: married (Ed)
Education: University of Massachusetts, Boston (B.A.)
Years in Current Position: 2 **Years in State Service:** 14

JOB DESCRIPTION:
Oversight of more than $200 million in state and federal funds.

Elizabeth E. Laing

Chairman

Board of Conciliation and Arbitration
Address: 100 Cambridge Street, Room 1105, Boston, MA 02202
Telephone: (617) 727-3466 ext. 308 **Fax:** (617) 727-4961
Staff: James Kelley, Vice-Chairman
Reports to: Governor A. Paul Cellucci

PERSONAL INFORMATION:
Born: January 23, 1948 **Place of Birth:** Massachusetts
Education: Emmanuel College (B.A., English/Art, '70); N.E. School of Law (J.D., '78); Katharine Gibbs School (Special Course for College Women, '70)
Previous Employment: Joint Labor Management Committee for Municipal Police and Fire (Staff Mediator, '85-'93); Commonwealth of Massachusetts (Assistant Attorney General, '76-'82)
Years in Current Position: 5 **Years in State Service:** 18

JOB DESCRIPTION:
The Chairman, as agency head, makes all final personnel, fiscal, administrative, legal, managerial, adjudicatory, litigation and other policy decisions.

1999 PRIORITIES:
Fast and efficient delivery of dispute resolution services to the labor management community; increase agency revenue, revise agency regulations to reduce unnecessary administrative burden.

ORGANIZATIONS:
Massachusetts Bar Association; Boston Bar Association; SPIDR; ALRA; AAA

Division of Industrial Accidents

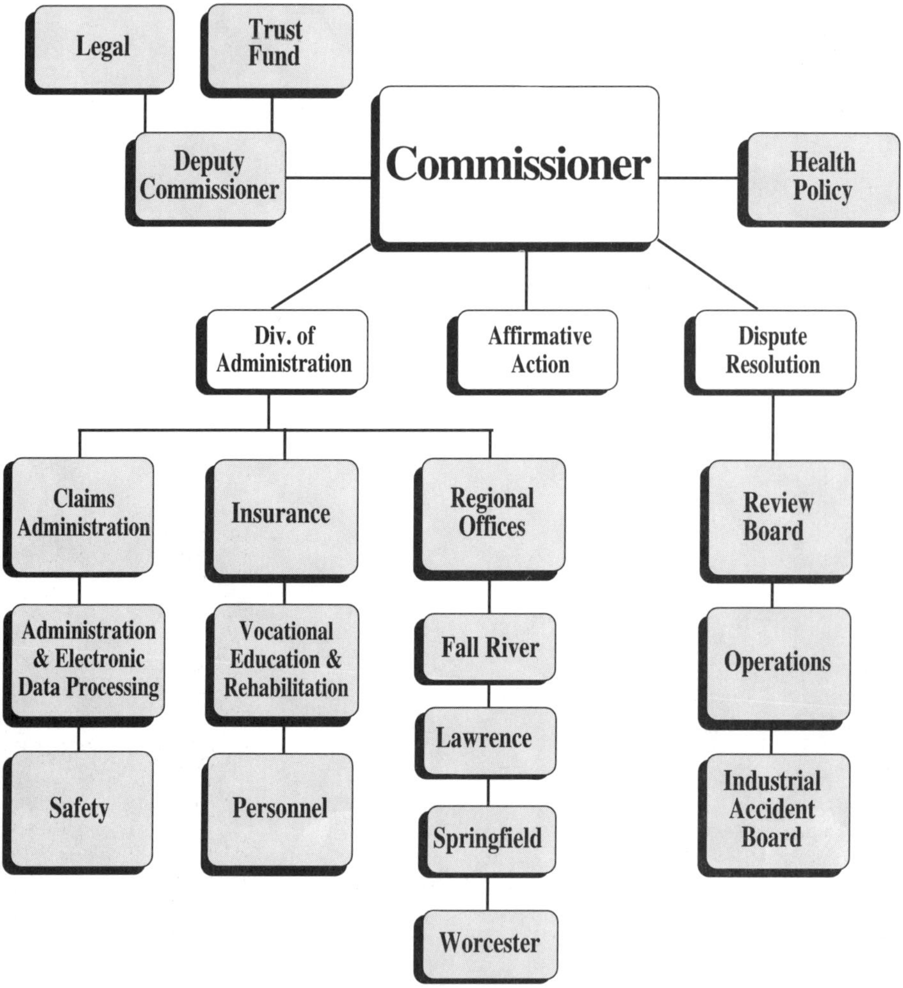

James J. Campbell

Commissioner

Division of Industrial Accidents
Address: 600 Washington Street, Boston, MA 02111
Telephone: (617) 727-4900 ext. 356 **Fax:** (617) 727-6477
Reports to: Director Angelo Buonopane

PERSONAL INFORMATION:
Born: November 2, 1943 **Place of Birth:** Lowell
Marital Status: married (Constance) **Children:** 3
Education: University of Massachusetts (B.S., '65)
Previous Employment: City of Lowell (City Manager, Assistant City Manager)
Years in Current Position: 8

JOB DESCRIPTION:
Executive and Administrative head of the Department of Industrial Accidents.

1999 PRIORITIES:
Reduce the cost of workers' compensation to employers; reform the present Workers' Compensation system; protect the legitimately injured worker.

ORGANIZATIONS:
International Association of Industrial Accident Boards and Commissions; Merrimack Valley Red Cross Association; Greater Lowell Boy Scout Council

John T. Dunlop

Chairman

Joint Labor-Management Committee
Address: One Ashburton Place, Room 610, Boston, MA 02108
Telephone: (617) 727-9690 **Fax:** (617) 727-5786
Staff: Mary Cappadona, Secretary
Reports to: Governor A. Paul Cellucci.

PERSONAL INFORMATION:
Born: July 5, 1914
Place of Birth: Placeville, CA
Marital Status: married (Dorothy Webb) **Children:** 3
Education: University of California, Berkeley (B.A., '35; Ph.D., '39)
Previous Employment: Harvard University (Lamont University Professor); U.S. Secretary of Labor ('75-'76)

Years in Current Position: 22 **Years in State Service:** 22

JOB DESCRIPTION:
Work with a committee comprised of six municipal officers, three professional firefighters and three police officers, nominated by their statewide organizations, to encourage the parties in collective bargaining disputes involving municipal police officers and firefighters to resolve the terms of collective bargaining agreements by mediation and other means. The committee encourages the parties to develop constructive approaches to their common employment relations problems.

1999 PRIORITIES:
To encourage direct collective bargaining settlements between parties; to reduce the time required to resolve disputes particularly those that require more than a year for resolution; and to increase the proportion of disputes (currently approximately 80 percent) that are settled voluntarily.

ORGANIZATIONS:
American Economics Association; Industrial Relations Research Association; National Academy of Arbitrators (Life Member)

Morris A. Horowitz

Vice-Chairman

Joint Labor-Management Committee
Address: One Ashburton Place, Room 610, Boston, MA 02108
Telephone: (617) 727-9690 **Fax:** (617) 727-5786
Reports to: Chairman John Dunlop

PERSONAL INFORMATION:
Born: November 19, 1919 **Place of Birth:** Newark, NJ
Marital Status: married (Jean) **Children:** 2
Education: New York University (B.A., '40); Harvard University (Ph.D., '54)
Years in Current Position: 19 **Years in State Service:** 19

JOB DESCRIPTION:
To encourage the parties in collective bargaining disputes involving municipal police officers and firefighters to accept the terms of collective bargaining agreements by mediation and other means.

ORGANIZATIONS:
American Economics Association; Industrial Relations Research Association; National Academy of Arbitrators; Society of Professionals in Dispute Resolution

Robert C. Dumont

Chairman

Labor Relations Commission
Address: 100 Cambridge Street, Room 1604, Boston, MA 02202
Telephone: (617) 727-3505 ext. 308 **Fax:** (617) 727-4402
Staff: Michael Wallace, Executive Secretary; John Cochran, Chief Counsel; Philip Holmes, Deputy Chief Counsel

PERSONAL INFORMATION:
Born: November 28, 1934 **Place of Birth:** Marlborough
Marital Status: single **Children:** 3
Education: Dartmouth College (A.B., '56)
Previous Employment: Dumont and Associates, Inc. (Founder and Principal); The New England (Vice-President of Personnel and Equal Opportunity); Commonwealth of Massachusetts (Personnel Administrator; Special Assistant to the Governor and Director of Office of State Service)
Years in Current Position: 2 **Years in State Service:** 6

JOB DESCRIPTION:
Enforce the Commonwealth's collective bargaining laws (M.G.L. c. 150A and c. 150E) and administer the operations of the Labor Relations Commission.

1998 PRIORITIES:
Ensure the fair and prompt resolution of cases before the Labor Relations Commission.

ORGANIZATIONS:
Northeast Human Resources Association

John A. King
Deputy Director

Division of Employment and Training
Address: 19 Staniford Street, Boston, MA 02114
Telephone: (617) 626-6600 **Fax:** (617) 727-0315
Staff: Susan Donnelly McKelliget, Chief of Staff
Reports to: Director Angelo R. Buonopane

PERSONAL INFORMATION:
Place of Birth: New York
Marital Status: married (Susan) **Children:** 2
Education: Trinity College (B.A.); Boston University (M.A.); Suffolk University Law School (J.D.)
Previous Employment: Mass. Division of Employment and Training, Policy Director
Years in Current Position: 1 **Years in State Service:** 20

JOB DESCRIPTION:
Manage the Massachusetts Unemployment Insurance program, operate the job service, and track trends in jobs and the economy.

1999 PRIORITIES:
Provide effective services to businesses and working people of Massachusetts

ORGANIZATIONS:
ABA, Massachusetts Service Alliance, Mass. Bar Association

Henry O. Marcy, 4th
Associate Director for Administration and Finance

Division of Employment and Training
Address: 19 Staniford Street, Boston, MA 02114
Telephone: (617) 626-6603 **Fax:** (617) 727-0315
E-mail: hmarcy@detma.org
Reports to: Deputy Director John King

PERSONAL INFORMATION:
Born: August 27, 1938 **Place of Birth:** Boston
Marital Status: married (Jean) **Children:** 3
Education: Harvard College (A.B., '60); Columbia University (M.A. ,'62); Simmons College (M.S., Library Science, '66)

Previous Employment: Massachusetts Office of the Inspector General (Chief, Management Division); State of Vermont (Administrative Director of Taxes; Comptroller and Commissioner of Management Information Systems; Commissioner of Budget and Management)
Years in Current Position: 7 **Years in State Service:** 11

JOB DESCRIPTION:
Responsible for Human Resources (personnel, labor relations, training, EEO/AA); Finance (budget, accounting, payroll, vendor payments, procurement, fiscal controls); MIS (mainframe operations, data communications network, PCs, LANs, systems development, etc.); Facilities Management (security, leasing, space design/moves, capitol improvements; General Office Services (central records, printing, inventory, mail, etc.).

1999 PRIORITIES:
Mainstreaming support functions; stability

ORGANIZATIONS:
American Society for Public Administration; American Library Association; Central Vermont Runners

Richard L. Dill

Associate Director of Unemployment and Field Operations

Division of Employment and Training
Address: 19 Staniford Street, Boston, MA 02114
Telephone: (617) 626-6604 **Fax:** (617) 727-0315
E-mail: rdill@detma.org
Staff: Jane Frain, Administrative Assistant
Reports to: Deputy Director John King

PERSONAL INFORMATION:
Born: May 24, 1939 **Place of Birth:** Norwood
Marital Status: married (Jessica Rogers Dill) **Children:** 1
Education: University of Massachusetts at Amherst (B.A., '61); Northeastern University (M.Ed., '68; C.A.G.S., '70; M.P.A., '80)
Previous Employment: Department of Employment and Training (Regional Director of Facilities Management, Director of W.I.N., Director of E.S. Automated Systems, Director of Staff Training); Brockton, Cambridge, 128 Professional Service Center (Local Office Manager)
Years in Current Position: 7 **Years in State Service:** 35

JOB DESCRIPTION:
Manage unemployment insurance services and field operations.

1999 PRIORITIES:
Implement state-wide virtual call center.

Robert J. Prezioso

Deputy Director

Division of Occupational Safety
Address: 100 Cambridge Street, 11th Floor, Boston, MA 02202
Telephone: (617) 727-3452 **Fax:** (617) 727-0726
E-mail: RobertPrezioso@USERS@LAB
Staff: Matthew Poirier. Administrative Assistant
Reports to: Director Angelo Buonopane

PERSONAL INFORMATION:
Education: University of Massachusetts at Boston (B.S., Management, '88); Harvard University (currently attending)
Years in Current Position: 2 **Years in State Service:** 8

JOB DESCRIPTION:
To protect the health and safety of workers in Massachusetts.

1999 PRIORITIES:
Conduct more thn 5,000 consultation and enforcement site visits in public and private workspaces in Massachusetts. Promulgate more user-friendly regulations; conduct free training seminars; and improve outread materials.

ORGANIZATIONS:
National Safety Council; Boston Society of Architects; Boston Atheneum

Paul Aboody, Jr.

Manager, Occupational Hygiene Program

Division of Occupational Safety
Address: 1001 Watertown Street, West Newton, MA 02465
Telephone: (617) 969-7177 **Fax:** (617) 727-4581
Staff: Nancy Comeau, Supervisor of Occupational Health Section; Joseph LaMalva, Supervisor OSHA Consultation Program; Robert Kenrick, Chief of Laboratory
Reports to: Deputy Director Robert J. Prezioso

PERSONAL INFORMATION:
Born: September 20, 1940 **Place of Birth:** Worcester
Marital Status: married (Patricia Ann) **Children:** 4
Education: St. Anselm College (B.A. '63); Worcester State College (M.Ed. Biology, '74); Harvard School of Public Health (various courses)
Previous Employment: Worcester Public Schools
Years in Current Position: 8 **Years in State Service:** 8

JOB DESCRIPTION:
To protect the workforce and promote the well-being of Massachusetts industries.

1999 PRIORITIES:
Increase investigations of workplaces for detection and prevention of occupational hygiene problems.

ORGANIZATIONS:
National Asbestos Council; American Conference of Government Industrial Hygienists

Stewart C. Field

Program Manager

Division of Occupational Safety
Address: 100 Cambridge Street, 11th Floor Boston, MA 02202
Telephone: (617) 727-3492 **Fax:** (617) 727-0726
E-mail: SField@state.ma.us
Staff: Steve Falcone, Admin I
Reports to: Deputy Director Robert Prezioso

PERSONAL INFORMATION:
Born: October 2, 1964 **Place of Birth:** Winchester
Marital Status: married (Heather Shannon)
Education: University of Massachusetts at Boston (B.A., '87); Boston University (M.S., '97)
Previous Employment: Massachusetts House of Representatives, Committee on Commerce and Labor
Years in Current Position: 2.5 **Years in State Service:** 9.5

JOB DESCRIPTION:
Implement the prevailing wage law; administer a joint state-federal occupational injury/illness survey; license and regulate employment agencies.

1999 PRIORITIES:
Adjust programs to accommodate new information technology; encourage multi-tasking of personnel through additional training opportunities.

Ernest W. Kelley

Manager, Lead and Asbestos Program

Division of Occupational Safety
Address: 333 East Street, Pittsfield, MA 01201
Telephone: (413) 448-8746 **Fax:** (413) 784-1163
Staff: Benjamin Tymann, Program Coordinaotr: Brian Wong, Field Supervisor; Frank Kramarz, Supervising Engineer; Richard Walsh, Chief Inspector
Reports to: Deputy Director Robert Prezioso

PERSONAL INFORMATION:
Born: April 8, 1946 **Place of Birth:** Greenfield
Marital Status: married (Hsiu-li Chan) **Children:** 2
Education: University of Massachusetts at Boston (M.S. '78)
Previous Employment: self-employed dairy farmer
Years in Current Position: 1 **Years in State Service:** 14

JOB DESCRIPTION:
To ensure that workers and the general public are protected from asbestos and lead hazards.

1999 PRIORITIES:
To maximise efficiency in the delivery services.

ORGANIZATIONS:
Forum on State and Tribal Toxics Action (FOSTTA)

Linda M. Hamel

General Counsel

Division of Occupational Safety
Address: 100 Cambridge Street, Room 1107, Boston, MA 02202
Telephone: (617) 727-3452 **Fax:** (617) 727-8022
E-mail: Linda M. Hamel@Users@LAB
Staff: Matt Poirier, Administrative Assistant
Reports to: Deputy Director Robert Prezioso

PERSONAL INFORMATION:
Born: May 9, 1958 **Place of Birth:** Portsmouth, NH
Marital Status: married **Children:** 1
Education: Dartmouth College (A.B., '80); University of North Carolina at Chapel Hill (J.D., '86)
Previous Employment: FDIC (1991-1996)
Years in Current Position: 2 **Years in State Service:** 2

JOB DESCRIPTION:
Provide General Counsel to state agency providing occupational safety to municipal and county employees, OSHA consultation program, private sector employees and regulation of lead and asbestos abatement and employment agencies.

1999 PRIORITIES:
Provide competent legal service to division.

Jill Nelson-Dowd

Manager Administrative Services

Division of Occupational Safety
Address: 100 Cambridge Street, 11th Fl , Boston, MA 02202
Telephone: (617) 727-3452 **Fax:** (617) 727-0726
E-mail: Jnelson-Dowd@state.ma.us
Staff: Patricia Washington, Business Management Specialist; Jean Reilly, Clerk; Mildred Rogers, Clerk
Reports to: Deputy Director Robert Prezioso

PERSONAL INFORMATION:
Born: Sept. 11, 1965 **Place of Birth:** Worcester
Marital Status: married (David Nelson) **Children:** 2
Years in Current Position: 1 **Years in State Service:** 12

JOB DESCRIPTION:
Managing all financial, payroll and personnel activities within the Division of Occupational Safety and Apprentice Training.

Suzanne Teegarden

President

Corporation for Business, Work, and Learning (CBWL)
Address: The Schrafft Center, 529 Main Street, Suite 1100, Boston, MA 02129
Telephone: (617) 727-8158 **Fax:** (617) 242-7660
E-mail: Steegarden@cbwl.org
Staff: Elaine Fox, Executive Assistant
Reports to: CBWL Board of Directors

PERSONAL INFORMATION:
Born: April 23, 1948 **Place of Birth:** Kansas City
Education: University of Kansas (B.A., '71); University of California at Berkeley (M.A., '83)
Previous Employment: Industrial Services Program (Executive Director); Re-employment Assistance Program (Director); Executive Office of Economic Affairs (Special Assistant)
Years in Current Position: 3 **Years in State Service:** 15

JOB DESCRIPTION:
Oversee and direct quasi-public agency responsible for workforce development and workplace services.

1999 PRIORITIES:
Improve efficiency and effectiveness among programs; improve connections between workplace and workforce services.

SECTION IV

Independent State Agencies

The organizations described in this section are important independent state agencies that had formerly been listed under the jurisdiction of the executive secretariats. While some of these agencies work in cooperation with the secretariats, they remain separate and distinct from state government.

Massachusetts Department of Education

The Department of Education, headed by the Commissioner of Education, is under the State Board of Education. It is responsible for pre-kindergarten, elementary, secondary, vocational-technical, and adult basic education programs. It serves school districts by establishing standards and programs for students that ensure high achievement; by administering a fair and equitable system of school finance; by working with school districts to create a governance structure that encourages innovation and accountability; by enhancing the quality and accountability of all educators; and by developing testing measures to hold students and schools accountable for educational achievement.

Massachusetts Health and Educational Facilities Authority (HEFA)

Robert J. Ciolek, Executive Director
99 Summer Street, Suite 1000
Boston, MA 02110-1240
Tel:(617) 737-8377 FAX (617) 737-8366

The Massachusetts Health and Educational Facilities Authority works with nonprofit institutions in Massachusetts to cost-effectively finance and refinance equipment, technology, buildings, and other capital projects through loans, leases, and bond issuances. HEFA also provides financial services, the award-winning PowerOptions program, and other programs to enable nonprofits to thrive in a constantly evolving economy. HEFA was established by the legislature in 1968, its board is appointed by the governor, and it is self-supporting without public funding. For more information visit the web site at www.mhefa.state.ma.us.

Massachusetts Housing Finance Agency (MHFA)

Steven D. Pierce, Executive Director
One Beacon Street
Boston MA 02108
Tel: (617) 854-1000 FAX (617) 854-1029

The Massachusetts Housing Finance Agency offers a variety of financial resources to promote decent, safe and affordable housing throughout the Commonwealth. Since its creation in 1966, MHFA's programs have helped tens of thousand of low and moderate income people buy their first home or rent affordable apartments. MHFA's programs also enable lenders to increase their investment in affordable mortgage and bond programs and developers to maximize the business opportunities in niche market areas. MHFA's commitment to challenge traditional lending practices combines innovation with sound business practices; a philosophy that reinforces the Agency's position as the leader in affordable housing finance in Massachusetts.

MassJobs Council

David S. Smith, Director
One Ashburton Place, Room 2111
Boston, MA 02108
Tel: (617) 727-7944 FAX (617) 727-0729

The MassJobs council is the principal Advisory Committee to the Governor regarding workforce development. Among the initiatives being pursued by this organization are Welfare to Work, School to Work and One-Stop Career Centers. The Board is made up of business leaders, labor union representatives, government officials, and educators.

Community Development Finance Corporation

Milton J. Benjamin, Jr., President
10 Post Office Square, Suite 1090,
Boston, MA 02109
Tel: (617) 482-9141 FAX (617) 482-7129

Massachusetts Community Development Finance Corporation is a quasi-public investment corporation. CDFC's primary goals are growth in the small business sector, creation of affordable housing, and commercial development in economically distressed communities. There is a nine-member board of directors consisting of members of the financial community, government department heads and union and citizen representation.

Disabled Persons Protection Commission

John D. Dunn, Jr. Executive Director
99 Bedford St.
Boston, MA 02111
Tel: (617) 727-6465 FAX (617) 727-6469 Hotline:(800) 426-0990

The Disabled Persons Protection Commission investigates and remediates cases of abuse of the Commonwealth's most vulnerable citizens. The Commission was created by M.G.L. c. 19C in 1987 as an independent investigations and oversight agency which investigates and remediates instances of abuse of disabled persons. In the last ten years the agency received more than 26,000 reports of abuse and presently receives an average of 360 reports of alleged abuse each month.

Office of Campaign and Political Finance

Michael J. Sullivan, Director
One Ashburton Place
Boston, MA 02108
Tel: (617) 727-8352 FAX (617) 727-6549
E-mail: OCPF@cpf.state.ma.us

The office of Campaign and Political Finance administers the state's Campaign Finance Law. Established in 1973, OCPF is the depository for disclosure reports filed by candidates and committees under M.G.L. Chapter 55. Candidates who report to OCPF are seeking statewide, legislative and county office, as well as Governor's Council candidates and some candidates running city-wide in cities with populations of least 100,000. Disclosure reports filed with OCPF, as well as other related documents and correspondence are available for public inspection.

Seaport Advisory Council

Richard S. Armstrong, Executive Secretary
49 Centre Street, Town Hall
Fairhaven, MA 02719
Tel: (508) 999-3030 FAX (508) 999-6442

The Massachusetts Seaport Advisory Council is a government council created in 1994 to coordinate state seaport policy. Its mission is to develop the full economic potential of the seaports of Massachusetts. The 15-member council is made up of private citizens appointed by the Governor, cabinet secretaries, and other representatives from state agencies that are related to seaport development.

The Council is based in Fairhaven and has a satellite office in Boston. It meets quarterly in different port cities and towns on a rotating basis. Meetings are open to the public. For more information visit the web site www.state.ma.us/seaports.

State Ethics Commission (ETH)

Stephanie S. Lovell, Executive Director
One Ashburton Place, Room 619
Boston, MA 02108
Tel: (617) 727-0060 FAX (617) 723-5851

Since 1963, the Massachusetts conflict of interest law has regulated the conduct of public officials and employees in the Bay State. Massachusetts General Laws c.268A limits what public employees may do on the job, what they may do after hours, and what they may do after they leave public service. It also sets standards of conduct required of state, county and municipal employees and officials.

The Commission staff is made up of four separate divisions, under the supervision of the executive director. The Legal Division provides free, confidential advice to public employees regarding the legality of proposed activities; it also represents the Commission in court. The Statements of Financial Interests Division administers the financial disclosure law and audits SFIs filed with the agency. The Public Education Division conducts seminars for public employees. The Enforcement Division investigates and prosecutes alleged violations of the laws.

Commission Members (1998)

Augustus F. Wagner, Jr., Chair
Nutter, McClennen & Fish, LLP

Lynne E. Larkin, Vice Chair
Attorney, Arlington, MA

Edward Rapacki
Ellis & Rapacki

Stephen E. Moore
Warner 7 Stackpole LLP

Paul J. Liacos
Chief Justice, Massachusetts Supreme Judicial Court (retired)

Office of the Inspector General (IGO)
Robert Cerasoli, Inspector General
One Ashburton Place, 13th Fl
Boston, MA 02108
Tel: (617) 727-9140 FAX (617) 723-3540

The IGO is a state watchdog agency with broad mandates to prevent and detect fraud, waste, and abuse in government. The office conducts operational and management reviews, analyzes legislation and regulations, provides technical assistance and conducts civil and criminal investigations. The Office has established a confidential toll-free hotline number -- 800-322-1323 -- and invites calls to report suspected fraud, waste, and abuse in government.

The Office was established in 1981 in the wake of a major construction procurement scandal. It employed a three-part prevention strategy: 1) Timely intervention - intervening in situations before fraud and abuse occurs by reviewing bills and recommending amendments to help protect against fraud or waste. The office also provides assistance to public agencies. 2) Dissemination of lessons learned - letting jurisdictions know about issues of interest to public officials. 3) Capacity building - providing training and technical assistance to public officials. The Massachusetts Certified Public Purchasing Official program and Procurement Bulletin are examples of capacity building efforts.

Board of Library Commissioners (BLC)
Keith M. Fiels, Director
648 Beacon Street, 5th Fl
Boston, MA 02215
Tel: (617) 267-9400 FAX (617) 421-9833
Web site: www.mlin.lib.ma.us

The Massachusetts Board of Library Commissioners supports, develops, coordinates, improves and promotes library services throughout the Commonwealth. The goals of the Board of Library Commissioners are to maintain strong, free public libraries, to coordinate and support statewide and regional programs and promote resource sharing and use of electronic information technology by libraries, and to provide for library services to blind and physically handicapped residents. The Board also advises municipalities and trustees regarding the operation and maintenance of public libraries and is responsible for the administration of state and federal programs for Massachusetts libraries.

The Board was established in 1890 under Chapter 78 of the Massachusetts General laws. It consists of nine commissioners appointed by the governor. A director, appointed by the Board, is responsible for administration of agency programs and services.

Massachusetts Convention Center Authority (MCCA)
Francis Joyce, Executive Director
Hynes Convention Center
900 Boyleston Street
Boston, MA 02118
Tel: (617) 954-2100 FAX (617) 954-2299

The Massachusetts convention Center Authority works in partnership with public and private entities in the state to bring meetings, congresses and conventions to Boston and Massachusetts. The M.C.C.A. owns and operates the John B. Hynes Veterans Memorial Convention Center in Boston, which, since its opening in 1988 as a national and international convention venue, has been occupied to capacity. The M.C.C.A. also took over and completed a two-year renovation of the 1,500-car Boston Common Garage, which it now manages.

In 1997 the Massachusetts State Legislature made the M.C.C.A. the owner of the Springfield Civic Center with responsibility for the design and construction of a $48.5 million expansion and renovation of that facility. At the same time the M.C.C.A. was charged with the design, construction, and operation of a new $537 million convention and trade show facility in South Boston.

Massachusetts Corporation for Educational Telecommunications (MCET)
John Flores, Executive Director
One Kendall Square, Building 1500
Cambridge, MA 02139
Tel: (627) 621-0290 FAX (617) 252-5729

MCET is the premier provider of outstanding educational programs, products and services using state-of-the-art technologies. Customers are life-long learners from K-12, higher education and the community at large in Massachusetts, the United States and the world. MCET has created a satellite network known as the Mass LearnPike, broadcasting from studios in Cambridge to all public school districts.

The Telecommunications Service Center offers services to education, business, non-profit and governmental institutions to provide technical assistance. Services include television broadcasting, satellite uplinking and downlinking, video production, worldwide video teleconferencing, audio bridging and mobile production and uplinking. Institutions of higher education partner with MCET to create programs on related issues to serve multiple campuses and learning sites.

Massachusetts Development Finance Agency
Michael P. Hogan, Executive Director
75 Federal Street, 10th Fl
Boston, MA 02110
Tel: (617) 451-2477 FAX (617) 451-3429

It is the mission of MassDevelopment to help build the communities of the Commonwealth by stimulating economic development. In 1995 the boards of directors of the state's largest economic development agencies initiated the process of affiliation to fashion a new Agency into a seamless system of support for Massachusetts's non-profits, businesses and health care institutions. Today MassDevelopment serves as the state's resource for financing and real estate development. By making strategic use of financing programs, and by leveraging long-standing relationships among public and private lending institutions, communities identify and capitalize on key development opportunities.

Massachusetts Educational Financing Authority (MEFA)
Dr. Peter Mazareas, Executive Director
125 Summer Street
Boston, MA 02110
Tel: (617) 261-9760 FAX (617) 261-9765

The mission of the Massachusetts Educational Financing Authority is to promote the economic development of Massachusetts higher education by offering a low cost college loan program, a prepaid tuition/college savings program, a college investment program with professionally managed funds, an international student loan program, and a public service early awareness and training program.

The Legislature established MEFA in 1981, at the request of colleges and universities for the purpose of assisting borrowers and colleges in financing the cost of education. MEFA is self-financing and receives no government interest subsidies or guarantees from the Commonwealth.

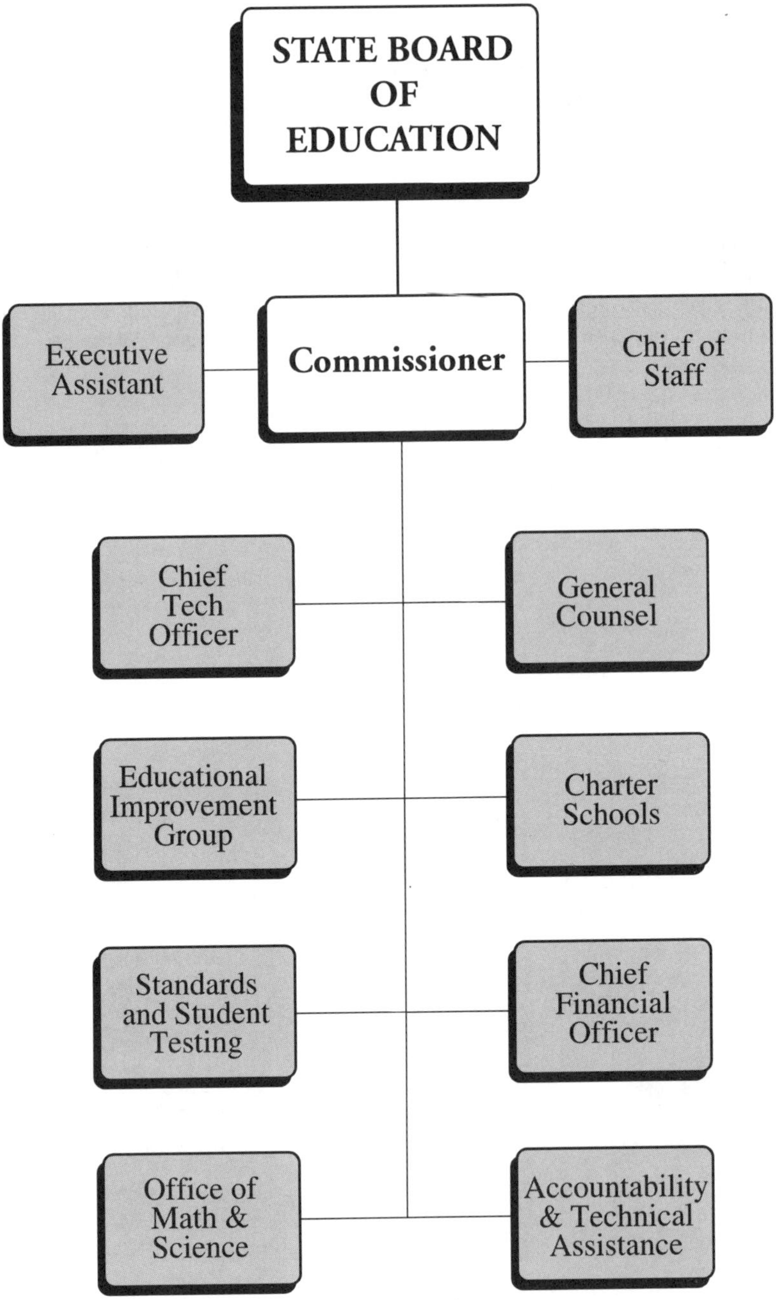
STATE BOARD OF EDUCATION
Executive Assistant
Commissioner
Chief of Staff
Chief Tech Officer
General Counsel
Educational Improvement Group
Charter Schools
Standards and Student Testing
Chief Financial Officer
Office of Math & Science
Accountability & Technical Assistance

Department of Education

STATE BOARD OF EDUCATION

Chairman	**John R. Silber**	(617) 353-4300
Vice-Chairman	**Roberta Schaefer**	(781)388-3300

DEPARTMENT OF EDUCATION

Interim Commissioner	**David P. Driscoll**	(781)388-3300
Deputy Commissioner	**vacant**	(781)388-3300
General Counsel/Board Liaison and Senior Associate Commissioner	**Rhoda E. Schneider**	(781)388-3300
Chief of Staff Office of the Commissioner	**Alan P.G. Safran**	(781)388-3300
Chief Financial Officer	**Jeff Wulfson**	(781)388-3300
Chief Technology Officer	**Greg Nadeau**	(781)388-3300
Director of Accountability	**Juliane Dow**	(781)388-3300
Director of Standards & Testing	**Jeffrey Nellhaus**	(781)388-3300
Director of Legislative Affairs	**Joseph Giannino**	(781)388-3300

Associate Commissioners:

Educational Improvement	**Carole Thomson**	(781) 388-3300
Charter Schools	**Scott Hamilton**	(617)727-0075
Administrator, Office for the Advancement of Math and Science	**Tom Noonan**	(781)388-3300

John R. Silber

Chairman, Massachusetts Board of Education

Department of Education
Address: 147 Bay State Road, Boston, MA 02215
Telephone: (617) 353-2208 **Fax:** (617) 353-9674
Staff: Mark G. White, Administrator for Education Reform
Reports to: Governor A. Paul Cellucci

PERSONAL INFORMATION:

Born: August 15, 1926 **Place of Birth:** San Antonio, TX
Marital Status: married (Kathryn) **Children:** 7
Education: Trinity University (B.A., summa cum laude, '47); Yale University (M.A., '52; Ph.D., '56)
Previous Employment: Boston University (Chancellor '96-present, President, '71-'96); University of Texas, College of Arts and Sciences (Dean, '67-'70); University of Texas (Professor, '55-'70); Yale University (Instructor, '52-'55)
Years in Current Position: 3 **Years in State Service:** 3

JOB DESCRIPTION:

To establish state policy for public education, from pre-kindergarten through twelfth grade.

1999 PRIORITIES:

Improve early childhood education, ensuring that children are learning to read well by second or third grade; reform bilingual and special education; develop academically reliable curricula; reform teacher certification and recertification; increase the time in school devoted to academic core disciplines; review school systems' budgets to ensure more funds are devoted to teaching and less to administration; and ensure safe schools for all children and teachers.

ORGANIZATIONS:

American Association of Higher Education (Member); American Philosophical Association; Americans for Medical Progress (Chairman); Aristotelian Society (Member); Bette Davis Foundation (Board of Directors); Boston Police Foundation (Board of Directors); British Institute of the United States (Board of Directors); Horatio Alger Association (Member); The Jamestown Foundation (Board of Advisors); Metaphysical Society of America (Member); Mutual of American Institutional Funds, Inc. (Board of Directors); National Association of Scholars (Board of Advisors); National Association of Schools and Colleges of the United Methodist Church (Board of Advisors); New England Holocaust Memorial Committee (Board of Directors); The Notes Club; Royal Society of Arts (Fellows); United States Strategic Institute (Vice Chairman); The University Club of Boston

David P. Driscoll

Interim Commissioner

Department of Education
Address: 350 Main Street, Malden, MA 02148
Telephone: (781) 388-3300 ext. 103 **Fax:** (781)388-3392
E-mail: ddriscoll@doe.mass.edu
Staff: Robin McCaffrey, Executive Assistant (ext.102)
Reports to: Board of Education

PERSONAL INFORMATION:
Born: October 9, 1942 **Place of Birth:** Melrose
Marital Status: married (Kathleen) **Children:** 4
Education: Boston College (A.B., Mathematics, '64); State College at Salem (M.Ed., '67); Boston College (D.Ed., '81)

Previous Employment: Melrose Public Schools (Superintendent, '84-'93; Assistant Superintendent, '72-'84; Mathematics Teacher, '66-'72); Western Junior High School in Somerville (Mathematics Teacher, '64-'66)
Years in Current Position: 1 **Years in State Service:** 34 (in Education)

JOB DESCRIPTION:
Provide overall leadership and management of the Department of Education in implementing all aspects of educational policy and laws affecting public schools.

1999 PRIORITIES:
Implementation of the Education Reform Act of 1993.

ORGANIZATIONS:
American Association of School Administrators; Chief State School Officers;; Harvard Round Table (past President); Merrimac Valley Superintendents Round Table

Alan P.G. Safran

Chief of Staff

Department of Education
Address: 350 Main Street, Malden, MA 02148
Telephone: (781) 388-3300 ext. 116 **Fax:** (781) 388-3392
Staff: Jan Feldman, Educational Specialist **E-mail:** asafran@doe.mass.edu
Reports to: Interim Commissioner David P. Driscoll

PERSONAL INFORMATION:
Born: November 5, 1958 **Place of Birth:** Albany, NY
Marital Status: married (Dana) **Children:** 2
Education: Princeton University (B.A., '80); George Washington Law Center (J.D., Law, '86)

Previous Employment: U.S. Senate Foreign Relations Committee (Spokesman); U.S. Senate Arms Control Observer Group (Spokesman); Queens County, NY (Assistant District Attorney); Massachusetts Republican State Committee (Executive Director and Press Secretary)
Years in Current Position: 4 **Years in State Service:** 4

JOB DESCRIPTION:
Lead responsibility support for the Commissioner.

1999 PRIORITIES:
Support work of Commissioner; Inform the public of developments and changes flowing from the Education Reform Act of 1993; support state teacher quality enhancement initiatives.

ORGANIZATIONS:
Massachusetts State Bar Association; New York State Bar Association

Rhoda E. Schneider

General Counsel, Board Liaison and Senior Associate Commissioner

Department of Education
Address: 350 Main Street, Malden, MA 02148
Telephone: (781) 388-3300 ext. 110 **Fax:** (781) 388-3396
Staff: Debra Comfort, Juliane Dow, Susan Papanek McHugh, Staff Attorneys; Kathy LeBlanc, Raud Jean-Louis, Support Staff
Reports to: Interim Commissioner David P. Driscoll

PERSONAL INFORMATION:
Education: Wellesley College (B.A .'70); Boston University Law School (J.D., '74)
Previous Employment: Department of Education (Staff Attorney, '74-'78); Executive Office of Human Services (Legal Assistant, '74)
Years in Current Position: 20 **Years in State Service:** 24

JOB DESCRIPTION:
Provide legal counsel to Commissioner and State Board of Education; advise and assist in overseeing implementation of laws affecting public schools and other programs under the Department's jurisdiction.

1999 PRIORITIES:
Assist Commissioner and State Board of Education in implementing comprehensive Education Reform.

ORGANIZATIONS:
Harvard Graduate School of Education, Summer Institute on School Law (Faculty Member); Massachusetts Continuing Legal Education, Inc. (Faculty Member)

Milton J. Benjamin, Jr.
President

Community Development Finance Corporation
Address: 10 Post Office Square, Suite 1090, Boston, MA 02109
Telephone: (617) 482-9141 **Fax:** (617) 482-7129
Staff: Lisa Maxwell, Executive Assistant & Human Resource Administrator; Joseph Cullen, Controller
Reports to: John E. Marston, Chairman, CDFC Board of Directors

PERSONAL INFORMATION:
Born: September 10, 1950 **Place of Birth:** New York, NY
Marital Status: married (Dr. Joan Wallace Benjamin) **Children:** 2
Education: Northeastern University (B.S., '78); Northeastern Law School (J.D., '81)
Previous Employment: Lena Park Community Development Corporation (General Counsel, Vice President of Economic and Community Development)
Years in Current Position: 11 **Years in State Service:** 11

JOB DESCRIPTION:
President of CDFC, a quasi-public investment corporation that provides financing for small businesses and real estate projects in the Commonwealth's low- and moderate-income communities.

1999 PRIORITIES:
Increase capital and capital sources for targeted financing.

ORGANIZATIONS:
Chairman, Commonwealth Enterprise Fund; Board Member Roxbury Comprehensive Health Center; Executive Member, Boston Chamber of Commerce; Board Member, Roxbury Comprehensive Community Health ; Trustee, Mass Eye a& Ear Infirmary.

John D. Dunn, Jr.
Executive Director

Disabled Persons Protection Commission
Address: 99 Bedford Street, Room 200, Boston, MA 02111
Telephone: (617) 727-6465 ext. 119 **Fax:** (617) 727-6469
Staff: Ella E. Alexander, Administrative Assistant **E-mail:** JDunn@DPPC.state.ma.us

PERSONAL INFORMATION:

Born: Oct. 6, 1962 **Place of Birth:** Bridgeport, CT
Education: UMass/Amherst (B.S. '85)
Previous Employment: Commonwealth of Mass., Commission for the Deaf and Hard of Hearing
Years in Current Position: 2 **Years in State Service:** 12

JOB DESCRIPTION:
Direct activities of independent state agency responsible for protection of disabled adults through investigation of abuse reports received via 24-hour abuse hotline; ensure provision of protective services and oversight of other state agencies.

1999 PRIORITIES:
Continued expansion of investigative capability; enhancement of oversight and abuse prevention activities

ORGANIZATIONS:
American Association on Mental Retardation.

Richard S. Armstrong
Executive Secretary

Massachusetts Seaport Advisory Council
Address: 40 Center St., Fairhaven, MA 02719
Telephone: (508) 999-3030 **Fax:** (508) 999-6442

PERSONAL INFORMATION:
Born: January 7, 1944 **Place of Birth:** Attleboro
Marital Status: married (Patricia) **Children:** 2
Education: MIT (S.B., '65, M.S. '66); Episcopal Divinity School (B.D. '69)
Previous Employment: Commonwealth of Massachusetts, Assistant Secretary of Environmental Affairs; Town of Falmouth, Chair, Board of Selectmen, owner/operator Fiddler's Cove Marina, N. Falmouth
Years in Current Position: 3 **Years in State Service:** 5

JOB DESCRIPTION:
Oversee the Seaport 2000 initiative for the Governor and coordinate the development of the Commonwealth's Seaports using funding from the $300 million Seaport Board.

1999 PRIORITIES:
Accelerate construction phase of planning as projects are finished with emphasis on dredging, rail links, and pier infrastructure.

ORGANIZATIONS:
Society of Naval Architects, Cape Cod Center for the Environment, Cape Cod Health Care Corporation.

Michael J. Sullivan
Director

Office of Campaign and Political Finance
Address: One Ashburton Place, Rm 411, Boston, MA 02108
Telephone: (617)727-8352 **Fax:** (617) 727-6549
E-mail: msullivan@cpf.state.ma.us
Reports to: Commission to Select the Director (see MGL 55,3)

PERSONAL INFORMATION:
Born: July 18, 1959 **Place of Birth:** Saugus
Marital Status: married (Lynn) **Children:** 3
Education: Tufts (B.A. '81)
Years in Current Position: 4.5 **Years in State Service:** 10

JOB DESCRIPTION:
Administration of the state's campaign finance law.

1999 PRIORITIES:
Educating candidates about the Clean Elections Initiative. Upgrading our web site. Continuing our seminar program.

ORGANIZATIONS:
Assoc. of New England Football Officials; North Shore Baseball Umpires Assoc.; Council on Government Ethics Law

Robert J. Ciolek
Executive Director

Massachusetts Health and Educational Facilities Authority
Address: 99 Summer Street, Suite 1000, Boston, MA 02110
Telephone: (617)737-8377 **Fax:** (617) 737-8366
E-mail: Bob@MHEFA.state.ma.us

Michael P. Hogan
Executive Director

Mass Development
Address: 75 Federal St., 10th Fl, Boston, MA 02110
Telephone: (617) 451-2477 **Fax:** (617) 451-3429
E-mail: mhogan@state.ma.us
Reports to: Edward Linde and Robert Beal, Co-Chairs, MassDevelopment Board of Directors

PERSONAL INFORMATION:
Born: April 12, 1960 **Place of Birth:** Worcester
Marital Status: married (Margaret Dwyer)
Children: 1
Education: St. John's Seminary, Boston College (B.S. '82)
Years in Current Position: 4 **Years in State Service:** 6

JOB DESCRIPTION:
Executive Director of MassDevelopment, a quasi-public economic and real estate development agency that serves the communities of the Commonwealth by stimulating economic development

1999 PRIORITIES:
Provide flexible financing solutions to help manufacturers, businesses and non-profit organizations create new jobs; administer $30 million Brownfields Redevelopment Funds and continue to attract new and expanding businesses to locate at Devens and other Massachusetts sites.

ORGANIZATIONS:
Director, Greater Marlborough Boys & Girls Clubs; Trustee, UMASS/Memorial Health Systems; C.V.E.D., N.A.I.O.P.

SECTION V

The Supreme Judicial Court

For more than 300 years the Massachusetts judicial system has been administering justice for the Commonwealth of Massachusetts. The Massachusetts Constitution was enacted in 1780, distributing power and mandating a complete separation of legislative, executive, and judicial powers.

In 1781, Chief Justice William Cushing, an early Chief Justice of the Supreme Judicial Court, wrote the first American Court decision abolishing slavery, an issue that dominated American politics for more than 80 years thereafter.

The late 18th and 19th centuries were occupied with shaping the institutions of government (especially the law and the courts) to the rapidly developing needs of a newly industrialized and commercial society, with its new subject areas for litigation. In the 1870s the focus of change was on police, municipal and district courts.

In the past century, the pattern of reorganization has been the creation of specialized courts and specialized procedures, rather than changes in the basic structure of the judicial system.

Specialized courts were set up for land registration (Land Court, 1898), juvenile matters (Boston Juvenile Court, 1906), and housing matters (first Housing Court in Boston, 1971). An Intermediate Appellate Court was established in 1972 (Appeals Court).

In 1976, as a result of continued congestion, delay and backlog, the Governor's Select Committee on Judicial Needs (Cox Commission) published a report with wide-ranging recommendations for the reorganization and management of the state's court system.

As a result, the Legislature enacted the Court Reorganization Act of 1978, which created the Massachusetts Trial Court headed by a Chief Administrative Justice.

In 1986, the Senate Committee on Ways and Means undertook a 10-month study to assess the degree to which the Cox Commission had been implemented and had been effective. The Committee published a report, *Agenda 90: Modernizing the Judiciary*, which found that "the administration of justice in Massachusetts is still suffering because Massachusetts courts are handling 21st century problems with 19th century resources." *Agenda 90* went on to make a number of recommendations to modernize both the functioning of the judiciary and the physical surroundings in which justice was being dispensed.

In 1990, Chief Justice Paul J. Liacos of the Supreme Judicial Court established the Chief Justice's Commission on the Future of the Courts to determine how the judiciary can best meet the changing needs of society in the 21st century. The Commission documented its findings and recommendations in a report to the Chief Justice in 1992, titled *Reinventing Justice, 2022*.

Copies of this report are available by writing to:

Supreme Judicial Court's
Public Information Office
218 Old Courthouse
Boston, MA 02108

The Massachusetts court system consists of two levels: the Appellate Courts and the Trial Court.

The Appellate Courts

The Supreme Judicial Court and the Appeals Court compose the Appellate Courts in Massachusetts. The Appeals Court was created as the intermediate appellate court in 1972.

The Supreme Judicial Court consists of a Chief Justice and six Associate Justices, appointed (as are all Massachusetts judges) by the Governor, with the advice and consent of the elected Executive Council, to hold office during good behavior until age 70.

The Appeals Court consists of a Chief Justice and thirteen Associate Justices.

In addition to its appellate functions, the Supreme Judicial Court retains broad original jurisdiction in certain classes of cases (often concerned with that of other courts), is responsible for the general superintendency of the judiciary and of the bar, makes or approves rules for the operation and procedures of all Massachusetts courts and, in certain circumstances, may be required to provide the Governor, the Executive Council, or either house of the Legislature with advisory opinions. The Justices of the Supreme Judicial Court also decide questions of Massachusetts law certified to them by federal courts or by the highest appellate courts of other states.

The Trial Court

The Court Reorganization Act of 1978 administratively unified the seven formerly separate and distinct trial courts of the Commonwealth into a single Trial Court consisting of seven departments: Superior Court, District Court, Probate and Family Court, Land Court, Boston Municipal Court, Juvenile Court, and Housing Court. A court reform act of 1992, in part, provided for a statewide Juvenile Court Department and a expanded Administrative Office under the Chief Administrative Justice for Administration and Management. The Offices of the Commissioner of Probation and the Jury Commissioner are also part of the judiciary.

The Administrative Office of the Trial Court, headed by the Chief Justice for Administration and Management, is responsible for the functional areas required by legislation: personnel and employee relations, fiscal and budgetary matters, property and facilities leasing, education and training, security, data processing, legal matters, research, and planning. The Court Interpreter Program, the Judicial Institute, and the Trial Court law libraries are also managed from this office.

Hon. John J. Irwin, Jr.,
Chief Justice for Administration and Management
Trial Court of the Commonwealth

District Court Department
Chief Justice:
Hon. Samuel E. Zoll
Number of Authorized Justices: 172
Location: 69 divisions statewide

Superior Court Department
Chief Justice:
Hon. Robert A. Mulligan
Number of Authorized Justices: 80
Locations: 14 divisions; one division per county located at the county seat; satellite sessions may be held at other locations.

Probate and Family Court Department
Chief Justice:
Hon. Sean Dunphy
Number of Authorized Justices: 49
Locations: 14 divisions; one division per county located at the county seat; satellite sessions may be held at other locations.

Juvenile Court Department
Chief Justice:
Hon. Martha P. Grave
Number of Authorized Justices: 37
Locations: 11 divisions; Boston, cities of Springfield and Worcester, Bristol County; in process of expanding structure.

Boston Municipal Court Department
Chief Justice:
Hon. William J. Tierney
Number of Authorized Justices: 11
Location: Boston

Housing Court Department
Chief Justice:
Hon. E. George Daher
Number of Authorized Justices: 9
Locations: Boston, Worcester, Hampden, Springfield, Northeastern, and Southeastern

Land Court Department
Chief Justice: Hon. Peter W. Kilborn
Number of Authorized Justices: 4
Location: Boston, with statewide jurisdiction

Office of the Jury Commissioner
Jury Commissioner for the Commonwealth:
Frank Davis
Location: Boston

Office of the Commissioner of Probation
Commissioner of Probation:
John J. O'Brien
Location: Boston

Massachusetts Court System

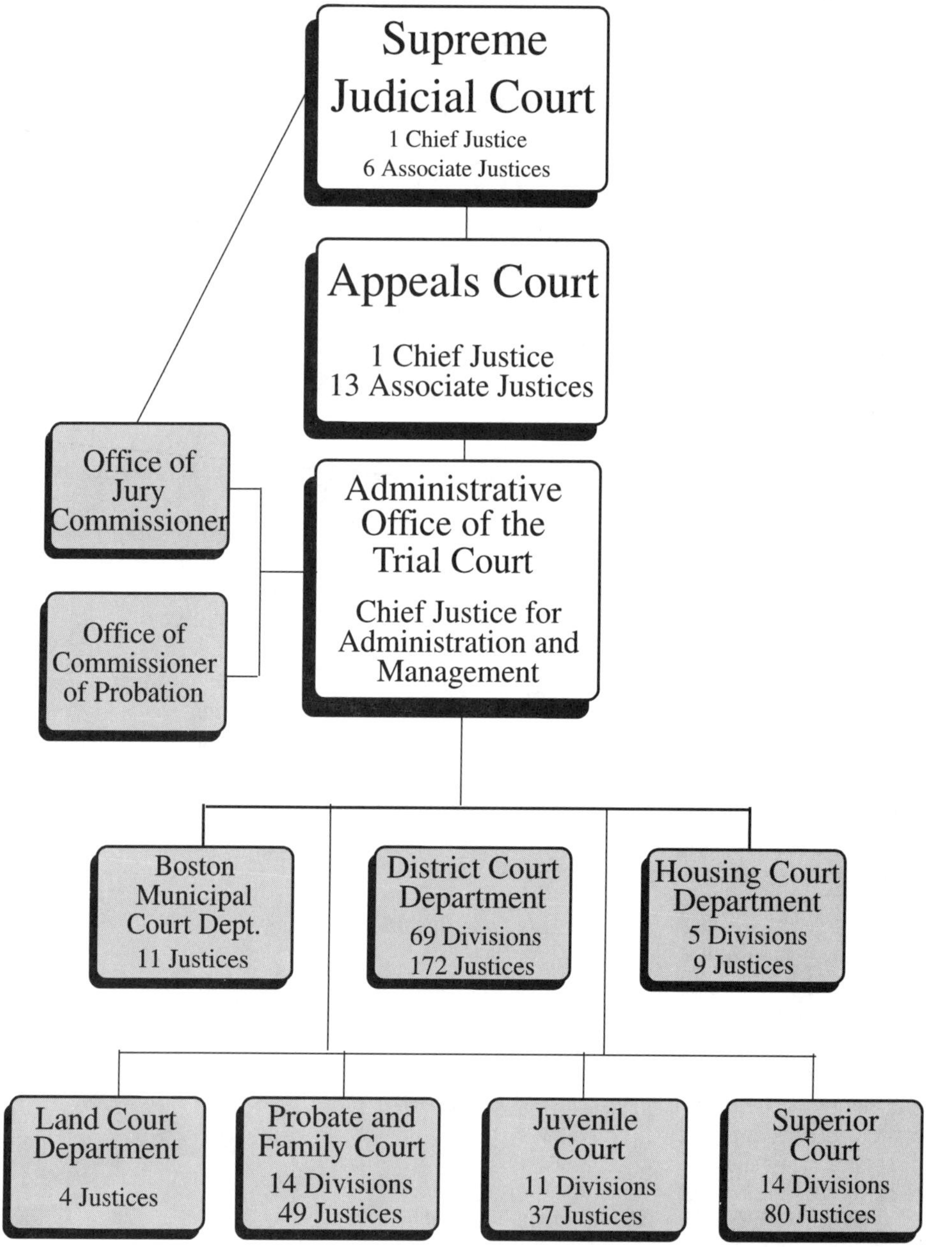
Supreme Judicial Court
1 Chief Justice
6 Associate Justices
Appeals Court
1 Chief Justice
13 Associate Justices
Office of Jury Commissioner
Administrative Office of the Trial Court
Chief Justice for Administration and Management
Office of Commissioner of Probation
Boston Municipal Court Dept.
11 Justices
District Court Department
69 Divisions
172 Justices
Housing Court Department
5 Divisions
9 Justices
Land Court Department
4 Justices
Probate and Family Court
14 Divisions
49 Justices
Juvenile Court
11 Divisions
37 Justices
Superior Court
14 Divisions
80 Justices

Chief Justice	**Herbert P. Wilkins**	(617) 557-1000
Associate Justice	**Ruth I. Abrams**	557-1000
Associate Justice	**Neil L. Lynch**	557-1000
Associate Justice	**John M. Greaney**	557-1000
Associate Justice	**Charles Fried**	557-1000
Associate Justice	**Margaret Hilary Marshall**	557-1000
Associate Justice	**Roderick L. Ireland**	557-1000

Administrators:

Administrative Assistant to the Justices	**Maria Zoe Mossaides**	557-1193
Business/Fiscal Manager	**Robert A. Burns, Jr.**	557-1070
Chief Staff Counsel	**Henry Clay**	557-1164
Clerk for the Commonwealth	**Jean M. Kennett**	557-1020
Clerk for Suffolk County	**Maura Sweeney Doyle**	557-1180
Counsel for Policy Development	**Barbara M. Diamond**	557-1156
Public Information Officer	**Joan Kenney**	557-1113

Herbert P. Wilkins

Chief Justice

Supreme Judicial Court
Address: 1300 New Courthouse, Boston, MA 02108
Telephone: (617) 557-1000 **Fax:** (617) 248-0771
Staff: Catherine Collins MacInnes, Administrative Assistant to the Chief Justice; Maria Zoe Mossaides, Administrative Assistant to the Justices; Maureen D. McGee, Legal Counsel to the Chief Justice

PERSONAL INFORMATION:
Education: Harvard University (A.B., '51); Harvard Law School (LL.B., '54)
Previous Employment: Palmer & Dodge (Partner,'60-'72; Associate '54-'60)
Years in Supreme Judical Court: 26
Years in Judiciary: 26

ORGANIZATIONS:
American Law Institute; American College of Trial Lawyers

Ruth I. Abrams

Associate Justice

Supreme Judicial Court
Address: 1300 New Courthouse, Boston, MA 02108
Telephone: (617) 557-1000
Staff: Joyce Hurley, Administrative Assistant

PERSONAL INFORMATION:
Education: Radcliffe College (A.B.); Harvard University Law School (LL. B.)
Previous Employment: Superior Court (Associate Justice); Supreme Judicial Court (Special Counsel); Assistant Attorney General (Appellate Section, Criminal Division), Middlesex County (Assistant District Attorney); Abrams, Abrams & Abrams (private practice)
Years in Supreme Judical Court: 21
Years in Judiciary: 26

John M. Greaney
Associate Justice

Supreme Judicial Court
Address: 1300 New Courthouse, Boston, MA 02108
Telephone: (617) 557-1000
Staff: Lynne Hanson, Judicial Secretary

PERSONAL INFORMATION:
Education: College of the Holy Cross (B.A.); New York State University School of Law (J.D.)
Previous Employment: Massachusetts Appeals Court (Chief Justice, '84-'89); Appeals Court (Associate Justice, '78-'84); Superior Court (Associate Justice, '75-'78); Hampden County Housing Court (Presiding Justice, '73-'75); Ely & King (Associate)
Years in Supreme Judical Court: 8
Years in Judiciary: 25

ORGANIZATIONS:
American Law Institute; American Bar Association Foundation

Neil L. Lynch
Associate Justice

Supreme Judicial Court
Address: 1300 New Courthouse, Boston, MA 02108
Telephone: (617) 557-1131
Staff: Ginny Thurler, Administrative Assistant; Charlene A. Caldeira, Law Clerk; Douglas A. Wolfson, Law Clerk

PERSONAL INFORMATION:
Born: June 26, 1930 **Place of Birth:** Holyoke
Marital Status: Married (Kathleen)
Education: Harvard University (A.B., '52); Harvard Law School (LL.B., '57)
Years in Supreme Judical Court: 18
Years in Judiciary: 18

Margaret Hilary Marshall

Associate Justice

Supreme Judicial Court
Address: 1300 New Courthouse, Boston, MA 02108
Telephone: (617) 557-1000 **Fax:** (617) 557-1091
Staff: Sally Locke, Administrative Assistant

PERSONAL INFORMATION:
Born: September 1, 1944
Place of Birth: Newcastle, Republic of South Africa
Marital Status: married (Anthony Lewis)
Children: 3 (stepchildren)
Education: Witwatersrand University, South Africa (B.A., '66); Harvard University (M.Ed., '69); Yale Law School (J.D., '76); Regis College (D.HL., Honorary, '93)
Previous Employment: Csaplor & Bok (Associate and Partner, '76-'89); Choate, Hall & Stewart (Partner, '89-'92); Harvard University (Vice-President and General Counsel, '92-'96)

Years in Supreme Judical Court: 2

Roderick L. Ireland

Associate Justice

Supreme Judicial Court
Address: 1300 New Courthouse, Boston, MA 02108
Telephone: (617) 557-1000 **Fax:** (617)557-1052

PERSONAL INFORMATION:
Born: December 3, 1944
Place of Birth: Springfield
Education: Lincoln University, (B.A. '66); Columbia University, (J.D. '69); Harvard Law School (L.L.M. '75); Northeastern University, (Ph.D. '98)
Previous Employment: Roxbury Defenders Committee (1972-74); Executive Office of Administration and Finance for the Commonwealth of Massachusetts, Assistant Secretary and Chief Legal Counsel, (1975-77); Board of appeal on Motor Vehicle Liability Policies and bonds, Chairman 1977; Boston Juvenile Court, Associate Justice, (1977-90) 12.5 years; Appeals Court, Associate Justice (1990-97) 7 years.

Years in Supreme Judicial Court: 2

Years in Judiciary: 21

Maria Zoe Mossaides

Administrative Assistant to the Justices

Supreme Judicial Court
Address: 1400 New Courthouse, Boston, MA 02108
Telephone: (617) 557-1193 **Fax:** (617) 557-1052
Staff: Henry Clay, Chief Staff Counsel; Barbara Diamond, Counsel for Policy Development; Robert Bloom, Deputy Administrative Assistant
Reports to: The Justices

PERSONAL INFORMATION:
Born: Sept. 6, 1951 **Place of Birth:** New York City
Marital Status: Married (V. Rev. Nicholas Apostola) **Children:** 3
Education: Mt. Holyoke College (A.B., '73); State University of New York at Buffalo (J.D., '77); Harvard University, JFK School of Government (M.P.A., '90)
Previous Employment: Division of Purchased Services (Assistant Commissioner); Office of the Comptroller (General Counsel to Comptroller); Department of Social Services (Deputy General Counsel); Office for Children (Director and General Counsel)
Years in Current Position: 9 **Years in State Service:** 19

JOB DESCRIPTION:
Court Administrator for the highest court in Massachusetts.

ORGANIZATIONS:
Massachusetts Bar Association, Public Law Section; Holy Trinity Nursing Home

Robert A. Burns, Jr.

Business/Fiscal Manager

Supreme Judicial Court
Address: 1300 New Courthouse, Boston, MA 02108
Telephone: (617) 557-1070 **Fax:** (617) 723-3577

PERSONAL INFORMATION:
Education: North Adams State College (B.A., '79); Suffolk University (M.P.A., '85)
Previous Employment: Executive Office of Human Services (Deputy Budget Director)
Years in Current Position: 7

ORGANIZATIONS:
Knights of Columbus (Andover)

Henry Clay

Chief Staff Counsel for Appellate Bureau

Supreme Judicial Court
Address: 1300 New Courthouse, Boston, MA 02108
Telephone: (617) 557-1164

PERSONAL INFORMATION:
Education: Dartmouth College (B.A., '64); Boston University School of Law (LL.B., '67)
Years in Current Position: 7

Jean M. Kennett
Clerk

Supreme Judicial Court
Address: 1412 New Courthouse, Boston, MA 02108
Telephone: (617) 557-1020
Staff: Susan Mellen, Assistant Clerk; L. Holliey White, Assistant Clerk pro tem

PERSONAL INFORMATION:
Education: Suffolk University (J.D., '81)
Previous Employment: Supreme Judicial Court for Suffolk County (First Assistant Clerk)
Years in Current Position: 13

ORGANIZATIONS:
Boston Bar Association; National Conference of Appellate Court Clerks

Barbara M. Diamond
Counsel for Policy Development

Supreme Judicial Court
Address: 1400 New Courthouse, Boston, MA 02108
Telephone: (617) 557-1156 **Fax:** (617) 557-1052

PERSONAL INFORMATION:
Education: Radcliffe College (B.A., '70); Harvard Law School (J.D., '73)
Years in Current Position: 6

Joan Kenney
Public Information Officer

Supreme Judicial Court
Address: 218 Old Courthouse, Boston, MA 02108
Telephone: (617) 557-1113 **Fax:** (617) 742-1807
Staff: Elizabeth Fearnley, Assistant Public Information Officer; Sonya Smiddy, Administrative Assistant
Years in Current Position: 10

Index of Names

A

B

C

D

E

F

G

L

M

N

O

T

V